Published by Manchester University Press,
Oxford Road, Manchester M13 9PL, UK
and 51 Washington Street, Dover,
New Hampshire 03820, USA

British Library cataloguing in publication data
Case studies in population biology.
   1. Animal populations
   I. Cook, Laurence M.
   591.52′ 48   QH352

Library of Congress cataloging in publication data
Main entry under title:
Case studies in population biology.
   Includes index.
   1. Population biology—England—Woodchester Park—Addresses, essays,
lectures. 2. Woodchester Park (England)—Addresses, essays, lectures.
I. Cook, Laurence Martin.
QH352.C37   1985   591.5′ 248   84-19451

ISBN 0-7190-1740-8 (cased)

Typeset by Graphicraft Typesetters Ltd.
Printed in Great Britain
by Unwin Brothers Ltd
The Gresham Press
Old Woking, Surrey
A member of the Martins Printing Group

Contents

Contributors

R.R. Askew: Department of Zoology, University of Manchester, Manchester M13 9PL, UK.

R.R. Baker: Department of Zoology, University of Manchester, Manchester M13 9PL, UK.

J.S. Bradley: School of Environmental and Life Sciences, Murdoch University, Murdoch, 6150 Western Australia.

M.V. Hounsome: Department of Zoology, Manchester University Museum, Manchester M13 9PL, UK.

W.I. Montgomery: Department of Zoology, Queen's University of Belfast, Belfast BT7 1NN, Northern Ireland.

R.J. White: Department of Biology, Building 44, The University, Southampton SO9 5NH, UK.

D.W. Yalden: Department of Zoology, University of Manchester, Manchester M13 9PL, UK.

Preface

There are between 1.5 and 15 million living species of plants and animals. The generation of diversity is a central process of evolution, but the reasons for it are imperfectly understood. Botany and zoology are concerned with the study of living systems at all levels from macromolecule to communities of species, a manifold approach which is necessary before we can hope to unravel a general picture of evolution. Population and evolutionary studies have been a feature of the zoology departments of Manchester and Liverpool Universities for many years. Emphasis has been placed on the need to relate theoretical models to real situations and teaching commitments to research. Field courses are an excellent way of combining both requirements, and they play a prominent role at Manchester and Liverpool.

This book presents a series of studies linked by the following common characters. They originate from observations made on field courses held at Woodchester Park Field Centre, Gloucestershire, UK; they are designed to investigate the factors determining numbers within species and coexistence between species of animals; and they are concerned with the problem of the extent to which theoretical models can be related to natural populations. The following pages present some data, provide some answers, and in so doing, give an account of the methodology of aspects of ecological field studies.

The contributions also record the influence of J. Gordon Blower on the development of ecological field studies in Manchester. It would not be his nature to wish his name to appear on every page, but his influence, pervades the book. His part has been to create the course at Woodchester Park (and earlier at other centres) and modestly but persistently to question the assumptions of population ecology in an effort to get the answers right. He will be remembered for this by generations of students. At a time when increasing emphasis seems to be placed on self-promotion and the acquisition of research grants, it is a pleasure to recognise the influence of a different type of approach. For Gordon Blower, satisfaction and self-confidence have been derived from a single-mined respect for the subject. This book is dedicated to him and to that aproach, following his retirement from formal teaching in September 1982.

The courses could not have run so successfully without the whole-hearted cooperation of Mr and Mrs A.R. Kelly. We thank them for the facilities they have provided at the Field Centre, both for the courses themselves and for research throughout the year. We are grateful to the people of Nympsfield for their welcome over seventeen years. A notable characteristic of the Manchester Zoology course has been the contribution of Richard Abbott. We thank him for his technical and logistic skills and for many liaison activities, always performed with a light touch.

L. M. Cook

1 R.R. Askew and D.W. Yalden

The Woodchester Park valley

Introduction

This book could be seen as an account of the population biology of a very few animal species in a limited area in south-west England. From another point view, it is also an account of how university research develops out of, and contributes to, university teaching. This is a theme frequently developed by university lecturers in justification of the apparently ambiguous role of a university; we hope that we have provided here a practical example of how teaching and research are mutually related. A third view of this book might be that it is an examination of a very important topic in population biology, namely, how one defines a population. We trust that this third view, at least, justifies the book.

Three separate threads have combined to produce the research described here. One is the educational background alluded to above; these studies developed out of field courses run for second-year zoology students at Manchester University. A second thread is the ecological and geographical background, providing appropriate animals in sufficient abundance for study. A third thread is the historical one, providing an appropriate base, a field centre, which we have been privileged to use for 17 years, enabling us also to observe changes in animal populations over that time span. These three threads will be elaborated further in this chapter.

Educational background

The Department of Zoology, University of Manchester, has run field courses in population biology each year since 1953. Initially, they were run at various locations in the Lake District, but, after interludes of one year each at Swansea (1965) and Snowdonia (1966), the courses have taken place at Woodchester Park in Gloucestershire since 1967.

The course lasts for two weeks, and in nearly every year has been held in the last week or so of June and the first week of July.

Initiating the course, establishing its content and its format, were among the most important contributions made by J. Gordon Blower to the academic life of Manchester's Department of Zoology. To outsiders, he is probably best known as a millipede specialist, author of the Linnean Society's Synopsis for that group (Blower, 1958, 1985). To us, his colleagues, he is formally Reader in Ecology (appointed in 1959, having served previously as a demonstrator from 1948 and as a lecturer from 1951), and informally the best teacher of undergraduates amongst us; several generations of students would, we know, concur with that judgement.

Among the other contributors to this volume, R.R. Askew, L.M. Cook and D.W. Yalden are also members of staff in the Department of Zoology at Manchester, and have attended the field courses at Woodchester Park in practically every year from 1967 onwards. Dr M.V. Hounsome was originally a postgraduate student in the department, and since 1974 has been Keeper of Zoology at Manchester Museum; he has attended the field courses, specifically to organise bird-ringing activities, since 1971.

One direct consequence of the use by Manchester of Woodchester Park has been that other universities have become aware of the suitability of the site for their own field courses. In some cases, this has arisen because Manchester postgraduates or staff have taken up appointments in other universities. Notable among these was the late Dr J.A. Bishop, a member of staff at Manchester in 1967–1968, who moved to Liverpool University's Department of Zoology in 1968 and started a tradition of use of Woodchester Park which continues to the present. Professor A.J. Cain was concerned with establishing Woodchester Park as a venue for field courses both during his time at Manchester (1963–1968) and then from Liverpool. Two of the present contributors, R.J. White and J.S. Bradley, became involved as postgraduates of Liverpool Department of Zoology. Of the other contributors, W.I. Montgomery was an undergraduate student and then a postgraduate at Manchester. Dr R.R. Baker, a member of staff at Manchester since 1974, actually became acquainted with Woodchester Park initially as a demonstrator at Newcastle upon Tyne Zoology Department through field courses introduced by another ex-Manchester postgraduate, Dr B. Shorrocks.

Run originally for students of Honours Zoology only, the courses have been duplicated for Biology students. The first course for them was organised in 1975 by R.R. Baker, and has run every year since then, usually in the fortnight following the zoology course. Thus we have, for more recent years, a month of information on some populations, notably birds and mammals.

The main emphasis of the Manchester field courses has been estimation of the size of animal populations. As Gordon Blower remarked in his introduction to the report of the first Woodchester Park field course in 1967, 'The most important characters of an animal population are the number of individuals and the age structure of these.' In most years, the first class exercise has been to examine the population of earthworms. Various sites around the Field Centre have been used, not always the same sites every year nor, in detail, the same procedures. Formalin extraction has always been the principal method, though in some years we have also attempted comparison with potassium permanganate used (like formalin) as a repellant, and with hand sampling. After this, the class has split into a number of groups, each studying the population of a very mobile group of animals by mark, release, recapture procedures. The traditional animals for teaching these techniques to zoology students in Britain have been grasshoppers, and these we too have studied in almost every year. We have also extended the techniques to populations of moths, damsel-flies, butterflies, small mammals and small birds in most years, and have on occasion applied them, either in class exercises or in individual student projects, to such diverse animals as the bug *Calocoris sexguttatus*, ants, wolf spiders, ladybirds, ground beetles, and even earthworms.

We had several reasons for selecting the topic of population estimation for such concentrated attention. It is essential in most practical and theoretical studies in animal ecology to have some idea of population size; in some studies (estimating levels of predation, for example), the absolute population size may be required, whereas in others a relative index may suffice (for example, when estimating selection pressures on different phenotypes). As an educational tool, we have found that approaching the study of animals through estimation techniques focuses the attention of students on the biological problems involved. The techniques of mark, release, recapture could perfectly well be taught using beads in a laboratory, or even taxis at an urban railway station (Bishop & Bradley, 1972), but the biological problems posed by, for instance, trap shyness and trap addiction, territoriality, migration and 'mortality' (whether real or statistical — loss of marks at ecdysis, for instance) are problems that force themselves on the students' attention.

Much of our effort on the field courses has been concerned with teaching the mathematical procedures, and much student effort has been expended in getting them correct. This led to the production of a student handbook (Blower *et al.*, 1981) summarising this aspect of our courses. Computer programs have recently taken the tedium from this part of the work. The question of the best statistical procedure to use remains an important one for discussion on the courses, and there is a difficult balance between what is efficient statistically and what is biologically practical. One recurrent theme in discussion, however, has been 'What *is* a population?'; this will be elaborated further in this volume. Students are frequently mystified but intrigued to spend five or six days studying a group of animals and then to realise, as they analyse their results, that they don't actually know how to define the population on which they have been working. The problem scarcely arises with grasshoppers or small mammals, which are perceived to be contained within some arbitrary grid or quadrat under study. It is most acute with birds and, especially, moths, which are highly mobile animals that are sampled only at one or a few points in a large 'home range', the points at which mist nets or moth traps are operated.

Some of the chapters that follow are directly concerned with this problem. Chapter 4, discussing the bird population of Woodchester Park over 13 years, derives directly from the field courses. The other chapters all concern animals that have been studied on field courses but have been pursued further by postgraduate students working over a three-year period for their doctorates.

Geographical and ecological setting

We could not have continued to visit Woodchester Park for so many years, and the postgraduate studies could certainly not have been concluded successfully, unless a suitable range of populations, of adequate size for study, had been assured. Other field-course sites which we have on occasion used have not attracted such constant attention, nor produced such intensive studies, suggesting that there is something a little special about Woodchester Park. If there is, then it stems from its geographical and ecological setting.

Geographically, Woodchester Park occupies a deep eastward-opening valley in the Cotswold Hills. It lies in the county of Gloucestershire, in vice-county 34 of the Watsonian system, and in the National Grid square SO 80; the buildings of the Field Centre, 'the Cottage', are at SO 812013. The valley opens near the small town of Nailsworth, 4 km away. Stroud is 6 km away to the north-east of the Field Centre; the nearest large towns are Gloucester (18 km N), Cheltenham (27 km NE) and Bristol (37 km SW) (Fig. 1.1). Most of the Park lies in the parish of Woodchester (Woodchester village is just 3 km north of Nailsworth), but the parishes of Nailsworth, King's Stanley and Nympsfield also impinge upon it. The Park is roughly 4 km long from east to west, approximately 1 km across at its widest from north to south, and has a map area of about 250 ha. In altitude it ranges from 213 m (700 ft) in the west to 75 m (250 ft) in the east. The

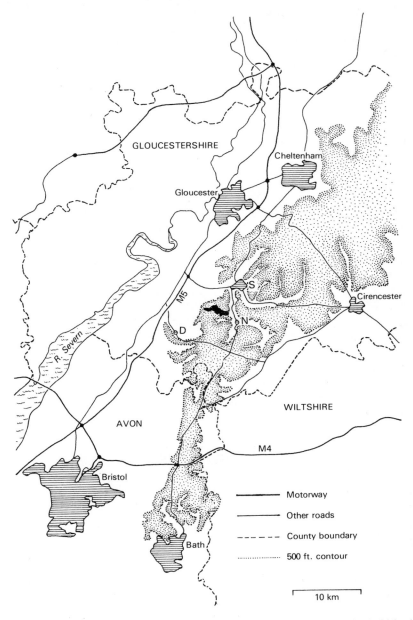

Fig. 1.1 Woodchester Park: regional setting. Woodchester Park (shaded black) occupies a valley which opens eastwards near Nailsworth (N), with Stroud (S) to the north and Dursley (D) to the south. (Based upon the Ordnance Survey Map with the permission of the Controller of Her Majesty's Stationery Office, Crown Copyright reserved.)

Fig. 1.2   Woodchester Park: local setting. Woodchester Park occupies part of three parishes, King's Stanley (K.S.), Nympsfield (N.) and Woodchester itself (W.). (Based upon the Ordnance Survey Map with the permission of the Controller of Her Majesty's Stationery Office, Crown Copyright reserved.)

valley is steep sided, incised into a plateau which is, all around, at an altitude of 150–230 m (Fig. 1.2).

This geography reflects very directly the geology of the area. The Park lies entirely on rocks of Jurassic age, notably the Inferior Oolite, a hard erosion-resistant limestone responsible for much of the scenic, as well as architectural, attraction of the Cotswold Hills. In the bottom of the valley, the Park rests on the Marlstone Rock Bed, an impervious clayey limestone which is frequently, as in the Park, the marker for a line of springs (Cave, 1977). Above this lies a bed of bright yellow sand, the Cotteswold Sands, about 30 m thick, and, in the valley, the usual site of badger setts. On top of the sands lie the limestones of the Lower and Upper Inferior Oolites, approximately 42 m thick, constituting the hard surface for the plateau in this region, and the summit of the scarp slope of the Cotswolds just a kilometre or less to the west and north of the Park (Fig. 1.3). In particular, Selsley Common, just north of the valley on the scarp slope and formed from the Upper Inferior Oolite, is important to us as a site where grasshopper population studies (see Chapter 3) and our class exercises on both grasshoppers and butterflies take place.

Climatically, Woodchester Park is in the relatively mild south west of Britain. The meteorological station at Cheltenham records a mean annual temperature of 10°C, with a mean daily maximum of 14°C and a mean daily minimum of 6.2°C; annual total rainfall has averaged (1916–1950) 69.3 cm (27.3 in). More significant for us than the long-term averages has been the variation in weather from year to year, since this has very marked repercussions on the fauna available to study on the field course each year.

We remember such extremes as the drought of summer 1976, and the long, hot spell that year which started during our field course, or the cool, wet spring of 1977 which resulted in us finding no adult grasshoppers, no Yellow Underwing moths, and too few butterflies to study.

Superimposed on this geographical and geological setting is an ecological setting which in part reflects the natural fauna and flora of the region, but even more the historical and agricultural history of the area. There are nine chambered tombs and tumuli within a 5 km radius on the surrounding plateau (notably 'Hetty Peglar's Tump', 2.5 km away to the south west), indicating that late Neolithic/Beaker Age people were well established in the area by 3000 BC. There are also two hill forts, presumably of Iron Age, at Uley Hill and Ring Hill, 3.5 km to the south, and 8 km to the north, respectively. Human occupation of the area in Roman times is also well attested by archaeological remains, notably the villa with its famous mosaic at Woodchester itself (Sheils, 1976). The former presence of Anglo-Saxon

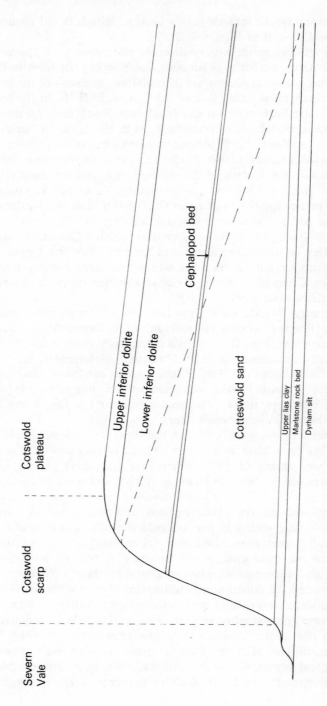

Fig. 1.3 Woodchester Park: geological setting. A schematic geological section through the Cotswold Scarp in the vicinity of Woodchester Park. The depths of the named strata are drawn roughly in proportion.

settlers is indicated less by archaeological remains than by their place names, which we still, in essence, use: Nailsworth (Naegl's enclosure), Woodchester (the Roman camp or settlement in the wood), Nympsfield (Nymed's field) and King's Stanley (stony clearing), the principal parishes, are essentially Old English names (Smith, 1964*a, b*), as are those of other local features. In the Domesday Book of AD 1086, Woodchester, Nympsfield and (King's) Stanley are recorded as manors, and they have a well-documented existence since then. (Nailsworth is exceptional, in that it developed as a non-conformist settlement from the seventeenth century onwards at the 'corner' of Horsley, Minchinhampton and Avening parishes and was created as a parish in 1892 (Herbert & Sheils, 1976).)

The human population of this area of Gloucestershire has probably always had a modest density, and this has undoubtedly contributed to the survival of some of the interesting patches of habitat in the area. At the time of the Domesday survey, AD 1086, the Cotswold plateau held three or four plough teams and six to seven recorded people per square mile (Darby & Terret, 1954). This was about the average density for the English Midlands generally, with parts of Leicestershire and Nottinghamshire more densely populated but Staffordshire, Shropshire and northern Warwickshire more sparsely occupied; it implies that the valleys, at least, were well farmed. King's Stanley had 18 men listed, and Woodchester had 16 villagers and 12 smallholders. At the start of the modern censuses, Nympsfield had 523 citizens in 1801, and 532 in 1811, but the population dropped steadily through the nineteenth century to only 216 people in 1901 (Minchin, 1907). There has been some modest increase this century, however, and 398 people were recorded at the 1971 census. In Woodchester, the population has been more stable, averaging 882 (range 816 (1861) to 974 (1871)) during the nineteenth century; in 1971, it was 820.

A park is recorded as early as 1311, but it was greatly enlarged by enclosure, absorbing open field and common land in Woodchester parish and overlapping into neighbouring parishes, in the early seventeenth century. In the early eighteenth century, it was described as the largest park in the county, with a boundary 7 miles in circumference. Spring Park, as it was often called, was later landscaped, perhaps by John Spyers who made a survey of it in 1782. The ownership of the manor, subsequently the park itself, is well documented from AD 1199 onwards. It belonged to the Ducie family from 1631 to 1846, when it was sold to William Leigh. He demolished the manor house, and started on the construction of a new house, the Mansion; meanwhile he lived in the Cottage which is now the Field Centre. The Mansion was, in fact, never completed, though it still stands as an imposing piece of architecture (Verey, 1969). The majority of the park is currently managed as a private forestry venture (Sheils, 1976).

One ecologically important feature which is clear from the historical records is the continuity of woodland in the area. In Woodchester parish, woodland is recorded in documents as early as AD 716, and wood sales were economically important in the fifteenth and sixteenth centuries. Nisbet & Vellacott (1907) quote Rudge (1807): '. . . the most extensive (beech woods) are . . . the magnificent woods at Spring Park, and on Frocester and Stanley Hills, belonging to Lord Ducie.' In King's Stanley, Domesday records woodland 1 × 1½ leagues in extent; subsequent records mention 80 acres of woodland in 1295, 161 acres in 1322, and 148 acres of 30- to 40-year-old beech in 1568 (Herbert, 1972). Although woodland history is not quite so well documented in Woodchester and Nympsfield, it seems certain that some of the steep slopes in the park have been continuously covered in woodland, albeit well-managed and exploited woodland. The preponderance of Beech (*Fagus sylvatica*) certainly reflects human management of the woodland (Thorley, 1981) rather than, as was once thought, the persistence of 'ancient beech woods', but the patches of deciduous woodland, which include Field Maple (*Acer campestre*), Gean (*Prunus avium*), and Yew (*Taxus baccata*), may well be relics of ancient woodland.

The history of open grassland habitats locally is less clear. By analogy with elsewhere in southern Britain, one may suppose that the limestone plateau was cleared of forest in or by late Neolithic times, say 4000 years ago. Probably areas of herb-rich limestone grassland, such as the lower slopes of Selsley Common, have had a continuous history of grazing since that time. We know that attempts to enclose Selsley were made, and successfully resisted, in 1831 and 1852; earlier, in 1766, its area was estimated at 150 acres. Common rights of grazing are still exercised, from May to October each year, under the control of the grazing committee of the parish council (Herbert, 1972). However, the upper, level part of the common was ploughed under the wartime emergency agricultural powers, and 40 years later that part of the common still has a herb-poor pasture, dominated by Ryegrass (*Lolium perenne*), which contrasts sharply with the herb-rich grassland on the slopes.

Within the park, most of the limestone grassland, and much of the deciduous woodland, has been replaced by conifer plantations (see Fig. 1.4). These are mostly of larch (*Larix* sp.), but include also cypresses (*Thuja*) and spruce (*Picea*); there are also some plantations of hybrid poplar (*Populus* × *euramericana*). Three meadows remain in the valley bottom, and small remnants of limestone grassland persist, notably at 'Inchbrook Meadow' to the east, just outside the park gates, and at the top of the valley to the west. The valley bottom contains

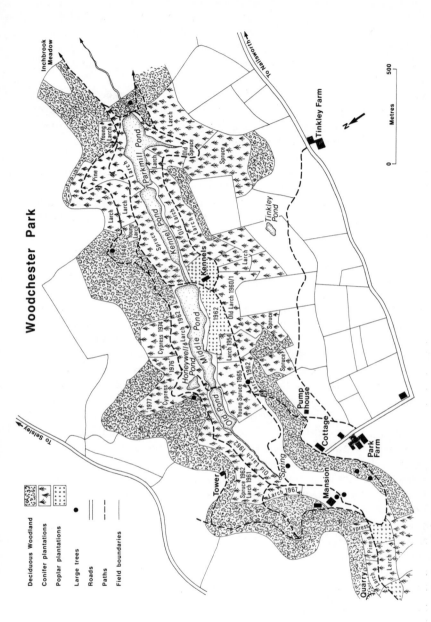

Woodchester Park

Legend:
- Deciduous Woodland
- Conifer plantations
- Poplar plantations
- Large trees ●
- Roads
- Paths
- Field boundaries

Inchbrook Meadow

To Selsley

To Nailsworth

Parkmill Pond
Spruce Pond
Kennel Pond
Middle Pond
Honeywell Pond
Old Pond
Tinkley Pond

Kennels
Tower
Spring
Pump house
Cottage
Mansion
Park Farm
Tinkley Farm
Quarry

Young Larch
Pine
Larch
Old Spruce
Spruce
Old Larch
Larch 1948
Young Larch
Cypress 1974
Honeywell/Larch 1962
1977
Cypress
1962
Old Larch 1960
Larch 1956
Spruce
Young Spruce 1965
Larch
Spruce 1962
Larch 1961
Old Larch 1962
Larch 1967
Cypress
Larch
Pine

N

0   Metres   500

Fig. 1.4 Woodchester Park: habitat types. A map of the Park showing particularly the different woodland blocks and, where we know them, the dates of planting. Unshaded areas are pastures (especially in the valley bottom) and arable land. (Based on aerial photographs, and drawn by Dr J.H. Tallis.)

five ponds, which date from late eighteenth-century landscaping, and these have a fringe of Alder (*Alnus glutinosa*) persisting around them. There are in addition a large number of fine specimen trees dotted about the park which presumably also date back to that landscaping: Beech (*Fagus sylvatica*), Oak (*Quercus robur*), Walnut (*Juglans regia*), and Cedar (*Cedrus libani*) are the most prominent.

Subsequent planting, particularly around the Cottage, has added further to the local diversity of the flora; individual specimens of Maidenhair Tree (*Gingko biloba*), Chilean Pine (*Araucaria araucana*), Holm Oak (*Quercus ilex*) and Portugal Laurel (*Prunus lusitanica*) are examples. Numerous shrubs of Box (*Buxus sempervirens*) and Cherry Laurel (*Prunus laurocerasus*) provide the understorey to the mammal grid on the wooded slope near the Cottage.

Given this diversity of habitats, semi-natural and manmade, and this diversity of flora, it is not surprising that the fauna is also diverse and interesting.

The fauna: composition and variation

Our knowledge of the fauna of the area remains patchy, despite our best endeavours. Much depends on the enthusiasm of particular specialists, and appropriate sampling methods for some groups have not been applied. Moreover, our activities have been confined to a short period of the year. At present, our fauna list contains about 1100 species. In some groups, we have recorded around 50% of the British or English fauna at Woodchester Park (Table 1.1), and given the habitat or temporal specialisations of many of the other species, we may consider that we have a reasonably complete inventory of the area's fauna for those groups. We have in the process recorded several rare or unusual species, which in itself encourages us to think that our list is reasonably complete in parts; certainly such rarities do much to convince us that the valley is a faunistically rich site and well worthy of study.

One of the foremost specialities is the Yellow-necked Mouse *Apodemus flavicollis* (Yalden, 1971); though present in scattered localities throughout south-east England and the Severn Valley, previous attempts to study its ecology in England had been frustrated by the low numbers that most people caught. Its abundance at Woodchester Park was essential to the studies discussed by Ian Montgomery in Chapter 5. Rare birds that we have recorded include Osprey *Pandion haliaetus* (1977) and Quail *Coturnix coturnix* (1982, 1983). Among the invertebrates, notable rarities include the Woodlouse *Ligidium hypnorum* and Harvestman *Homalenotus quadridentatus*, both found

Table 1.1 Approximate numbers of species in various taxonomic groups in the British fauna, and the number recorded at Woodchester Park.

	British fauna	Woodchester Park	(%)
Oligochaeta	26	15	58
Terrestrial Gastropoda	114	47	41
Isopoda	29[a]	13	45
Chilopoda	50	12	24
Diplopoda	52[a]	19	37
Opiliones	23	15	65
Odonata	42	9	21
Neuroptera	60	23	38
Lepidoptera — Rhopalocera	66	35	53
Diptera — Syrphidae	244	62	25
Siphonaptera	55	10	18
Coleoptera — Carabidae	352	23	7
Amphibia	6	4	67
Reptilia	6	3	50
Aves	193[b]	91	47
Mammalia	53	23	43

[a] Excludes hothouse aliens.
[b] English breeding birds.

in old grassland with a deep litter layer. A host of insects are usually feeding on the flowering umbels of Hogweed *Heracleum sphondylium*. Regularly seen are the large, black-and-yellow stratiomyid fly *Stratiomys potamida* and the Large Long-horn Beetle *Stenocorus meridianus*, both uncommon species in Britain. Of much greater rarity is the Bee Beetle *Trichius fasciatus*, a specimen of which was found on an umbel in 1978. The Bee Beetle occurs in Scotland and Wales but there are very few English records. Also often on Hogweed is the Scarlet Tiger moth *Callimorpha (Panaxia) dominula*, of which there are several colonies in the valley (see Chapter 2); this species has a patchy distribution restricted to southern England. The local Dragonfly *Cordulia aenea* breeds in Middle Pond although its occurrence is rather sporadic, and the huge Bush Cricket *Tettigonia viridissima* is encountered from time to time in Inchbrook Meadow. The scarce Chafer *Omaloplia ruricola* occurs still on Rodborough Common, a well-known locality for it, and in the valley two species of beetles that are characteristic of old woodland have been found. They are *Platystomos albinus* and *Oncomera femorata*. The latter is usually taken from Ivy but it is regularly found in an old rambler rose growing against the Cottage wall. Two woodwasps (*Xiphydria camelus*, associated with dying Alder, and *Urocerus gigas*, which oviposits in felled or damaged conifers) both occur in the valley. A parasite of the last species, *Rhyssa persuasoria*, an ichneumon with a spectacularly long ovipositor, has occasionally been entangled in the ornithologists' mist nets. Other rare parasitic Hymenoptera include the chalcids *Perniphora robusta* (1976, the third British record), *Lariophagus rufipes* (1969, second British record) and *Chrysonotomyia germanica* (1971, first discovery in Britain).

Observing animals and plants in a limited area over a period of many years, albeit for only a brief period in each year, allows an appreciation of the changes, some slow and some rapid, that occur in all populations. No two years are alike and this generates undiminishing interest and excitement. Each field course produces surprises with previously overlooked species being discovered, new species appearing in the valley, and familiar animals varying in their abundance. Populations of animals change in size between generations and within a generation, as numbers decline from their maximum at birth. Numbers of breeding adults, however, usually vary between rather narrow limits. Rare species generally remain rare and common species stay common. This stability indicates that natality and mortality rates are balanced, not precisely in every generation, but on average over a series of generations. The level of every population is adjusted to the carrying capacity of the environment, and if this capacity remained stable, population sizes would vary little between one generation and the next. But of course the environment is continually changing and demanding readjustment in the population levels of plants and animals. Environmental changes are sometimes rapid and dramatic, and sometimes very gradual with almost imperceptible effects. One has only to see the fossil brachiopods in the limestone of the valley to appreciate that the area was once submerged beneath the sea. On a very much smaller timescale, changes to the environment have taken place since our first visit in 1967.

On the steep northern slope, just outside the park gates at Inchbrook, is an area of unused limestone grassland. We have watched the gradual invasion of this grassy slope by Hawthorn and Oak and the replacement of its varied flora, which included Rockrose *Helianthemum nummularium*, Thyme *Thymus drucei*, Centaury *Centaureum erythraea*, Viper's Bugloss *Echium vulgare*, and Bee Orchid *Ophrys apifera*, by ranker herbage. The original limestone flora flourished under the grazing pressure of rabbits, but decimation of the rabbit population by myxomatosis in the 1950s allowed shrubs and trees to become established. Floral change has orchestrated faunal change. A colony of the Small Blue butterfly *Cupido minimus*, whose caterpillars feed in the flower-heads of Kidney-vetch *Anthyllis vulneraria*, has slowly declined, as too have numbers of the grasshopper *Stenobothrus lineatus*. Gordon Blower's description of the slope in 1967 as a Fabrian meadow is sadly no longer apt.

Dutch Elm disease arrived in the valley in 1971 or 1972, rather later than in the surrounding countryside, but by 1981 all mature Elm trees were dead or dying and only a few Wych Elms remained unaffected. Biological consequences of the disappearance of the Elm are difficult to predict. Two species of butterfly, the Comma *Polygonia c-album* and the White-letter Hairstreak *Strymonidia w-album*, have caterpillars that feed on foliage of Wych Elm, and a decline in their numbers might he anticipated. The White-letter Hairstreak was last plentiful in 1976 and has not been seen since, but the Comma, whose caterpillars will feed on Nettle and other plants in addition to Elm, was plentiful in 1982 both in the valley and elsewhere in England.

Large parts of the valley are given over to commercial forestry. Ecological changes in a fast-growing conifer plantation are rapid and profound, and their effect on bird life is especially striking. We have witnessed a succession of warbler species in a growing Larch plantation to the east of the Mansion. The ground was cleared and planted with Larch, probably in 1964 (in 1978 the trees showed twelve to thirteen annual rings). At the time of our first field course in 1967, the small trees were screened by a dense undergrowth of tall grasses, Bracken, Rosebay Willowherb and patches of Brambles. Whitethroats *Sylvia communis* were exceedingly common and the song of Grasshopper Warblers *Locustella naevia* was almost incessant, with an estimated six males in the area. Only two singing Willow Warblers *Phylloscopus trochilis* were present. In the following years, as the trees grew and the grassy areas disappeared, Grasshopper Warblers declined and the last was heard in 1972. Whitethroats also became progressively scarcer, although their decline in the plantation coincided with a national fall in numbers by about 80% in 1969 (Winstanley *et al.*, 1974). As numbers of these two warblers were reduced, the number of Willow Warblers increased to attain a maximum in about 1973. Further growth of the trees, and some clearance of the undergrowth, made the plantation less attractive to Willow Warblers and by 1978 they were scarce. Since 1978, however, the trees have become tall enough for Chiffchaffs *P. collybita*, and this is now the dominant warbler in the plantation.

Progressive, unidirectional faunal changes stemming from environmental alterations are just one of the sources of annual variation. They are predictable, or at least would be predictable if our knowledge were more complete. As yet quite unpredictable, however, is variation generated by climatic differences between years. This affects especially those organisms that complete a generation in a year or less, particularly insects, but what happens to insect populations has a quite profound effect upon the entire ecosystem. We view the valley through a small window in time, four weeks from the end of June, and what we see varies with the degree of advancement of the season. This is primarily governed by the weather, a prolonged period of warm spring weather advancing the biological cycles of many organisms, both plants and animals, but with different organisms responding differently to the same weather. It is hardly surprising, therefore, that different biological indicators of the state of the season are seldom unanimous.

One of the best guides to the state of the season is the age structure of grasshopper populations. Short-horned grasshoppers overwinter in the ground as eggs, and the nymphs hatch in spring when the herbage on which they feed begins to grow. They pass through a sequence of four nymphal instars before the adult stage is reached. The date of hatching from the egg, and the duration of each instar, are apparently temperature dependent, for there is a good positive correlation between air temperatures from April to the date of the field course and the proportion of grasshoppers that are found to have attained the adult stage (Fig. 1.5). Of the three common species studied, *Chorthippus*

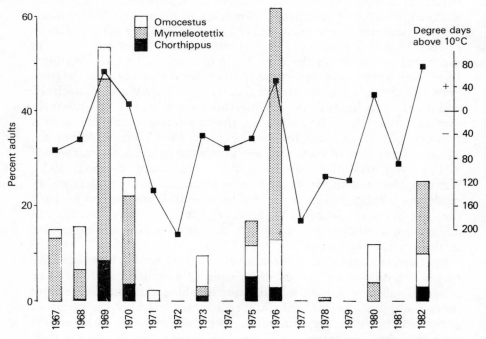

Fig. 1.5 Grasshopper numbers and weather. The percentage of adult grasshoppers in each year's catch compared with the 'growing season'. Growing season is here calculated as the accumulated degree-days above 10°C from 1 April to the third day of the field course each year.

parallelus is always the latest to mature, but in some years *Myrmeleotettix maculatus* became adult before *Omocestus viridulus* whereas in other years the order is reversed. *Omocestus* inhabits more luxuriant ground vegetation than does *Myrmeleotettix*, and it is probable, although we have no data to test the hypothesis, that *Myrmeleotettix* is able to take advantage of short periods of sunshine which rapidly warm the partially bare ground it usually frequents. Grasshopper and meteorological data show 1972, 1974, 1977, 1979 and 1981 to be very late years; in none was any adult grasshopper found.

Damselflies are, like grasshoppers, one of the animal groups upon which we practise mark, release, recapture population studies. From 1972 until 1977, the population of insects along the path crossing Kennel Dam was investigated. Four damselfly species were present in the waterside vegetation, *Ischnura elegans*, *Coenagrion puella*, *Enallagma cyathigerum* and *Pyrrhosoma nymphula*. A fifth species, *Erythromma najas*, frequents the lily-pads on Middle Pond. Numbers of individuals of each of the four more accessible species, captured over the five or six days of each year's project, are presented in Table 1.2. Every year *Pyrrhosoma* was present in only very small numbers and the most numerous species was either *Ischnura* (three years) or *Enallagma* (also in three years). Examination of temperature data (from the Birmingham Weather Centre) shows that *Ischnura* dominated the collections in the three years (1972, 1974 and 1977) of lowest April–May–June temperatures, whereas in the three warmest years

Table 1.2 Percentage representation of *Ischnura elegans*, *Coenagrion puella*, *Enallagma cyathigerum* and *Pyrrhosoma nymphula* in annual samples of damselflies from Kennel Dam and Tinkley Pond. Temperature deviations from the mean maxima for the months April, May and June (Birmingham Weather Centre) are given. p denotes present in negligible numbers.

Site and year	Numbers of damselflies caught	Per cent *Ischnura*	Per cent *Coenagrion*	Per cent *Enallagma*	Per cent *Pyrrhosoma*	Deviation From mean maximum temperature (°C) for April–June
Kennel Dam						
1972	178	53.9	33.7	12.4	p	− 6.7
1973	855	45.1	3.9	51.0	p	− 1.7
1974	842	68.6	11.3	20.1	p	− 2.4
1975	1044	18.6	21.9	58.6	0.9	− 1.1
1976	1226	16.7	29.7	53.6	p	+ 3.5
1977	335	46.3	34.3	14.9	4.5	− 5.6
Tinkley Pond						
1978	1390	90.8	8.7	0.3	0.2	− 4.5
1979	1718	84.0	11.3	0.2	4.5	− 4.0
1980	1118	84.6	8.8	3.0	3.6	0
1981	1059	79.9	9.2	1.0	9.9	− 3.7
1982	995	94.0	4.5	1.3	0.2	+ 2.6

Enallagma was the commonest species. In 1978 the study moved to Tinkley Pond, a small, isolated pond in pastureland near the top of the valley's southern slope. Here *Ischnura, Coenagrion, Enallagma* and *Pyrrhosoma* were again present although in different proportions from those at Kennel Dam. *Ischnura* is clearly the dominant species at Tinkley Pond, exceeding in numbers the three other species together, and *Enallagma* is usually the least numerous. There is no suggestion from the Tinkley Pond data (Table 1.2) that *Ischnura* is proportionately more numerous in late years.

Earthworms are another group that feature in class exercises, and for which, therefore, we have several years' data. Although they have been studied to provide an example of static sampling, the results have wider value; many species, including the Badger *Meles meles* (Kruuk, 1978), Fox *Vulpes vulpes* (Macdonald, 1980) and various thrushes, depend heavily on earthworms for much of their diet. Our sampling has been carried out at three sites, Mansion Meadow, Spring Meadow and the Orchard; we have usually sampled all three sites each year, and taken 25 samples, each of $0.1\,m^2$, at each site. The earthworms have been extracted by repulsion with formalin (Raw, 1959). The population estimates have varied from year to year between 12 and 276 per square metre at Spring Meadow; similar variation has been recorded at the other sites (Table 1.3).

In Spring and Mansion Meadows, the yearly variation is quite strongly correlated with the June rainfall ($r = 0.56$): see Fig. 1.6. There is, further, an interesting negative correlation at these two sites between the percentage of pigmented worms and the total sample of worms: when few worms are obtained, most of them are pigmented. Pigmented worms, principally *Lumbricus*, are those that live in burrows and come to the surface at night to feed on dead vegetation, which they pull into their burrows; these are the worms on which Badger, Fox and thrushes prey. By contrast, the unpigmented worms, primarily species belonging to *Allolobophora*, do not come to the surface, but often aestivate in dry weather; they are likely to be more important to the Mole *Talpa europaea* (Haeck, 1969). We have investigated the low catches in dry years by hand sorting; this has revealed that the unpigmented worms are indeed coiled up tightly, aestivating, and thus unable to respond to formalin. Thus in dry years, out class samples contain fewer worms, but most of them are the active, pigmented ones. There is, of course, one important lesson here for other ecologists interested in earthworms as prey; the mass of worms can be sampled effectively by formalin (since *Lumbricus terrestris* is much the heaviest worm, and quite numerous) but the greatest number of worms, the smaller unpigmented species, may not be amenable to sampling in this manner if conditions are dry.

Table 1.3 Earthworm numbers and rainfall. Earthworm numbers are the total in a 2.5 m² sample (25 × 0.1 m² samples) and the percentage of pigmented worms in these samples, for the three sites, Orchard, Mansion Meadow and Spring Meadow. Rainfall (mm) is the monthly, two-monthly, or three-monthly total for Birmingham.

Year	Orchard		Mansion		Spring		Rainfall		
	N	% pigmented	N	% pigmented	N	% pigmented	June	May–June	April–June
1970	—	—	135	38.5	—	—	48	78	166
1971	365	30.7	—	—	479	13.2	74	111	164
1972	368	56.0	433	26.1	433	38.3	62	130	177
1973	96	52.1	164	65.9	247	62.3	74	175	240
1974	145	100.0	—	—	97	100.0	42	75	90
1975	18	100.0	56	100.0	30	100.0	18	40	102
1976	47	68.1	83	77.1	133	60.2	21	72	88
1977	144	13.2	257	28.0	—	—	118	158	209
1978	56	28.6	—	—	200	35.0	37	70	115
1979	7	42.9	{94	55.3	170	52.4	16	140	209
			{80	62.5					
1980	249	27.7	383	38.6	689	29.8	107	130	148
1981	334	50.9	419	75.2	289	57.1	22	111	150
1982	246	47.6	242	41.7	279	58.1	145	174	198
1983	154	83.8	111	93.7	97	62.9	21	121	220

Regression of % pigmented on log N:

	b	t_b	r	t_r
M + S	− 23.68	5.14	0.738	4.34
O	− 5.13	0.77	0.227	0.73

Regression of log N *on rainfall*:

June	0.0102	3.04	0.562	2.77
May–June	0.0092	2.66	0.511	2.46
April–June	0.0053	1.57	0.332	1.50

Moth sampling using mercury-vapour light-traps has been a prominent feature of the field courses, and our data provide a long-term record of the moth fauna of the valley. Robin Baker has shown that moth-traps sited only a few metres apart may collect samples of moths that differ in their composition qualitatively and quantitatively, but an overall picture of the moth fauna can be obtained by examining moth samples collected on the Cottage lawns over the 16 years of our visits (excepting 1972, which was a poor moth year and sampling was not undertaken). Data for yearly samples are presented in Table 1.4 (microlepidoptera are excluded). Species diversity (α) rises and falls from year to year and there is no clear long-term trend and no obvious correlation with weather. We had thought that diversity might decline with the growth of conifer plantations and a general simplification of the valley's flora, but this is not apparent in the data. Highest values for species diversity were obtained in 1979 (both zoology and biology field courses). The two most abundant species in the samples overall

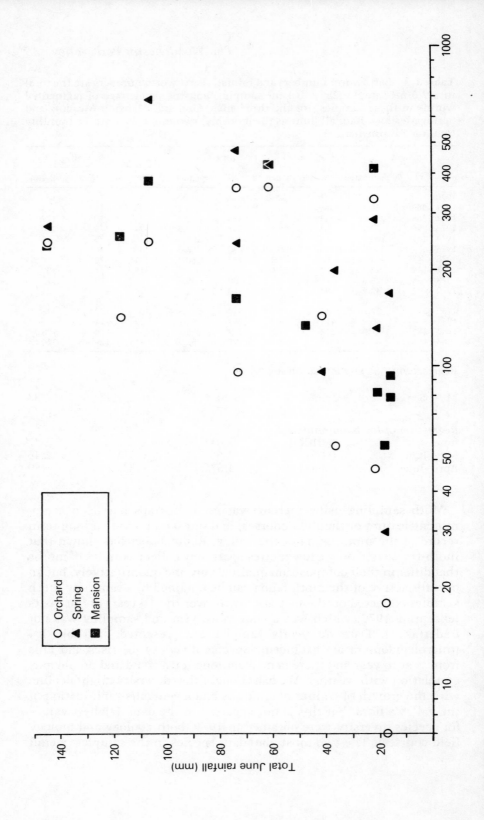

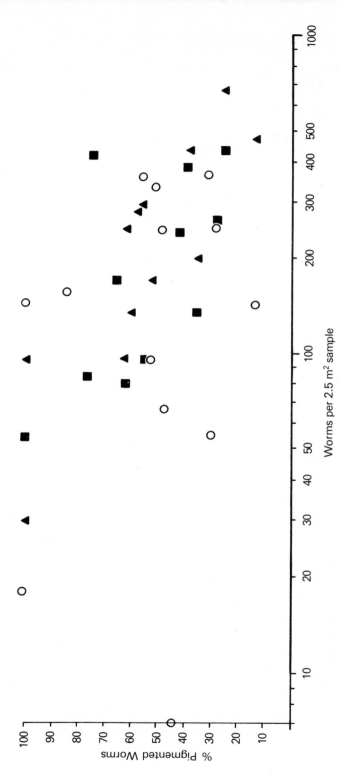

Fig. 1.6 Earthworm numbers and rainfall. Top: Earthworm numbers per 2.5 m² sample, at three sites for 12 years, plotted against June rainfall in those years. Bottom: Earthworm numbers per 2.5 m² sample, for three sites and 12 years, plotted against the percentage of pigmented worms in those samples (see Table 1.3).

Table 1.4 Annual variation in moths caught at Woodchester Park in relation to variation in weather.

Year	Date	N moths per trap night	LYU + HD[a] (% total moths)	Ratio LYU:HD	Warmth of spring[b]	Warmth of nights[c]	Spring rainfall (mm)[d]	Severity of winter[e]
1967	3 July	67.9	28.4	1.13	399	167	135	—
1968	29 June	551.6	56.4	3.95	415	165	331	44
1969	9 July	220.5	30.6	1.96	531	198	249	53
1970	25 June	368.3	84.1	0.64	476	147	166	60
1971	23 June	67.2	31.1	0.18	330	86	164	24
1973	3 July	515.5	68.3	9.25	424	167	240	20
1974	27 June	107.0	66.8	0.66	401	147	90	21
1975	30 June	90.3	55.5	0.37	418	147	102	18
1976	25 June	572.7	68.7	0.09	512	170	88	32
1976	12 July	190.3	25.8	0.91	767	324	88	32
1977	20 June	97.4	24.3	0.0	280	77	209	34
1977	10 July	53.0	32.6	0.05	424	174	209	34
1978	26 June	43.5	55.7	0.20	353	148	115	34
1978	13 July	37.3	36.2	4.40	472	235	115	34
1979	25 June	32.0	11.6	0.86	349	140	209	79
1979	13 July	49.7	26.9	1.44	510	265	209	79
1980	23 June	56.2	68.7	0.31	491	113	148	60
1980	12 July	55.9	69.9	1.96	633	195	148	60
1981	22 June	14.7	16.8	0.16	376	110	150	53
1981	10 July	30.9	36.3	2.78	524	204	150	53
1982	21 June	145.0	58.8	1.80	540	140	198	62
1982	9 July	644.5	60.8	6.11	711	244	198	62

[a] HD, Heart-and-Dart *Agrotis exclamationis*; LYU, Large Yellow Underwing *Noctua pronuba*.
[b] Warmth of spring: degree-days, April to third day of field course, with maximum temperature above 10°C.
[c] Warmth of nights: degree-days, June, with minimum temperature above 5°C.
[d] Spring rainfall: total rainfall (mm) April–June inclusive.
[e] Severity of winter: number of frost-days in preceding winter.

are the Large Yellow Underwing (*Noctua pronuba*) and the Heart-and-Dart (*Agrotis exclamationis*). A sample dominated by a small number of common species will be a sample of low species diversity and there is an inverse relationship between the proportion of a sample composed of these two species and sample diversity ($r = -0.49$, $P < 0.02$). The Heart-and-Dart usually emerges before the Large Yellow Underwing, although there is a great deal of overlap, and there should therefore be a tendency for the ratio Large Yellow Underwing : Heart-and-Dart to be high in 'early' years and low in 'late' years. It is noteworthy that the ratio is always higher for the biology course than for the zoology course in the same year, the biology course following the zoology course. Large Yellow Underwings exceeded Heart-and-Darts on the zoology courses of 1967, 1968, 1969, 1973 and 1982. These were all early or moderately early years with warm springs, but so too were 1970, 1974, 1975, 1976 and 1980, in which Large Yellow Underwings were not especially abundant. A ratio between the numbers of two species is a measure subject to a variety of disturbances. It is interesting, therefore, to find a correlation between the Large Yellow Underwing : Heart-and-Dart ratio and the numbers of two butterfly species observed on censuses of the Woodchester Park valley. The Marbled White *Melanargia galathea* and Meadow Brown *Maniola jurtina* are satyrid butterflies with grass-feeding caterpillars, both common in the valley. The Marbled White emerges later than the Meadow Brown and there is a good correlation ($r = 0.95$, $P < 0.004$) between Large Yellow Underwing : Heart-and-Dart and Marbled White : Meadow Brown ratios for the 6 years on which butterfly censuses have been conducted on the zoology course (Table 1.5). This suggests that the phenology of these four species, all of which have caterpillars that feed near to the ground surface, is similarly influenced by conditions prevailing in a year.

In an attempt at further analyses of the variation in our moth catches from year to year, we applied a stepwise multiple regression analysis, comparing the number of moths caught per trap night with four climatic variables : (i) warmth of spring, (ii) spring rainfall, (iii) warmth of the nights prior to and during our course, and (iv) severity of the previous winter (Table 1.4). Three of these were significantly correlated with moth numbers, warmth of spring and spring rainfall being positively correlated but winter severity being negatively correlated; in other words, warm, wet springs following mild winters tend to result in a high moth catch. However, these three variables only accounted for about 39% of the variation in moth catch from year to year, so that other factors are also important. We can, at present, only guess at what these might be; the size of the predator population(s), the amount of moonlight on the nights we are trapping (see Chapter 6 by Dr Baker) and the strength of the wind might be among them.

Butterflies have been recorded regularly, but a quantitative census,

Table 1.5 Ratios of numbers of Large Yellow Underwings (LYU) to Heart-and-Darts (HD), and of Marbled Whites (MW) to Meadow Browns (MB) recorded on zoology field courses. There is a strong correlation between the two ratios ($r = 0.95$, $P < 0.004$).

	LYU : HD	MW : MB
1977	0	0
1978	0.20	0.01
1979	0.86	0.37
1980	0.31	0.47
1981	0.16	0
1982	1.80	1.43

in which a record is kept of numbers of each species seen in defined sections of the valley, was started only in 1977. Thirty-five species have been recorded from the valley (Table 1.6). Twenty butterfly species were recorded in the first two years (1967 and 1968), and five more in 1969 and 1970. The next two years, 1971 and 1972, were both late years and produced the first record of the Pearl-bordered Fritillary and the only records of the Wall and Duke of Burgundy Fritillary. These are all butterflies with a spring flight period which is normally over before the end of June. The next significant year was 1976 with its hot summer coinciding with the first biology field course in mid-July. During this course, Gatekeeper, Brimstone and Small Copper (surprisingly not found previously) were added to the list, and on an afternoon

Table 1.6 Butterfly species recorded from the valley. Year first recorded and number of years (out of 16) in which recorded also given.

Dingy Skipper	1970 (4)	Marbled White	1967 (16)
Erynnis tages		*Melanargia galathea*	
Grizzled Skipper	1968 (3)	Ringlet	1967 (16)
Pyrgus malvae		*Aphantopus hyperantus*	
Small Skipper	1967 (8)	Meadow Brown	1967 (16)
Thymelicus sylvestris		*Maniola jurtina*	
Large Skipper	1967 (16)	Small Heath	1967 (15)
Ochlodes venata		*Coenonympha pamphilus*	
Green Hairstreak	1970 (2)	Wall	1971 (1)
Callophrys rubi		*Lasiommata megera*	
White-letter Hairstreak	1970 (3)	Speckled Wood	1967 (16)
Strymonidia w-album		*Pararge aegeria*	
Small Copper	1976 (4)	Gatekeeper	1976 (2)
Lycaena phlaeas		*Pyronia tithonus*	
Holly Blue	1973 (3)	Marsh Fritillary	1976 (1)
Celastrina argiolis		*Euphydryas aurinia*	
Small Blue	1976 (8)	Pearl-bordered Fritillary	1971 (4)
Cupido minimus		*Boloria euphrosyne*	
Common Blue	1968 (9)	Small Pearl-bordered Fritillary	1979 (1)
Polyommatus icarus		*Boloria selene*	
Brown Argus	1968 (3)	Dark-green Fritillary	1967 (5)
Aricia agestis		*Argynnis aglaja*	
Duke of Burgundy	1972 (1)	Silver-washed Fritillary	1970 (7)
Hamearis lucina		*Argynnis paphia*	
Brimstone	1976 (1)	White Admiral	1982 (1)
Gonepteryx rhamni		*Ladoga camilla*	
Orange Tip	1970 (3)	Peacock	1967 (9)
Anthocharis cardamines		*Inachis io*	
Green-veined White	1967 (16)	Painted Lady	1968 (5)
Pieris napi		*Cynthia cardui*	
Small White	1968 (15)	Red Admiral	1968 (9)
Pieris rapae		*Vanessa atalanta*	
Large White	1968 (14)	Small Tortoiseshell	1968 (15)
Pieris brassicae		*Aglais urticae*	
		Comma	1969 (8)
		Polygonia c-album	

visit to the valley on 8 June a number of Marsh Fritillaries was seen. This last was an unexpected discovery since the valley is an unlikely habitat for the species. The White Admiral, first seen in 1982, is the latest species to be added and may reflect an expansion in range rather than the discovery of a previously overlooked butterfly.

Similar changes in other groups include the Mandarin Duck *Aix galericulata*, first recorded in the valley in 1978 and present in most subsequent years, and the appearance of Roe Deer *Capreolus capreolus* in 1982 and Muntjac *Muntiacus reevesi* in 1983. Conversely, the Great Crested Grebe, *Podiceps cristatus*, which bred successfully in 1967, the year of our first visit, and increased to four or five pairs by 1975, has failed to breed since 1979; increased disturbance and vegetation clearance, accompanying increased angling activity at about that time, is probably responsible.

Such changes, both gains and losses, emphasise the dynamic aspects of ecology. It is these that maintain our interest in the site, and provide much of the interest also in the subsequent chapters.

References

Bishop, J.A. & Bradley, J.S. (1972) Taxi-cabs as subjects for a population study. *Journal of Biological Education*, **6**, 227–31.

Blower, J.G. (1958) *Millipedes*. Linnean Society Synopses of the British Fauna, **11**.

Blower, J.G. (1985) *Millipedes*. Linnean Society Synopses of the British Fauna, **00** (2nd edn).

Blower, J.G., Cook, L.M. & Bishop, J.A. (1981) *Estimating the Size of Animal Populations*. London: Allen & Unwin.

Cave, R. (1977) Geology of the Malmesbury District. NERC/IGS Memoir for One-inch Geological sheet 251 (NS) London: HMSO.

Darby, H.C. & Terret, I.B. (1954) *The Domesday Geography of Midland England*. Cambridge: Cambridge University Press.

Haeck, J. (1969) Colonization of the mole (*Talpa europaea* L.) in the Ijsselmeerpolders. *Netherlands Journal of Zoology*, **19**, 145–248.

Herbert, N.M. (1972) King's Stanley, in *Victoria History of the County of Gloucestershire*, vol. 10, Pugh, R.B., ed. London: Oxford University Press, pp. 242–57.

Herbert, N.M. & Sheils, W.J. (1976) Nailsworth, in *Victoria History of the County of Gloucestershire*, vol. 11, Pugh, R.B., ed. London: Oxford University Press, pp. 207–17.

Kruuk, H. (1978) Foraging and spatial organisation of the European badger *Meles meles* L. *Behavioural Ecology and Sociobiology*, **4**, 75–89.

Macdonald, D.W. (1980) The Red Fox, *Vulpes vulpes*, as a predator on earthworms, *Lumbricus terrestris*. *Zeitschrift für Tierpsychologie*, **52**, 171–200.

Minchin, G.S. (1907) Table of population, in *Victoria History of the County of Gloucestershire*, vol. **2**, Page, W., ed London: Constable, *pp*. 173–87.

Nisbet, J. & Vellacott, C.H. (1907) Forestry, in *Victoria History of the County of Gloucestershire*, vol. 2, Page, W., ed. London: Constable, pp. 263–86.

Raw, F. (1959) Estimating earthworm populations by using formalin. *Nature, London*, **184**, 1661–2.

Rudge, T. (1807) *A general view of the agriculture of the county of Gloucestershire*. Drawn up for the consideration of the Board of Agriculture. London.

Sheils, W.J. (1976) Woodchester, in *Victoria History of the County of Gloucestershire*, vol. 11, Pugh, R.B., ed. London: Oxford University Press, pp. 294–304.

Smith, A.H. (1964a,b) *The Place-names of Gloucestershire*, Parts 1 and 2. English Place-names Society, **38** and **39**. Cambridge: Cambridge University Press.

Thorley, A. (1981) Pollen analytical evidence relating to the vegetation history of the chalk. *Journal of Biogeography*, **8**, 93–106.

Verey, D. (1969) Woodchester Park, Gloucestershire. *Country Life*, **145**, 284–8.

Winstanley, D., Spencer, R. & Williamson, K. (1974) Where have all the Whitethroats gone? *Bird Study*, **21**, 1–14.

Yalden, D.W. (1971) A population of the yellow-necked mouse *Apodemus flavicollis*. *Journal of Zoology, London*, **164**, 244–50.

2   R.J. White

Some population study methods illustrated with the Scarlet Tiger moth

Introduction

In this chapter the emphasis is on the properties of a population which must be investigated in order to obtain an adequate understanding of the important processes shaping the population. One aim of the chapter is to show that capture–recapture sampling methods can reveal much more about populations than just their size. For example, the extra effort involved in a marking scheme which allows individuals to be recognised pays considerable dividends. Data from several adjacent colonies of the moth *Callimorpha (Panaxia) dominula* (L.) are used to derive estimates for dispersal rates, spatial distribution, survival rates and population size. These parameters are obtained separately for the two sexes, whose behaviour differs, and for the different colonies.

A second objective is to summarise current knowledge of the population structure and dynamics of the Scarlet Tiger moth colonies at Woodchester. It is hoped that this will show how a full understanding of a natural population can only be achieved by the integration of several lines of investigation: in the present study these are the capture–recapture analysis of the adults, quadrat-based sampling of the larval stages, and simulation as a means for both suggesting and testing hypotheses about the ways in which the observed population properties arise. The usefulness of such an understanding is demonstrated in the interpretation of some morphological data reflecting underlying genetic diversity both within and between colonies.

Animals living in discrete populations, that is to say in well-defined areas or 'colonies' separate from other such areas, have several advantages over more widespread species. One is that the scope of the study is automatically defined; if more than one colony is being studied, then the effort is broken into manageable pieces. Thinking about the differences between the populations is a powerful way of stimulating new ideas; some of these may lead to the formulation of hypotheses which can then be tested. This is a crucial aspect of any scientific study, and is frequently neglected in ecological surveys.

Ecology

Callimorpha dominula is a brightly coloured day-flying tiger moth. It is distasteful to birds (Kettlewell, 1973: p. 277) and has warningly coloured forewings in black with white and yellow spots. The hind-wings are red with black markings.

The eggs are smooth and non-adhesive and are scattered by the female with no particular regard for the food plants of the larvae. There is a wide range of these (Table 2.6), but usually only two or three are eaten to any extent in a given colony. The half-grown larvae hibernate in dead leaves or grass tussocks, and complete their growth in the spring. Pupation takes place in May, apparently in leaf litter. Kettle-well (1943) and Fisher & Ford (1947) describe the life cycle in greater detail.

The adults occur at Woodchester in late June and for most of July, the exact period of the flying season varying from year to year. They emerge soon after dawn. Females start to produce a male-attracting pheromone (Kettlewell, 1943, 1946) around noon, and by late after-noon have usually commenced copulation. Females mate once only but some males may mate several times.

Previous work on the Scarlet Tiger moth has been fairly extensive. Cockayne (1928) and Kettlewell (1943) discuss the variation found in the species. An ecogenetic approach has been taken by Fisher & Ford (1947), Sheppard (1951), and Sheppard & Cook (1962), studying, at a colony near Cothill, Berkshire, a polymorphism controlled by a single gene locus. The frequency of the gene and the population size of the colony have been monitored for many years (Ford, 1975).

Cook (1960, 1961) made an ecological study, suggesting that in Britain the moth is on the edge of its range and may show certain adaptations such as greater specialisation in habitat and food-plant choice than is found in the rest of Europe. This work has been followed up by Cowley (1976), who made a quantitative assessment of the moth's life cycle in two Woodchester colonies (Coaley Peak and Marmontsflat Wood).

White (1974) also studied these colonies, with others, but concentrated on aspects of the variability and dispersal of the adult stage. Some of the results of these two studies are reported here.

Distribution

The moth is found in colonies, up to a few hundred metres across, from which it rarely strays. The distribution of the moth in Britain is described by Cook (1959), and a further list of colonies is provided by

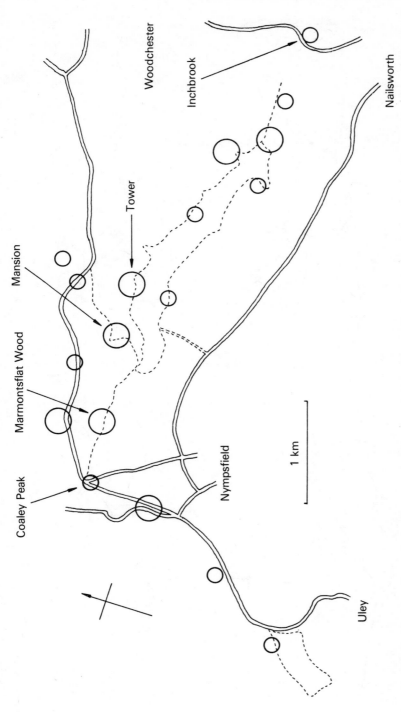

Fig. 2.1 Distribution in and around the Woodchester valley. This map is based on sightings from 1971 to 1974. Large and small circles represent the position but not the shape of large and small colonies. The colonies mentioned in the text are identified. Roads and footpaths are marked.

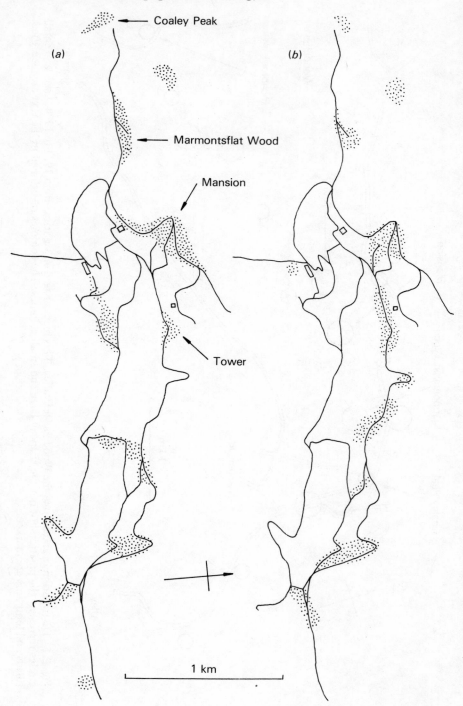

(a)

(b)

Coaley Peak

Marmontsflat Wood

Mansion

Tower

1 km

White (1974: Appendix I). These colonies occur in widely scattered groups, often associated with river systems. One such group is centred on the Woodchester valley and adjacent hills in the southern Cotswolds and consists of over 20 colonies (Fig. 2.1). Eleven of these extend along the limestone scarp from Stinchcombe Hill near Dursley to Scottsquar Hill north of Stroud. Ten colonies are known from the valley itself, from Marmontsflat Wood at the upper, western end, to Inchbrook at the eastern end. Not all the valley colonies now remain, but in 1973 there were 14 colonies within a radius of 2 km from the Woodchester Park Field Centre (Fig. 2.2).

The adult populations

Capture-recapture methods

Sampling A capture–recapture analysis, as the name implies, assumes that each individual in a population can be classified when encountered or 'captured' according to the time of any previous capture. The encounter of a previously recorded individual is known as a 'recapture'. Normally individuals cannot be recognised on sight, and some form of marking must be adopted.

There are two types of marking commonly used: date marking and individual marking. When date marking is used, each individual is given a mark which identifies the time of its capture. If a marked individual is recaptured, it is given another date mark. Thus individuals can be classified according to their 'capture history', but two individuals with the same capture history cannot be distinguished. This type of marking is relatively simple since only a small number of distinct marks is required, and only one type of mark is needed on any one sampling occasion. However, in a study involving many sampling occasions, it may be difficult to design marks which might be needed in any combination. Date marking is adequate for all the commonly used methods of capture–recapture analysis, and its use is described by Blower *et al.* (1981).

Individual marking involves giving each individual its own unique mark. This may require a more complex marking scheme than date marking, but more information is potentially available since each individual can be recognised. It is always possible to reconstruct the

Fig. 2.2 (opposite)   The valley colonies. The main Woodchester valley tracks are shown twice, with stippling representing the Scarlet Tiger moth distribution based on information (*a*) from 1970 to 1974, and (*b*) for 1982 and 1983. Population parameters are discussed in the text for those colonies identified and for the earlier period of study.

same data tables as provided by date marking studies, and hence the same methods of analysis are applicable. However, if additional information such as capture location is recorded at every sighting, the data may be used for other purposes such as movement studies in addition to the estimation of the usual population parameters such as population size and survival rate provided by the basic capture–recapture analysis methods.

The extra information obtainable from the use of individual marks is so desirable that date-specific marking should not normally be considered. Giving individuals distinct marks usually involves little extra effort when they are first encountered, and on subsequent recapture occasions the need for further marking is avoided. In most field studies the time spent marking individuals is a small proportion of the total effort expended, so the aim should be to recover as much information as possible from each recapture.

Parameters usually estimated   The most obvious parameter of a population is its size, the number of individuals it contains at a given moment. In addition, two other parameters determine the changes in the population size from one time to another. These are the 'residence rate', which is the probability of an individual remaining in the population from a given instant for a further unit of time (or the proportion of such individuals in the Fisher–Ford method), and the 'dilution rate', which is a measure of the number of new individuals entering the population. The common capture–recapture estimation methods provide estimates of these parameters for the time of each sampling occasion.

It is important to note that, in a study of a single population in a defined area, it is not possible to distinguish between individuals which die and those which leave the area, or between those which are newly 'born' or freshly emerged and those which have just entered the area. Thus the residence rate is a combination of the rates of survival (or mortality) and emigration, and the dilution rate is a combination of the rates of birth (natality) and immigration. In the rest of this chapter, the term 'survival rate' will be used loosely in the sense of the residence rate defined above.

Principles of the estimation methods   The fundamental principle of the various capture–recapture methods discussed here is that of the 'Lincoln' or 'Peterson' Index. A known number of individuals in a population are marked or are otherwise distinguishable, and a random sample of individuals is then taken from the population. The product of the number of marked individuals in the population and the proportion of marked individuals in the random sample is an estimate of the total size of the population.

Normally the marked individuals in the population are put there by means of a sample which is caught, marked, and released on an occasion prior to the random sample used to obtain the population estimate. A crucial assumption of this estimation process, and of the more complex methods derived from it, is that the second sample is truly random in the sense that the probability of capture of an individual is independent of whether or not the individual is marked. There are many ways in which this requirement may not be met, and any one of these may seriously bias the results.

It is highly desirable that some consideration be given to testing whether the data to be analysed meet this fundamental assumption. In general this cannot be done after the data have been collected since none of the suggested statistical tests seems to be effective (Roff, 1973). Therefore some preliminary experimental studies are required that are specifically designed to test the hypothesis of 'equal catchability'. Experiments of this type, such as those of Morton (1982), have not been carried out using *C. dominula*.

Sequential sampling methods Some other limitations of the simple Lincoln Index method are overcome in the more advanced methods. One such drawback is that no mortality of the marked individuals may occur between the first (marking) and second (estimation) samples, for otherwise the number of marked individuals at the time of the second sample would not be accurately known. Reducing the time interval between the samples is not usually advisable since one of the ways of trying to get a reasonably random second sample is to allow enough time for the marked individuals to recover from their capture and to disperse throughout the study area. Another difficulty with the simple Lincoln Index approach is that it is frequently not possible to get large enough samples on either the first or the second occasion for an accurate estimate. The samples must both be large because the precision of the estimate depends on the number of marked individuals (recaptures) in the second sample.

Both limitations can be avoided by the use of more than two sampling occasions. The number of marked individuals in the population gradually increases as the result of successive sampling operations, thus providing more recaptures. Also, several population estimates can be obtained, since most sampling occasions serve both to mark new individuals and to obtain estimates of the proportion which are already marked. By distinguishing different classes of capture history, the various methods obtain estimates for the survival and dilution rates. The ways in which this is done largely explain the differences between the methods.

The choice of capture–recapture analysis method   The earliest of the methods considered here is that of Fisher & Ford (1947), who described a method derived from the study of Dowdeswell *et al.* (1940). In this method a single survival rate is assumed to apply throughout the period of study, irrespective of the weather, the age of the individuals, or other factors.

This method is based on a theoretically unsatisfactory 'deterministic' model, which defines the survival rate as the proportion of individuals alive at a given time that are still alive one day (or other unit of time) later. However, the survival or otherwise of a single individual is in reality statistically unrelated to the survival of other individuals, and more modern methods are all based on a 'stochastic' model whereby the survival rate is defined as the probability of a single individual surviving from one time to the next. The actual proportion that survives is therefore subject to random fluctuation.

However, the Fisher–Ford method has often been used in entomological studies, despite its deterministic nature, because a single survival rate estimate is obtained. A standard error for the survival rate estimate can be obtained as described by Leslie & Chitty (1951). The Fisher–Ford method often proves more effective than other methods when sampling is at irregular intervals and the sampling fraction is low (Bishop & Sheppard, 1973).

Other methods, which provide a series of survival rates, require more extensive data, particularly more recaptures, to obtain equally good estimates of population size. This is an inevitable result of the general statistical rule that the estimation of more parameters requires more data. Recently, Jolly (1982) has developed a stochastic method (his method B) which assumes a single constant probability of survival. There is little experience of the use of this method as yet, but it should probably replace the less soundly based Fisher–Ford method.

Jolly's previous (1965) method A is the best known of the methods that estimate a series of survival rates. Standard errors are provided for all the main series of estimates, that is survival rate, population size, and dilution rate. Another method is that of Manly & Parr (1968). This method estimates more or less the same quantities as Jolly's method A, but does so by using the capture histories in a different way. In particular, it needs a substantial number of individuals which have been captured at least three times. This requirement makes it even more dependent on the availability of good data than Jolly's method A, but if the number of recaptures are high, it can produce estimates which are less affected by possible age-dependent survival than those of the other methods. It is frequently assumed in insect studies that mortality is fairly random and does not depend on the age of the insect; thus the Manly–Parr method has not been extensively used by entomologists.

The most commonly used methods are those of Fisher & Ford, Jolly (1965), and Manly & Parr. Most recent studies of butterfly populations have used Jolly's method A, although Cook *et al.* (1976) used all three methods in a study of a tropical butterfly, *Heliconius charitonius* (L.). It is suggested that future studies should consider the use of Jolly's (1982) method B. However, computer programs for this method, desirable in view of the repetitive nature of the calculations, are not yet widely available.

Requirements　For capture–recapture methods to be successful, there is obviously a need to use organisms which can be caught alive in sufficient numbers and which can be marked easily. Insects have been used extensively for this purpose, and Ehrlich & Davidson (1960) suggest an individual marking system for butterflies and provide a compendium of useful sampling techniques. It is necessary either that the animals should disperse well within the area being sampled or that sampling should be even over the entire area.

A reasonable sampling intensity is required to produce sufficiently accurate estimates. Because of the underlying Lincoln Index formula, the precision of the population estimate depends on the smallest value involved, which is the number of recaptures. Thus a study in which few recaptures are obtained on some occasions will not provide accurate estimates for those occasions. A preliminary study is often advisable to establish whether the sampling effort which is practicable is capable of producing good results. Often the only criterion by which the estimates can be judged is their own internal consistency: wild fluctuations from day to day are unlikely to reflect the true situation.

Sometimes there are trade-offs involved when planning a sampling programme. For example, the use of the Fisher–Ford or Jolly B methods may provide better population size estimates at the expense of the loss of information about whether the survival rate is fluctuating. The choice of the sampling interval is also important. Daily samples are frequently chosen for the data collection, but in the analysis of a long sequence of samples with few recaptures, it may be better to group the daily samples into larger units.

It is also possible that several smaller analyses of the data should be made in preference to one large analysis. In the work described below, separate analyses were performed for each sex and for different colonies. This is necessary if such subpopulations are likely to provide different estimates of important parameters. On the other hand, if the population is subdivided too much, the estimates obtained in each analysis may become highly inaccurate.

Alternative strategies   A different approach to the calculation of a mean survival or residence rate is based on the decline in the probability of recapture with the time since an individual's first encounter (Watt *et al.*, 1977; Tabashnik, 1980). Such estimates can usefully be compared with those obtained from the standard capture–recapture methods, possibly using the formula of Scott (1973*b*) to obtain a mean survival rate from those methods which do not provide one.

There are several alternatives to the multiple sample capture-recapture study if the population size is the main parameter of interest. If the sampling intensity is high enough for individuals to be encountered repeatedly during the course of one sampling occasion, the methods of Craig (1953) and Eberhardt (1969) can be used. These methods can also in some circumstances be used to determine whether the population is open (subject to immigration) or closed. In this way the ambiguity in the interpretation of the dilution rate may be resolved.

For the estimation of the population size of active and conspicuous organisms such as some Lepidoptera, there are various 'transect' methods which rely on the application of constant searching effort in a fixed transect or other defined area of the population. In these methods, such as those of Douwes (1970) and Pollard (1977), the insects are merely counted without the need for capture. Hence the advantage of low disturbance to the population is balanced by the inability to obtain subsidiary information such as survival and dispersal rates. Douwes (1970) has compared the results with Jolly's method A. However, these methods are not necessarily mutually exclusive. The advantages of both can be had if marking and recapturing are carried out on separate occasions. Conspicuously marked individuals need not be disturbed when 'recaptured' if individual marks are used.

Brown & Ehrlich (1980) found that the Jolly method A population size estimates correlated very well with the numbers of individuals captured in each sample, given a constant sampling effort on each occasion. This can be useful to fill in gaps in the Jolly estimates caused by few or no recaptures on some occasions. Such gaps are particularly prone to occur at the beginning and end of the adult 'flying season' in Lepidoptera.

The adult capture-recapture programme

The following colonies were included in the complete study: Coaley Peak, 1971–1976; Marmontsflat Wood, 1970–1976; Mansion, 1972–

1974; Tower, 1973 only. Data for 1974 to 1976 inclusive are not analysed here.

Sampling methods Sampling was carried out daily, except during exceptionally bad weather. Two methods were used to capture moths: the netting of both sexes as they flew past or were encountered on herbage or Hogweed flowers (*Heracleum sphondylium* L.), and the trapping of males in assembly traps. The traps used the scent of one or two virgin females to attract the males. Assembly trapping was not used at the Coaley Peak colony, or at Marmontsflat Wood in 1971. The technique of searching and netting was employed in all colonies except at Marmontsflat Wood in 1970.

The use of assembly trapping necessitated early-morning searches for eligible newly emerged females. They were usually placed in the traps by about 1200 GMT. Male moths are attracted to the females mainly during the afternoon, and the traps were emptied in the evenings. In this way, male moths were not confined in the traps (which would reduce their dispersal and perhaps increase their survival) for more than a few hours.

Each moth was given a unique mark (if it was not already marked) and its location and the way in which it was caught were recorded. In addition, the moth's sex and condition (subjective estimates of the degrees of fading and wing damage similar to those of Watt *et al.*, 1977) were recorded, together with whether it was 'normal' or exhibited any unusual wing pattern.

Dispersal rates and spatial distribution Distances flown by re-captured moths are shown as a histogram in Fig. 2.3, expressed as the distance moved per day between successive captures. The main feature is the very short distance moved by such a large moth. Mean movement rates are summarised in Table 2.1. The rates are correlated with the length of the colony, being about one-twentieth of it in all colonies except Tower. This colony may really be an outlying part of the Mansion colony.

The distances moved by a few individuals, however, were very much greater than the mean distance. In the years 1971, 1972 and 1973, no moths were observed to move between Coaley Peak and any other colony. The distance from Coaley Peak to the edge of the nearest other colony studied (Marmontsflat Wood) is 500 m. In 1972 and 1973 when the Mansion colony was included, five moths out of a total of 409 recaptures moved from Marmontsflat Wood to Mansion or the reverse. One out of the ten 1973 recaptures at Tower had come from Mansion.

These movements were all less than 800 m. In the years 1949 to

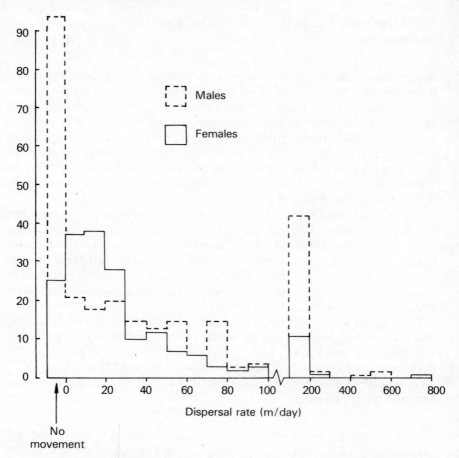

Fig. 2.3 Distances flown by recaptured moths. Data from Marmontsflat Wood and Mansion, 1971–1973. Note the change in the scale of dispersal rate to accommodate the larger distances travelled. The large number of male recaptures showing no movement was due to the use of traps of fixed locations. Where a moth was recaptured more than once, each recapture has provided a separate estimate of the daily rate of movement.

1968, out of about 200 recaptures in which this could have been detected, no moths moved between the Cothill and Sheepstead Hurst colonies (Ford, 1975), which are about 2 km apart.

The possible influence of this dispersal behaviour on the distribution of the colonies of the mainly diurnal Scarlet Tiger moth will be considered later in this chapter. In Chapter 6, Robin Baker discusses some influences on the movement of night-flying moths and shows how a knowledge of these factors is not only of intrinsic interest, but

Table 2.1 Adult dispersal and survival rate estimates.

Year	Colony	Number of recaptures		Dispersal rate[a]		Survival rate[b]	
		Males	Females	Males	Females	Males	Females
1971–1973	Coaley Peak	34	127	7.0	5.6	0.79	0.72
1970	Marmontsflat Wood	119	—	17.3	—	0.44	—
1971–1973	Marmontsflat Wood	186	122	18.2	15.2	0.64	0.66
1972–1973	Mansion	84	62	26.0	13.3	0.66	0.66
1973	Tower	5	4	7.6	52.4	0.61	0.57

[a] The dispersal rate is expressed in metres per day, calculated from the distance between successive captures.
[b] The survival rate is the estimated probability of survival for one day (24 h) using the Fisher–Ford method.

also calls into question the possibility of designing a sampling programme.

More detailed methods for quantifying and analysing individual movements are illustrated by Scott (1973a; 1975). Such information may be obtained at very little extra cost if individual marking is used, especially if the rather tedious analysis is done by computer.

Population size estimates Instantaneous population sizes are shown graphically in Fig. 2.4. In an insect population where the adults are only found at a particular time of the year, it is useful for the sequence of sampling occasions to span the whole 'season'; in this case it is

Table 2.2 Adult population size estimates.

Year	Colony	Number of recaptures		Population size estimates[a]		
		Males	Females	Males	Females	Total
1971	Coaley Peak	14	28	109	97	192
1972	Coaley Peak	17	58	115	89	206
1973	Coaley Peak	3	41	26	125	165
1970	Marmontsflat Wood	119	—	3221	—	6443[b]
1971	Marmontsflat Wood	21	31	1370	1126	3340
1972	Marmontsflat Wood	79	20	4441	865	6214
1973	Marmontsflat Wood	86	71	2875	1853	5191
1972	Mansion	41	6	4259	1476	7505
1973	Mansion	43	56	5129	4924	11053
1973	Tower	5	4	899	915	2012

[a] Population sizes were estimated by the Fisher–Ford method.
[b] Twice the estimate for males.

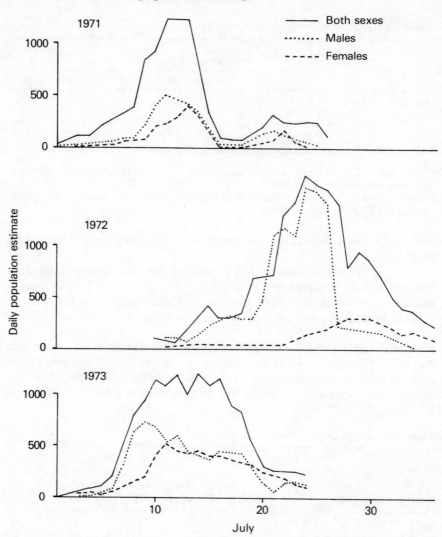

Fig. 2.4 Daily population sizes for Marmontsflat Wood. The estimates were obtained using the method of Fisher & Ford, applied separately to the male and female data. The estimates for the two sexes combined were produce from the pooled data; these estimates differ slightly from the sum of the separate male and female estimates.

possible to obtain an estimate of the total number of individuals passing through the adult stage in one year, for example by summing the numbers of individuals estimated to have died each day. The total number of adults emerging in each population is shown in Table 2.2.

The main conclusions are that the Coaley Peak colony is very small, whereas the Marmontsflat Wood and Mansion colonies are much larger. The latter two colonies are of comparable size to the Cothill colony (Ford, 1975).

These sizes have no bearing on the relative permanence of the colonies. At the time of writing (1983) the Coaley Peak colony has persisted at approximately the same size, though its densest part has shifted to the other side of a road. The Mansion colony appears subjectively to have declined greatly since the studies reported, and Marmontsflat Wood has become nearly extinct. It may be that these observations can be explained by the unchanged roadside conditions at Coaley Peak and the growth of trees in the woods at Marmontsflat and Mansion which has greatly reduced the availability of food plants.

There is a tendency for the estimated male populations to be larger than those of the females. A possible explanation for this lies in the fact that it was very difficult to sample Marmontsflat Wood and Mansion evenly, owing to the presence of dense thickets and tempting paths. The higher dispersal rate of males (Fig. 2.3, Table 2.1) would thus mean that we sampled them more randomly than the females, which showed less tendency to move in or out of the areas sampled. It should always be remembered that, if only parts of a population can be sampled, the results may underestimate the true size of the whole population. This underestimation will be reduced if the animals disperse well, for then their behaviour will tend to ensure random sampling of individuals, as assumed by the analysis methods.

Survival rates and longevity   The survival rates are low by comparison with those reported from Cothill, which are usually around 0.8 per day. The mean Woodchester rate of $s = 0.66$ corresponds to an expected lifespan or period of residence of $-1/\ln s = 2.4$ days. Probably the true figure is higher, since the combination of uneven sampling and relatively low dispersal would mean the loss of many marked individuals into impenetrable thickets where they would not be recaptured and would therefore appear to have left the population.

The use of a different sampling technique in 1970 has resulted in a survival rate for Marmontsflat Wood males which is significantly lower than in the other analyses. This is in contrast to the dispersal rate estimates, which were unaffected (Table 2.1). Only assembly trapping of males was used in 1970; there were no searches to capture individuals of both sexes. The apparently low survival estimate may be due to a more extreme form of the inadequate sample distribution mentioned previously. The highest survival rates were those found at Coaley Peak, where the whole colony is easily accessible and was sampled evenly.

The larval populations

Quadrat sampling methods

Quadrat sampling methods are widely used by plant ecologists but are also useful in animal studies, especially where the individuals are relatively immobile. Quadrats are usually sample plots of a fixed size which are positioned randomly within the area to be studied. The number of individuals within each quadrat is counted.

If the area to be surveyed is heterogeneous, 'stratified random' sampling can be useful. In this method the area is divided into homogeneous sub-units, each of which is sampled randomly but with a number of quadrats proportional to the area of the sub-unit.

The larvae of the Scarlet Tiger moth are well suited to quadrat sampling, since they are conspicuous even when small, do not move fast and hence cannot easily escape from the sample area. Thus relatively accurate counts can be made. Within the colonies sampled, there was no marked heterogeneity in the vegetation, so that randomly positioned quadrats gave a good estimate of both total numbers present, and their 'dispersion' or pattern of distribution. Clearly it is useful to know the numbers present. In this study, where the numbers of adults were also being estimated, it is possible to derive estimates for the mortality at various stages of the life cycle, as will be shown later.

Dispersion   The pattern of distribution of animals is important for three reasons:

   (a) It may give clues to the preferred habitats or food plants.
   (b) Changes in dispersion with time may be related to the action of density-dependent mortality factors.
   (c) The pattern of dispersion may affect the analysis of the quadrat counts.

The size of the quadrat should be appropriate to the population density and to the scale of the dispersion pattern. Careful attention should be given to the dispersion of the population, as this may suggest factors controlling the density in different areas.

Fitting distributions   One way of summarising the dispersion of a sampled population is to form a frequency distribution of the various numbers of individuals per quadrat. Several mathematical models provide expected frequency distributions which can be compared with that observed. A useful introduction to these is given by Elliott (1977).

Two such mathematical distributions are the Poisson and the Negative Binomial. The Poisson distribution describes a random dispersion in which there is an equal probability of an organism occupying any point in the study area and where the presence of one individual at a point does not influence the probability of another individual occupying the same point. As such it can never be precisely reproduced by any real organisms since each individual does not occupy a point but takes up a finite amount of space. However, it is sometimes found that observed distributions are indistinguishable from a Poisson series. A given Poisson distribution is distinguished from another only by its mean density. Thus the mean is the only 'parameter' of a Poisson distribution which must be determined from the observed distribution before the expected one can be calculated.

The Negative Binomial distribution is one of a number of alternative ways of describing a clumped distribution, where the probability of finding an individual varies from place to place. In the case of *Callimorpha dominula*, a clumped distribution of larvae might arise either from non-random deposition of eggs by female moths, or from a tendency of larvae to be attracted to particular food plants (Cowley, 1976: pp. 32, 41). The Negative Binomial has two parameters, the mean density, and the quantity k, which is an expression of the degree of clumping. The parameter k has to be calculated before the expected distribution can be determined. Low values of k indicate high degrees of clumping; when k becomes infinite, the Poisson distribution is reached.

Results for the larval populations

Random quadrats 1 m^2 were used, and Poisson and Negative Binomial distributions were fitted to the data obtained, using the methods described by Elliott (1977). Table 2.3 illustrates this process with one set of quadrat data for the Marmontsflat Wood colony in September 1972.

The example shows a very poor fit to the Poisson distribution and a very good agreement with a Negative Binomial distribution. This provides both strong evidence for a non-random distribution of caterpillars and an estimate of their degree of aggregation. The agregation is thought to be related to the distribution of clumps of the food plants, especially Hemp Agrimony (*Eupatorium cannabinum* L.) (Cowley, 1976). A summary of the density and dispersion estimates for all the larval samples is given in Table 2.4.

The population size estimates do not generally show the steady decline that would be expected for each generation from September to May. For example, the estimates for January and March 1972 are unex-

Table 2.3 Larval dispersion parameter estimates.

Number per quadrat	Observed frequency[a]	Poisson Expected	Poisson χ^2	Negative Binomial Expected	Negative Binomial χ^2
0	56	0.7	890.6	56.4	0.0
1	11	3.7		10.5	0.0
2	6	9.1	1.1	6.0	0.0
3	6	15.1	5.5	4.3	0.7
4	4	18.8	11.7	3.3	0.1
5	2	18.8	15.0	2.6	0.1
6	2	15.6	11.9	2.2	
7	1	11.1	10.0	1.9	0.6
8	1	6.9	5.0	1.6	
9	2	3.8	0.9	1.4	
10	3	1.9		1.3	1.3
11	1	0.9	46.7	1.1	
12–21	5	0.6		6.9	0.5
22–58	7	0.0		7.3	0.0
Total	107	107.0	998.3[b]	107.0	3.4[c]

[a] September 1972 data from Marmontsflat Wood.

[b] This χ^2 value with 8 degrees of freedom indicates a highly significant departure of the observed data from a random (Poisson) distribution ($P << 0.001$).

[c] There is no evidence (χ^2 with 7 df, $P > 0.5$) for any departure from the Negative Binomial distribution expected with a mean density of 5.03 per square metre and a clumping parameter $k = 0.19$.

Table 2.4 Repeated sampling of larvae at Marmontsflat Wood.

Date	No. of quadrats n	Dispersion[a] k	Density/m^2 Mean	Density/m^2 95% Fiducial limits		Colony area $(\times 10^3 \, m^2)$	Population estimate
31 March 1971	26	0.68	6.15	3.82	10.63	31	191 000
21 April 1971	72	0.52	3.75	2.69	5.39	31	116 000
8 May 1971	76	0.76	2.04	1.51	2.80	31	63 000
18 September 1971	70	0.24	3.33	2.08	5.73	22	72 000
13 November 1971	33	0.83	3.36	2.22	5.30	22	73 000
28 January 1972	62	0.52	1.53	1.03	2.34	27	42 000
9 March 1972	63	0.50	1.73	1.17	2.64	27	47 000
10 April 1972	70	0.52	5.11	3.67	7.37	27	140 000
19 May 1972	47	0.46	2.49	1.59	4.10	27	68 000
23 September 1972	107	0.19	5.03	3.36	8.22	27	137 000
27 March 1973	76	0.62	3.57	2.64	4.94	18	64 000
10 May 1973	79	0.73	3.65	2.76	4.92	18	66 000

[a] k is the aggregation parameter of the Negative Binomial distribution.

pectedly low. These apparent fluctuations may be partly explained by a failure to find all the larvae in a quadrat during the winter months.

Life tables Life tables provide the starting point from which various methods of analysis can assess the relative importance of different mortality factors. In this context, 'importance' does not necessarily mean 'magnitude'; it is not always the largest factor that best predicts future population size trends or is responsible for regulation of the numbers in a population. A discussion of the various analysis methods is presented by Southwood (1978).

As an example, an age-specific life table or 'budget' is shown in Table 2.5 for the Marmontsflat Wood colony. Estimates of the numbers of adults and larvae have already been discussed. Where more than one estimate exists in one year for a given stage in the life cycle, as for the spring larvae in 1972, the most appropriate estimate has been chosen giving allowance to considerations such as the previously mentioned likelihood of underestimation in winter, and the underestimation of larvae in very late samples because of pupation. The

Table 2.5 Age-specific life table or budget for Marmontsflat Wood.

Year Stage	Numbers entering stage	Fecundity per adult female[a]	Mortality during stage Apparent	Mortality during stage Real
1971				
Spring larvae and pupae	116 000		0.97	—
Adults	3 300	56.4		
Ova and newly hatched larvae	93 000		0.23	0.23
Autumn larvae including overwintering	72 000		$(-0.94)^b$	$(-0.73)^b$
1972				
Spring larvae and pupae	140 000		0.96	$(1.44)^b$
Adults	6 200	84.2		
Ova and newly hatched larvae	261 000		0.48	0.48
Autumn larvae including overwintering	137 000		0.52	0.27
1973				
Spring larvae and pupae	66 000		0.92	0.23
Adults	5 200	68.5		
Ova and newly hatched larvae	178 000		—	—

[a] Assuming half the total adult population estimated are females.
[b] Estimates enclosed in brackets are biologically impossible.

estimates for the numbers of eggs laid by the adults are derived from knowledge of the numbers and survival rates of females in the field and the daily rates of egg-laying in the laboratory.

Mortality rates in the table are presented in two ways. 'Apparent' mortality is expressed as the fraction of the number present at the beginning of the stage which die within the stage; 'real' mortality is expressed as a fraction of the estimated number of eggs. Because of a lack of confidence in the accuracy of some of the population estimates, the mortality figures must be regarded as tentative and will not be discussed further. However, the high mortality during or immediately before the pupal stage is noteworthy: this is unusual in Lepidoptera.

The distribution of colonies

To estimate population parameters is merely to describe past events. It is also important to predict what may happen in the future or in other populations not yet studied. The predictions may have their own usefulness, which may be small if undetected factors are at work, or they may be used to test hypotheses. Testing hypotheses is, of course, central to a proper scientific investigation: based on a certain provisional model or set of hypotheses, predictions are made and then subsequently compared with further data to determine whether the model is sufficient to account for all relevant observations. It is all too common for postulated 'models' merely to 'predict' the observations on which they were based; interpretations of multiple regression analyses often suffer from this fault.

In this section a hypothesis which might explain the observed local distribution of colonies is suggested and then investigated using computer simulation.

The problem of colony distribution

The moth's ecological requirements would seem to be very general. In Table 2.6 a brief summary of the known requirements is given. It can be seen that the range of habitat types in which colonies occur is very wide, and that the food plants eaten by the larvae are common. These requirements have been discussed in more detail by Cook (1961), White (1974) and Cowley (1976).

The observed distribution of colonies   However, populations are only found in a minute fraction of the places that appear to be capable of supporting the species. A possible explanation would, of course, be the

Table 2.6 Ecological requirements of the Scarlet Tiger moth.

Habitat types	Major larval food plants
Roadside verges and hedges	*Filipendula ulmaria* (L.)
Rough or waste ground	*Rubus fruticosus* agg.
Banks of streams, rivers and canals	*Urtica dioica* L.
Open woodland, clearings and edges	*Corylus avellana* L.
Reed beds	*Fagus sylvatica* L.
Dune slacks	*Salix caprea* L.
Undercliff	*Primula vulgaris* Huds.
Rough herbage on downland	*Symphytum officinale* L.
	S. × *uplandicum* Nym.
	Galeobdolon luteum Huds.
Larval requirements (Kettlewell, 1943)	*Eupatorium cannabinum* L.
	Taraxacum officinale Weber
Leaf litter or thick undergrowth	
for hibernation and pupation	Adult moths (especially males)
Partial shade	require nectar-producing flowers
Freedom from permanently wet ground	e.g. *Heracleum sphondylium* L.

requirement for some unknown factor which is only present in existing colonies and not found elsewhere.

This hypothesis may be tested by setting up artificial colonies in sites presently unoccupied by the moth. If this is done with sufficient numbers of larvae, then the new colony persists if the site is suitable on the basis of the known criteria, and becomes extinct if it is not (Kettlewell, 1943, 1973). A colony has been set up by P.M. Sheppard (pers. comm.) at West Kirby on the Wirral in Merseyside that has thrived for a number of years, despite being well outside the present range of the species.

Thus it appears that many places not occupied may be ecologically suitable, at least for several years, and a different explanation must be sought. The limited dispersal powers of the Scarlet Tiger moth might be sufficient to explain its absence from northern England, if it is slowly recolonising the country after the last Ice Age, but this theory does not seem able to explain the smaller-scale gaps in its distribution, such as its absence from Somerset when it is widespread in the surrounding counties. Neither does it explain the apparent contraction of the range from East Anglia and Kent since the nineteenth century (Cook, 1959).

The absence of the moth from certain 'suitable' areas may be explained if the environment varies with time in its ability to support the species. Periods of bad weather at critical phases of the life history or the sudden discovery of a colony by a poorly regulated parasite or disease organism might cause occasional extinctions. There is some evidence that it is common for colonies of many species to become extinct and be refounded by migration from neighbouring colonies (den Boer, 1981). The ultimate suitability of a site may thus depend on the presence of other colonies in the area.

Another difficulty lies in the species' micro-distribution. Figure 2.2 shows the distribution of colonies in the Woodchester valley, based on several years of captures and sightings. In many cases there is uniformly suitable habitat available from the centre of one colony, through the intervening gap and on into the heart of the next colony. These continuities occur mainly in an east–west direction along the paths shown. A striking feature of the distribution is the nearly constant 600 m spacing of many pairs of neighbouring colonies.

Clearly there is some additional factor, other than simple ecological requirements, controlling distribution at the local level. An explanation for such a regular spacing, whether of moth populations or of plants in a desert, must be sought in some interaction between the regularly distributed entities rather than in their environment. One such interaction is the attraction of males to females by the pheromone produced by the latter.

A hypothesis concerning the distribution of colonies   Suppose that a colony is already in existence, and female moths occur sparsely at the edges and abundantly in the centre, as might be expected. Males will thus be attracted towards the centre of the colony. Although some males mate with more than one female, on average each male must mate once only as there is no evidence of a large difference in numbers or survival rate between the two sexes, and females only mate once. Hence females will be less likely to be fertilised near the edge of the colony, or they will lay fewer fertile eggs after later insemination because of the scarcity of males. Conversely, females in the centre of the colony should be able to start laying eggs soon after emergence (Fig. 2.5). It is also possible that this effect may be enhanced by the depletion of males on the leeward edge of the colony. This may occur because of the normal behaviour of searching male moths to fly upwind (see, for example, Birch & Haynes, 1982). If the wind changes direction, the only area continuously occupied by searching males will be the centre.

These phenomena, if they exist, will result in lower fecundity of females around the edges of the colony, and thus tend to prevent the expansion of the colony. It also seems intuitively possible that large colonies may break up into smaller ones because chance aggregations of females, or aggregations in particularly favoured spots, may result in the formation of a number of nuclei which would then behave as separate colonies. Also, the centres of large colonies might 'die out'

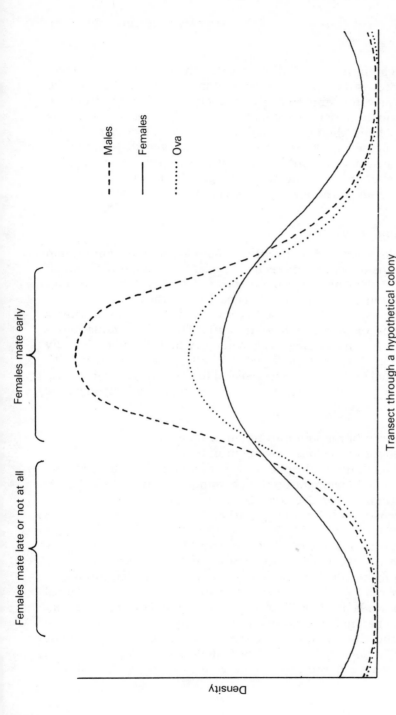

Density

Females mate late or not at all

Females mate early

Males ---- ----

Females ——

Ova ....

Transect through a hypothetical colony

Fig. 2.5 A hypothesis concerning the origin and maintenance of a clumped distribution. The figure represents the main idea on which the simulation described in the next was based. The horizontal axis passes from the edge of one colony through the intervening gap into the next colony and on to the edge of a third. The existing distribution of female moths is assumed to induce a male distribution which is slightly more extreme. The low proportion of male moths at the colony edges reduces the fertility of the females, which in turn causes the distribution of the resulting ova and later stages to partly reflect the male distribution. The existing variations in density are thus preserved or enhanced in the absence of any variations in habitat suitability.

because of overexploitation of habitat resources and cause the same result.

Testing the hypothesis   The hypothesis that the regular local arrangement of colonies is due to the male searching behaviour will now be explored. Clearly the importance of the effect will depend on the values of parameters such as the male and female dispersal rates, the attractability of the pheromone, and whether the effect can produce the observed colony structure from an initial even distribution or perhaps from just one ancestral colony. It is very difficult to imagine field experiments to investigate these points. In this case it is convenient to employ the technique of computer simulation.

Computer simulation

A model of dispersal and distribution   Before computer simulation can be used, it is necessary to specify a model of the hypothesis much more precisely than has been done above. The simulation program itself was written to investigate the behaviour of the model.

Generations are assumed to be discrete, and the moths inhabit a linear sequence of identical habitat units. Thus the simulation is more realistic for the Coaley Peak colony, which is approximately linear, than for Marmontsflat Wood. Some limited experience with two-dimensional models, however, has led to the same general conclusions. There are five variable quantities or parameters which affect the operation of the model:

  m, the amount of random movement of males
  f, the amount of random movement of females
  p, the attractability of the pheromone, that is, the amount of directional male movement up the pheromone gradient
  d, the strength of density-dependent population regulation
  e, the intensity of habitat exploitation

Initially, moths are assumed to be distributed evenly along the length of the environment. Both males and females are subject to limited random movement, the amount of this being determined by parameters m and f. Males are additionally affected by directional movement towards areas of increasing pheromone density. The concentration of pheromone is assumed to be proportional to the density of females, and thus males are attracted to regions of high female density. The amount of this directional male movement depends on the local steepness of the pheromone gradient and on the value of parameter p.

The operation of the model proceeds in cycles, equivalent to generations. In each cycle, events occur in the following order:

(1) Female moths emerge and begin to produce pheromone.
(2) Male moths move deterministically in the direction of any pheromone gradient, and simultaneously they disperse randomly. The dispersal component is approximately normally distributed.
(3) Female moths mate with males. The number that do so depends on the availability of males.
(4) Females move randomly and then deposit their eggs.

It is assumed that no movement occurs during the developing stages or before females mate. The number of moths that survive to start a new cycle at (1) depends on parameters d and e. These two parameters cause the colonies to vary spatially in their ecological suitability, but there is no predetermined tendency for the colony edges or areas outside the colonies to be less suitable. Indeed these parameters tend to cause the opposite.

Investigating the model   Many simulations were performed using this model, varying all of the parameters. The width of the simulated colonies, where these were formed, was from 6 to 12 of the habitat units. Colonies in the field are 200 to 400 m across, so one unit of the simulations is equivalent to about 33 m. The spacing of the simulated colonies was 15 to 20 units, which is equivalent on this basis to 500–670 m.

In the simulations, stable colonies were formed most frequently with male moths moving a mean distance of 0.75 units, that is 25 m, and females a distance of 0.5 units or 17 m. This accords well with the observed distances of about 30 m and 20 m respectively for real moths, at least in the larger colonies. The distances moved by individual moths in their whole lifespan are slightly more than their daily movement rates given in Table 2.1. An alternative view of this is that when the simulation is scaled to reflect the actual movement distances of moths, the simulated colonies possessed approximately the size and separation found in the field. Stable colonies were not formed if the males and females moved equal distances.

The simulations were sensitive to parameter p, the extent to which the movement of male moths was influenced by variations in pheromone level, which are assumed to be equivalent to variations in the density of females. If this pheromone effect is too small, no colonies form and the moths remain more or less evenly distributed. If, on the other hand, it is too large, the colonies contract too much and become extinct. There are no field data available for the influence of

Section through several colonies

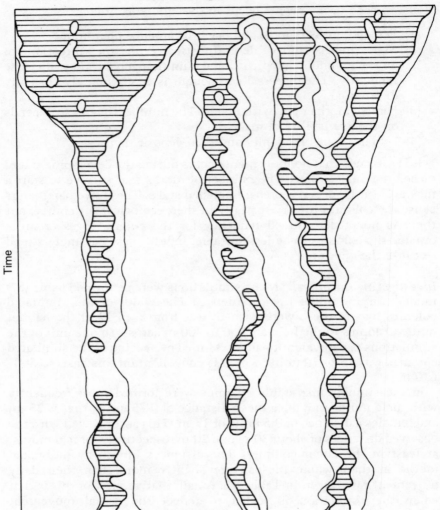

Fig. 2.6 Simulated changes in distribution with time. A typical simulation result is shown in which an initially uniform distribution of individuals has changed with time into a colonial distribution. In this case, three stable colonies have eventually formed in the absence of any variation in habitat suitability. The density of the distribution is represented by two levels of contour. The horizontal bars in the denser portions of the distribution are spaced at intervals of one generation. The scale of the horizontal or distance axis is discussed in the text where the size and spacing of the simulated colonies is shown to be similar to the dimensions of real colonies.

female distribution on male flight behaviour, so this aspect of the simulations cannot be fully assessed.

The effect of parameter d was to determine whether the simulated moths maintained a fairly constant population size, or declined to extinction, or became so common and widespread that no separation into colonies was observed.

With small values of parameter e, colonies, once established, tended to remain in one place, as shown in Fig. 2.6. With higher values, colonies tended to drift in location or to divide into two as the central area of the colony became depleted in habitat resources. There is some evidence that natural colonies do not remain fixed either (Fig. 2.2; Kettlewell, 1973).

Figure 2.6 shows that separation of an initially even distribution into a number of discrete colonies can occur. Other simulations have been performed starting from a single colony. In this case, large values of parameter e are needed for the initial colony to divide repeatedly so that the whole length of the simulated habitat becomes occupied by several colonies.

The results of the simulations agree well with the facts known at present about the small-scale distribution of colonies. However, the hypothesis proposed was developed with these facts in mind and it has not yet been rigorously tested by the process of making and testing predictions. This might involve, for example, further work on the behaviour of adult moths, especially males.

Population genetics of wing-pattern variation

What is a population?

So far I have not carefully defined what I mean by a population. Ecologists and geneticists tend to have different definitions.

Definitions of a population   To an ecologist a population is delimited primarily by convenience. It is that part of the whole species which is currently being studied in some area and whose individuals are assumed not to vary, or at least whose range of variation is represented evenly throughout the area. Implicitly it is the scope of any generalisations he may make from his study.

Geneticists have a slightly different definition. A 'genetical' population is one whose individuals, through sexual reproduction, share a common pool of genes. Frequently, the assumption is that mating is random within the population so that gene frequencies are homogeneous throughout its area. The latter situation constitutes a

'Mendelian' population, though these occur more often in models and hypotheses than in the field.

Animals that form discrete colonies or occupy disjunct patches of habitat are automatically divided into populations in the ecological sense. It is necessary to be careful not to assume that the colonies are therefore also genetically homogeneous Mendelian populations.

The genetics of colonies In the case of the Scarlet Tiger moth the colonies can be treated as populations in the ecological sense. However, especially in large colonies, the average distance moved by a moth in its lifespan is considerably less than the distance from one side of a colony to the other. For example, large colonies like those at Marmontsflat Wood and the Mansion are about 400 m across, at least in the longest dimension (Figs 2.1 and 2.2). This contrasts with the distances moved by individual adult moths (Fig. 2.3 and Table 2.1), which in large colonies average 13–26 m per day. In the average lifespan of 2.4 days, the movement of an individual moth would be perhaps 20–30 m.

Thus complete mixing of the individuals in a population does not occur, mating cannot be at random, and the opportunity therefore arises for random or selective processes to result in genetically divergent local groups of individuals within a colony. There is some support for this possibility from multivariate studies similar to that described below. There is also the circumstantial evidence that occasionally distinctive forms of the adult moths are found as groups of two or three individuals in the same part of a colony. For example, in 1972 at Marmontsflat Wood, two individuals of the variety *ocellata* (Kettlewell, 1943) and one of its possible homozygote *illustris* were found within a few metres of each other (White, 1974: p. 114). Such groups of individuals might share one or more parents or grandparents and their presence in a restricted area implies imperfect mixing of the gene pool.

Variation

Sampling genotypes Despite the sampling problems such genetic heterogeneity might cause, a comparative study of the variation of adult moths in a large number of colonies was performed, including some of those at Woodchester. Larvae were sampled from the colonies in spring when they were nearly fully grown, and then reared into adults under uniform conditions.

This sampling procedure is preferable to the sampling of adult moths for two reasons. Because of the high natural mortality during or immediately before the pupal stage (Table 2.5), large samples of caterpillars can be removed from a colony without seriously reducing the numbers of adults. The second advantage is the removal of much of the effect of environmental variation on the resulting adult wing pattern during the critical pupal stage. The adult variation thus observed is slightly less than that found in wild-caught moths and can be presumed to be mainly genetic in origin.

Recording and analysing variation The morphological features recorded were coded into 51 characters or variables, mainly describing details of the colour pattern of the wings. One variable represented the wingspan and four summarised variation of the thoracic and abdominal colour pattern. Many analyses were performed (White, 1974) but the one reported here involved 22 samples of moths from 17 colonies including Marmontsflat Wood (two samples) and Inchbrook (one sample) in the Woodchester area. The other colonies were a representative selection from the British distribution of the Scarlet Tiger moth.Three-hundred-and-sixty-one moths were included. The data were subjected to a canonical discriminant analysis. This method aims to display the relative differences between the samples in terms of the distances between points representing the samples on a two-dimensional scatter plot. Each character is automatically weighted or scaled according to the extent to which its variation between samples exceeds its variation within samples, or in other words according to its ability to discriminate the samples.

Colonies and variation One view of the result is shown in Fig. 2.7. The first canonical axis (of colony differences) has been omitted and axes two and three have been used in this plot. This is because the first axis served only to separate two samples taken in 1960 and 1962 by L.M. Cook from the remaining samples collected in the years 1969 to 1973. Such a difference might be due to temporal trends or to differences in rearing techniques and is not considered further.

The two samples from Marmontsflat Wood appear in the upper left corner of the plot and the mean of each sample is enclosed in a circle the diameter of which represents the 95% confidence interval for the location of the sample mean. The Inchbrook colony sample from the other end of the Woodchester valley, however, is more distinct, implying some degree of difference between the colonies.

Local evolution The other samples on the plot show an interesting large-scale geographical separation. Those to the left near the Woodchester samples come from Gloucestershire, Wales, Devon and Hampshire, and those to the right are from colonies in Wiltshire and Berkshire. It is tempting to speculate on the existence of a small degree of evolutionary divergence between these two areas, but further analyses are required to confirm this. In particular, the degree of spatial heterogeneity within colonies must be evaluated before confidence can be placed in samples purporting to represent the whole colony.

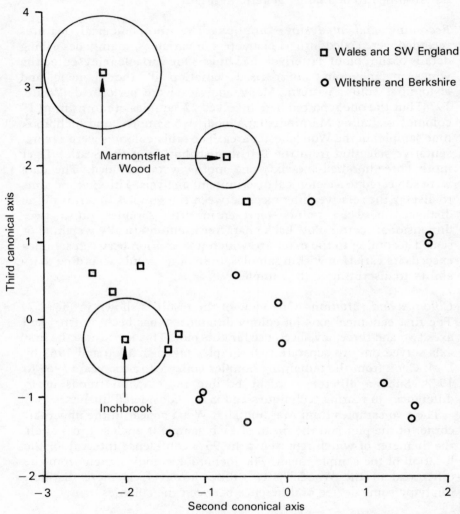

Fig. 2.7 Canonical analysis of variation between colonies. The analysis summarises the morphological differences between samples of moths from various colonies in England and Wales. Distances between points on the graph reflect overall differences in wing pattern between colonies. The axes are graduated in units equal to one standard deviation of the individuals within samples. Further explanation appears in the text.

A complete population study

These studies on the Scarlet Tiger moth have demonstrated some of the methods available for the analysis of populations. The intention was to show how an autecological project can benefit from the interaction of several lines of approach. The *Callimorpha* work is not an ideal or complete study; it might be improved in many ways. Nevertheless, it was chosen to illustrate this chapter because of its relevance both to the Woodchester valley and to the biology of discrete populations.

There are many questions to consider both when planning a population study and while reviewing its progress. Some of these are

Table 2.7 Objectives of a population study programme.

(A) Define the scope of the study: locations, times, species and relationships of interest
(B) Description of the populations: (often for preliminary or base-line monitoring)
   (a) Population parameters to be estimated
      (i) Numerical — population size (instantaneous, total generation)
            — factors causing size fluctuations (survival, natality, immigration and emigration rates)
      (ii) Dispersion — area occupied
            — density (average and at specific points)
            — location of individuals, territories, etc.
      (iii) Dispersal — type, direction and rate of movement
   (b) Environment parameters to be estimated vary with the organism chosen: see Andrewartha & Birch (1954)
   (c) Categorisation. Different estimates may be needed for any of the above parameters according to
            — sex, type or age of individuals
            — time of day or year
            — location
(C) Hypothesis formation:
   (a) Identify factors which might
            — determine the values of the parameters above
            — explain differences between categories for the parameters
   (b) Propose a model with potentially quantifiable unknown values
(D) Hypothesis testing:
   (a) Qualitative. Can a relationship be demonstrated between an effect and its postulated cause?
            — experimental demonstration
            — statistical demonstration
   (b) Quantitative. — determine the values specified in C(b) and their standard errors of estimation
            — show that the mathematical model successfully predicts population parameters not used in developing the model

summarised in Table 2.7, which concentrates on the objectives rather than on the detailed methods for accomplishing them. The organisation of the table highlights the logical stages of an investigation. Obviously, subject areas must be defined before studies can commence. It is not enough to describe a population and estimate parameters; hypotheses should be formed and tested. The testing may require the hypotheses to be revised and earlier stages of the investigation to be refined or repeated in an iterative process which will lead to a better understanding of the population.

For example, hypotheses about the regulation of the population size might be suggested after an initial period of study by considering whether the estimated survival rates are affected by predation, parasitism, disease, overcrowding or available food supply, and whether these factors might explain any observed differences in survival at different locations. This is an illustration of phase C(a) in Table 2.7. The next step is to define a model or set of equations in which, for example, the population size is reduced by x individuals per predator per day.

Such a model can be tested qualitatively, as in section D(a) of the table, by an experimental comparison of normal survival with survival in field cages from which the predator is excluded, or by a statistical comparison, possibly using regression analysis, of the survival in areas with differing predator densities. A quantitative demonstration of the hypothesis would require the experimental or statistical determination of the value of x and the other unknowns in the model. Only then can the model be used to make predictions.

The predictive ability of a model may have a purely academic value in demonstrating the applicability of the model and therefore establishing that the population processes are adequately understood, or it may have an applied value. Much ecological research is now aimed at predicting the effects of present or proposed changes in the environment. Green (1979) gives a valuable account of the design alternatives for such studies, and many of his exhortations should be heeded by all population biologists.

Acknowledgements

The larval data were collected by Mrs M.L. Cowley, who also assisted with the adult capture–recapture fieldwork. Dr E.A. Drew and Dr K.T. O'Grady helped with the latter. Many ideas have been discussed with Dr J.A. Bishop, Dr J.S. Bradley, Mr A.C. Morton, Professor P.M. Sheppard and Dr L.M. Cook (who also provided the 1970 Marmontsflat Wood data).

References

Andrewartha, H.G. & Birch, L.C. (1954) *The Distribution and Abundance of Animals*. Chicago: University of Chicago Press.

Birch, M.C. & Haynes, K.F. (1982) *Insect Pheromones*. London: Edward Arnold. (Institute of Biology, Studies in Biology, No. 147.)

Bishop, J.A. & Sheppard, P.M. (1973) An evaluation of two capture-recapture models using the technique of computer simulation, in *The Mathematical Theory of the Dynamics of Biological Populations*, Bartlett, M.S. & Hiorns, R.W., eds. London: Academic Press, pp. 235–44.

Blower, J.G., Cook, L.M. & Bishop, J.A. (1981) *Estimating the Size of Animal Populations*. London: Allen & Unwin.

Brown, I.L. & Ehrlich, P.R. (1980) Population biology of the checkerspot butterfly, *Euphydryas chalcedona*. Structure of the Jasper Ridge colony. *Oecologia*, **47**, 239–51.

Cockayne, E.A. (1928) Variation in *Callimorpha dominula* L. *Entomologist's Record and Journal of Variation*, **40**, 153–60.

Cook, L.M. (1959) The distribution in Britain of the Scarlet Tiger Moth, *Callimorpha (Panaxia) dominula* L. *Entomologist*, **92**, 232–6.

Cook, L.M. (1960) *A Study of Peripheral Populations with Special Reference to the Moth* Panaxia dominula. Oxford University: unpublished D.Phil. thesis.

Cook, L.M. (1961) Food plant specialization in the moth *Panaxia dominula* L. *Evolution*, **15**, 478–85.

Cook, L.M., Thomason, E.W. & Young, A.M. (1976) Population structure, dynamics and dispersal of the tropical butterfly *Heliconius charitonius*. *Journal of Animal Ecology*, **45**, 851–63.

Cowley, M.L. (1976) *The Ecology of Two Populations of the Scarlet Tiger Moth* Panaxia dominula L. *and its Relation to Food Plant Specialisation*. Liverpool University: unpublished M.Sc. thesis.

Craig, C.C. (1953) On the utilisation of marked specimens in estimating populations of flying insects. *Biometrika*, **40**, 170–6.

den Boer, P.J. (1981) On the survival of populations in a heterogeneous and variable environment. *Oecologia*, **50**, 39–53.

Douwes, P. (1970) Size of, gain to and loss from a population of adult *Heodes virgaureae* L. (Lep., Lycaenidae). *Entomologica Scandinavica*, **1**, 263–81.

Dowdeswell, W.H., Fisher, R.A. & Ford, E.B. (1940) The quantitative study of populations in the Lepidoptera. I. *Polyommatus icarus* Rott. *Annals of Eugenics*, **10**, 123–36.

Eberhardt, L.L. (1969) Population estimates from recapture frequencies. *Journal of Wildlife Management*, **33**, 28–39.

Ehrlich, P.R. & Davidson, S.E. (1960) Techniques for capture-recapture studies of Lepidoptera populations. *Journal of the Lepidopterists' Society*, **14**, 227–99.

Elliott, J.M. (1977) *Some Methods for the Statistical Analysis of Samples of Benthic Invertebrates*, 2nd edn. Ambleside: Freshwater Biological Association, Scientific Publication No. 25.

Fisher, R.A. & Ford, E.B. (1947) The spread of a gene in natural conditions in a colony of the moth *Panaxia dominula* L. *Heredity, London*, **1**, 143–74.

Ford, E.B. (1975) *Ecological Genetics*, 4th edn. London: Chapman & Hall.

Green, R.H. (1979) *Sampling Design and Statistical Methods for Environmental Biologists*. New York: Wiley.

Jolly, G.M. (1965) Explicit estimates from capture–recapture data with both death and immigration — stochastic model. *Biometrika*, **52**, 225–47.

Jolly, G.M. (1982) Mark–recapture models with parameters constant in time. *Biometrics*, **38**, 301–21.

Kettlewell, H.B.D. (1943) A survey of the insect *Panaxia* (64) (*Callimorpha*) *dominula*, L. *Transactions of the South London Entomological and Natural History Society (1942–3)*, 1–49.

Kettlewell, H.B.D. (1946) Further observations on *Panaxia dominula*. *Entomologist*, **79**, 31–2.

Kettlewell, H.B.D. (1973) *The Evolution of Melanism*. Oxford: Clarendon Press.

Leslie, P.H. & Chitty, D. (1951) The estimation of population parameters from data obtained by means of the capture–recapture method. I. The maximum likelihood equations for estimating the death rate. *Biometrika*, **38**, 269–92.

Manly, B.F.J. & Parr, M.J. (1968) A new method of estimating population size, survivorship, and birth rate from capture–recapture data. *Transactions of the Society for British Entomology*, **18**, 81–9.

Morton, A.C. (1982) The effects of marking and capture on recapture frequencies of butterflies. *Oecologia*, **53**, 105–10.

Pollard, E. (1977) A method for assessing changes in abundance of butterflies. *Biological Conservation*, **12**, 115–34.

Roff, D.A. (1973) An examination of some statistical tests used in the analysis of mark-recapture data. *Oecologia*, **12**, 35–54.

Scott, J.A. (1973*a*) Population biology and adult behaviour of the circumpolar butterfly, *Parnassius phoebus* F. (Papilionidae). *Entomologica Scandinavica*, **4**, 161–8.

Scott, J.A. (1973*b*) Convergence of population biology and adult behaviour in two sympatric butterflies, *Neominois ridingsii* (Papilionoidea: Nymphalidae) and *Amblyscirtes simius* (Hesperioidea: Hesperiidae). *Journal of Animal Ecology*, **42**, 663–72.

Scott, J.A. (1975) Flight patterns among eleven species of diurnal Lepidoptera. *Ecology*, **56**, 1367–77.

Sheppard, P.M. (1951) A quantitative study of two populations of the moth *Panaxia dominula* (L.). *Heredity, London*, **5**, 349–78.

Sheppard, P.M. & Cook, L.M. (1962) The manifold effects of the *medionigra* gene of the moth *Panaxia dominula* and the maintenance of a polymorphism. *Heredity, London*, **17**, 415–26.

Southwood, T.R.E. (1978) *Ecological Methods with Particular Reference to the Study of Insect Populations*, 2nd edn. London: Chapman & Hall.

Tabashnik, B.E. (1980) Population structure of Pierid butterflies. III. Pest populations of *Colias philodice eriphyle*. *Oecologia*, **47**, 175–83.

Watt, W.B., Chew, F.S., Snyder, L.R.G., Watt, A.G. & Rothschild, D.E. (1977) Population structure of Pierid butterflies. I. Numbers and movements of some montane *Colias* species. *Oecologia*, **27**, 1–22.

White, R.J. (1974) *Local Evolution in the Scarlet Tiger Moth* Panaxia dominula *(L.)*. Liverpool University: unpublished Ph.D. thesis.

3   J.S. Bradley

Comparative demography of four species of grasshopper on a Common site

Introduction

Aims of the chapter

The principal analytical tool of demographic studies of plants and animals is the life table, which summarises age-dependent mortality and fertility. Southwood (1978) describes the construction of life tables suitable for animal populations, and Harper (1977) shows that this technique can also be applied to plants. The life table enables one to best visualise the relative contributions of survival and reproduction to the mean fitness of the population; the more comprehensive the life table, the more accurately can these contributions be described. With this increasing accuracy comes the possibility of more detailed comparisons between populations, either intraspecifically, when different genotypes or phenotypes can be considered in studies of selection or population regulation, or interspecifically, in studies of niche definition and competition.

The chief difficulty in using life tables is that of obtaining the raw data from which to construct them. Estimates of either age-dependent survival or the numbers in each age category of a population are required, as well as information on reproduction. In human demographic studies or laboratory experiments, these estimates can be obtained from absolute counts. In plants and sessile animals, where individuals generally stay put, absolute counts again can be used. Mobile animals, however, create problems because the investigator generally has to resort to random sampling or capture–recapture models to assess the population. Where the animal passes through a number of stages, life-table parameters can be estimated independently for each stage. However, this often represents an inefficient use of data because the information about each stage may be small, or the analytical tools at the disposal of the investigator may not provide the most desirable parameter. For example, random sampling readily generates estimates of population size, but estimates of loss or gain are more difficult to obtain. The solution is to use a comprehensive life-table model, which amalgamates data from all stages and provides estimates of mortality and duration in each stage.

The purpose of this chapter is to show how the comparative demography of four sympatric species of grasshopper can be investigated, using a form of life table, described by Read & Ashford (1968), which provides direct estimates of population size and survival from data obtained by random sampling. It achieves this by sacrificing generality and simplicity of computation in favour of specificity and accuracy. With the current general availability of computing facilities, computational simplicity should *not* be favoured over accuracy in biological analysis, and I hope to demonstrate that the greater detail which can be derived from specific models, as opposed to general models, makes the extra computational effort well worth while.

Site of investigation

The investigation described in this chapter was carried out on a mixed colony of grasshoppers occupying Selsley Common, a region of grazed grassland situated on the western scarp slope of the Cotswold Hills (map reference SO 826027). The investigation took place during 1971–1973.

The Selsley colony was selected for investigation because a considerable body of information on it was already available. The zoology departments of both Manchester and Liverpool Universities ran annual field courses in the Woodchester area, Manchester from 1967, and Liverpool from 1969. An integral part of all field courses was a capture–recapture study of the Selsley grasshoppers.

Selsley Common forms part of the scarp slope of the Cotswolds, running down from the east to the Severn Valley, and is situated approximately 3 km SSW of Stroud. There is a WNW and a W facing slope of approximately 30° rising to several hectares of pasture. Figure 3.1 is a map of part of the Common, and shows the areas involved in the study.

This area is situated on the face of the escarpment. It is grazed, but not so heavily as the top. It is crossed by a number of narrow, terraced, cattle tracks. The slope is fairly even, but there are occasional hollows, and several shallow troughs run down it.

The subsurface rock of Selsley is oolitic limestone and consequently the Common is well drained. The soil is shallow, 15–23 cm on the face of the slope. It is calcareous and stony. Pockets of deeper soil occur in the troughs and hollows on the face.

The scarp face is covered by a fairly typical limestone flora. The

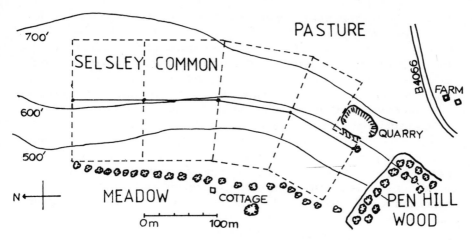

Fig. 3.1 A map of Selsley Common showing the central 400 m transect and the regions 100 m above and below it that were sampled in 1972. Contours at 100 ft intervals are also indicated.

most common grasses are *Agrostis tenuis* Sibth, *Bromus erectus* Huds, and *Festuca ovina* L. Other grasses at high density are *Sesleria caerulea* (L.), *Koeleria cristata* (L.), *Dactylis glomerata* L., *Poa compressa* L., *Poa angustifolia* L., *Poa pratensis* L., *Lolium perenne* L., *Holcus lanatus* L., *Briza media* L. and *Anthoxanthum odoratum* L. The presence of such species as *K. cristata* and *S. caerulea* indicates the dry conditions of the soil (see Hubbard, 1968).

Other important components of the flora, in terms of proportion of cover, are *Cirsium acaule* Scop., the ground thistle (this plant makes grasshopper sampling a hazardous operation!), *Plantago media* L., *Plantago lanceolata* L., *Leontodon taraxacoides* (Vill.) and *Achillea millefolium* L. Various sedges (*Carex* spp.) and mosses also form a considerable part of the flora.

Description and biology of the species

Five species of grasshopper occur on Selsley Common. These are: *Chorthippus parallelus* (Zetterstedt), *C. brunneus* (Thunberg), *Omocestus viridulus* (L.), *Stenobothrus lineatus* (Panzer), and *Myrmeleotettix maculatus* (Thunberg). All five species are classified in the sub-family Acridinae of the family Acrididae, the true, or short-horned, grasshoppers (Ragge, 1966).

During the period of investigation, *C. parallelus*, *C. brunneus*, *O. viridulus* and *S. lineatus* occurred at a sufficiently high density on Selsley to make a detailed study of their demography possible.

However, *M. maculatus* was sporadically distributed, with a low population density.

The adult forms of these species are easily distinguishable in the field. *Chorthippus parallelus* is medium sized and is characterised by vestigial hindwings. The forewings are very shortened in the female, and reduced in the male. However, a rarely occurring form is macropterous, and can fly. The species is universally distributed over Britain. It inhabits a wide selection of grassland habitats but prefers moist conditions. A large grasshopper, *C. brunneus* is universally distributed in Britain with the exception of northern Scotland. Like *C. parallelus*, it can inhabit a large range of habitats, but prefers arid conditions. It is common on urban wasteland and building sites, on sand dunes and exposed rocky outcrops, as well as lightly grazed dry land. It does not occur in lush pastures. *Stenobothrus lineatus* is a medium-sized grasshopper, restricted in range to southern England, and it prefers dry locations, especially limestone grassland. Another medium-sized grasshopper is *O. viridulus*, which favours lush grassland; it is universally distributed in Britain.

Grasshoppers, as all Orthoptera, exhibit incomplete metamorphosis; that is, a pupal stage is missing from the life history and the juvenile instars resemble the adult in general form. Species indigenous to Britain exhibit very similar and uniform life histories. They are all univoltine (i.e. one generation per year), and develop through four juvenile instars. Very infrequently, *C. parallelus* passes through an extra stadium (Richards & Waloff, 1954).

The female oviposits at regular intervals after fertilisation. The eggs are laid, several at a time, in egg-pods. The pod consists of secretions of the accessory glands exuded at the time of oviposition, which bind the eggs into a solid mass. The egg-pods of the four species considered here are distinctive and easily identified. The pods of *S. lineatus* and *O. viridulus* are laid among the bases of grass stems, close to the ground. The pods of *C. parallelus* and *C. brunneus* are laid below the surface of the soil, up to 2 cm deep. The laying period and number of eggs laid vary from species to species. In general, adults are present during the summer and early autumn. The eggs undergo an obligate egg diapause over winter, and hatch in the spring. A temporary phase, the vermiform larva, emerges from the egg and forces its way out of the egg-pod and out of the soil, if the pod is situated beneath the surface. After a few hourse, the vermiform larva moults into a nymphal stage, which resembles an adult grasshopper except for the former's complete lack of wings and small size. The vermiform stage is of very short duration, and the complete nymph is present in the vermiform sac before hatching. This stage is not, therefore, a true stadium, but rather represents an extra protective cuticle enveloping the first instar.

In the first two instars, the wings are present only as inflated lobes on the tergites of thoracic segments 2 and 3. In the third instar, the wings become reflected and obviously veined, but generally extend only to the posterior margin of the first abdominal tergite. In the fourth instar, the wings extend to the fourth abdominal tergite, and the external genitalia are fully developed.

Each stadium may last for a period of approximately 1–3 weeks, and newly moulted individuals are obvious because of their soft cuticle and faint pigmentation. The cuticle takes up to 24 h to harden. In referring to the instars, I have adopted the convention used in Richards & Waloff (1954) in giving them Roman numerals. Therefore, Instar I refers to the first instar and Instar V refers to the adult.

The determination of the instar to which an individual belongs or of the species to which an adult belongs is a relatively easy matter. This is not true of the identification of species within the juvenile instars, especially Instars I and II. Keys to the identification of adults are given in Ragge (1966), and in Richards & Waloff (1954) who also give keys to the identification of instars and of species within each stadium. Their keys are a guide, but cannot distinguish juveniles in every case.

During the sampling programme described in this chapter, I overcame the difficulty of identification in two ways:

(a) I collected egg-pods and reared hatchlings of the common species, and carefully learnt the appearance of the juvenile stages until I could distinguish between them without the need for clearly defined keyable characters.
(b) When samples included nymphs of the earlier instars, I took them back to the laboratory and examined them under a binocular microscope.

As a check, I kept nymphs singly in cages until they moulted into a clearly identifiable state. In no case did I find mis-identification of the species during sampling.

The abundance and distribution of grasshoppers

The sampling programme

The most efficient method of sampling grasshoppers depends upon the habitat. In long grass, rhythmic sweeping with a large net is probably the most efficient (Clarke, 1948). However, netting is certainly not efficient where the sward is relatively short, as in the case of Selsley Common.

In short turf, the grasshoppers are easily observable if the grass is searched intensively and disturbed to induce them to leap. Once the grasshopper has been located, it can be caught very simply by holding a specimen tube in front of it. If the grasshopper does not enter the tube voluntarily, it can be induced to do so by a light touch on the rear of the abdomen. For the sequential sampling study, I used the standard technique of taking randomly located quadrats. I marked out the sampling area with a central transect consisting of five marker canes placed at intervals of 100 m, at an approximately constant altitude, half-way up the face of the slope.

The region sampled consisted of the area within 100 m above and below this line, with the exception of the southern end of the transect where the region of the quarry was excluded. The quarry represented a sheltered habitat, and previous experience had shown that grass-hoppers lingered here at the end of the season, when they had dis-appeared from the face of the slope. The sampling area is illustrated in Fig. 3.1.

The quadrats consisted of a 1 m² frame covered with a funnel of butter muslin. They were placed by pacing out the coordinates from the central transect, and the location was checked using a prismatic compass.

The accuracy of the results from the sampling experiment depends upon how accurately the samples were taken. There are three principal sources of error in the sampling technique:

(a) Disturbed grasshoppers may escape from the area of the quadrat as it is placed.
(b) Trapped individuals may not be observed and counted.
(c) Counted individuals may be mis-identified.

I attempted to minimise source 'a' by approaching into the sun and from slightly below where I intended to place the quadrat, and then placing it as quickly and quietly as possible. I also watched carefully to see if any grasshoppers leaped out of the area. None was seen to do so.

The magnitude of source 'b' depends on how thoroughly the area beneath the quadrat is searched. The fact that the turf was short, and that the grasshoppers had a tendency to leap up on to the white muslin funnel when disturbed, made efficient searching easier. I attempted to

Fig. 3.2 (opposite)   The change in density with time for each instar and each species. The density is measured in individuals per square metre, and is estimated from the rolling average of three consecutive sampling dates. Day zero is 1 April. In (*a*), the top graph represents the first instars, and the bottom graph the adults. The total densities irrespective of instars are presented in (*b*). The heavy solid line represents, *O. viridulus*; *S. lineatus* is represented by the heavy broken line; *C. parallelus* by the light solid line and *C. brunneus* by the light broken line.

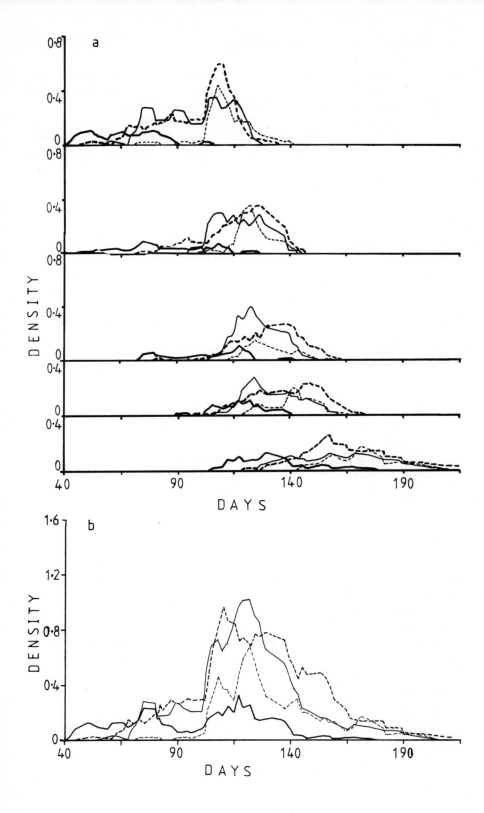

assess the size of 'b' by a small experiment. I searched a series of five quadrats taken in 1971 when the number of individuals on the Common was at its highest. After searching each quadrat, I left the frame for 10 min, and then searched intensively again. In each case the second search revealed no further individuals. A period of 10 min may not have been long enough for well-hidden grasshoppers to change their positions, but this result does indicate that more searching effort would be unlikely to improve the results.

Relative abundance of the species

Figure 3.2 presents the smoothed results of the sequential sampling, expressed as grasshoppers in each instar per square metre. The graphs indicate that *O. viridulus* tends to run through its life history in advance of the others, since individuals of the species are the first to appear in each instar and the first to disappear. The other three species group closely together, with perhaps *S. lineatus* running a little ahead.

The graph of total numbers also indicates that *S. lineatus* and *C. parallelus* achieve higher densities than *O. viridulus* and *C. brunneus*; *O. viridulus* has the lowest density.

It is important to note that these graphs give no information on the total number of grasshoppers hatching in each species, nor on their longevity. A high density could be achieved in a species which has fewer individuals hatching, but where the hatch is very synchronised and the death rate is small. The sampling data suggest that the timing of the life history of the four species is very similar but the abundance different. However, an exact comparison of their dynamics must involve the construction of life tables where the effects of different development rates can be disentangled from differences in survival.

Dispersion and development with respect to height and aspect of the scarp slope

The four species considered in this chapter are not closely related. The two members of the genus *Chorthippus* differ distinctly in morphology and courtship song (Broughton, 1972), suggesting that they have been isolated genetically for a considerable time. In Britain, *O. viridulus*, *C. parallelus* and *C. brunneus* are practically ubiquitous, whereas *S. lineatus* is very near the limit of its range in the Cotswolds (Ragge, 1966). Nevertheless, they occupy very similar environments, and have almost identical life histories.

Studies of their biology and ecology suggest that they are responsive to similar environmental factors. In a colony at Silwood Park, Berkshire, Richards & Waloff (1954) estimated the numbers emerging between 1947 and 1951 and showed that the population sizes of the four species tended to fluctuate together rather than independently.

Since the species are genetically distinct, however, we should expect them to achieve optimum fitness in different microhabitats. The microclimate of the slope is likely to be largely a function of altitude and aspect, and consequently separation with respect to these variables may represent niche separation. The amount of time spent in different microclimates is certainly likely to affect an individual's growth rate and longevity, giving rise to differences in dynamics between the species.

The distribution of the four species in 1972 was examined in detail. The data are divided into two parts: samples taken between 10 May and 12 July, and those taken from 14 to 28 July. These dates include the early instars of all four species when population densities are at their highest. Since sampling was random, the frequency of occurrence of the various species scored for the different areas of the Common is an indication of their relative abundance.

The results are analysed using the G-test (Sokal & Rohlf, 1969). The

Table 3.1 A partitioned G-test using the method described in Sokal & Rohlf (1969) to test the independence of four factors on the 1972 sampling density. The altitude classification is squares above the central transect vs squares below. The distance classification consists of the four 100 m portions of the central transect. The time classification is individuals sampled before 12 July vs individuals sampled afterwards.

Hypotheses tested	Degrees of freedom	G	P
Square × species independence	21	224.9	<0.005
Altitude × distance independence	1	26.8	<0.005
Altitude × species independence	3	30.6	<0.005
Distance × species independence	3	67.7	<0.005
Altitude × distance × species interaction	3	16.2	<0.005
Altitude × distance × species independence	10	141.4	<0.005
Remaining square × species comparisons (1 vs 2) (3 vs 4) (5 vs 6) (7 vs 8)	11	83.5	<0.005
Square × time independence	7	167.8	<0.005
Species × time independence	3	42.1	<0.005
Square × time × species interaction	21	10.6	$0.975 > P > 0.9$
Square × time × species independence	52	445.3	<0.005

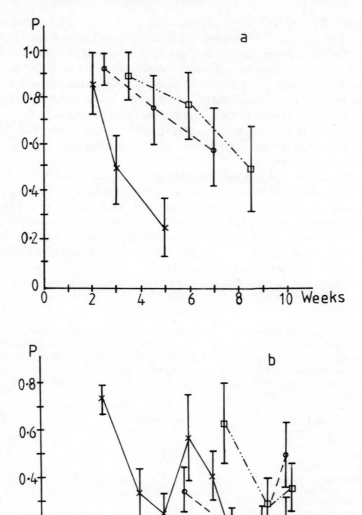

Fig. 3.3 The proportion (P) of individuals caught below the base-line transect, plotted against time in weeks. The point scaled as week 1 is 1 June. The solid lines with crosses refer to Instar I, the broken lines with circles to Instar II, and the dotted lines with squares to Instar III. The vertical bars refer to standard deviations. Only the first three instars have been included, because of the low density and spread of the later stages. Graph (*a*) refers to *O. viridulus*, graph (*b*) to *C. parallelus*, graph (*c*) to *S. lineatus*, and graph (*d*) to *C. brunneus*.

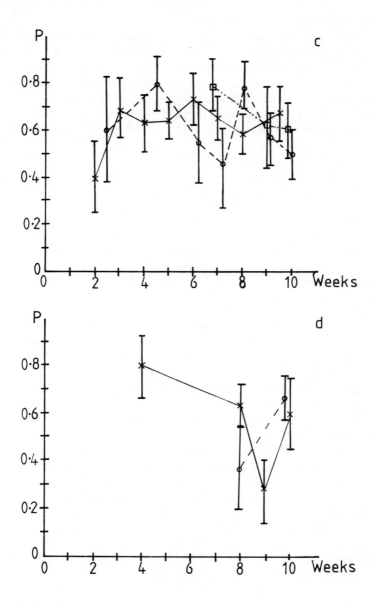

G-statistic follows a χ^2 distribution with the appropriate degrees of freedom, but is simpler to partition.

The data are partitioned by date, square and species, and a comparison is made between the upper four and the lower four squares (Table 3.1). With one exception, the null hypotheses have very low probabilities. The G-test assumes that the distribution sampled is a Poisson, which is not so (the distributions are discussed later in this chapter). However, the probabilities obtained are much too small to be the result of failure of this requirement to be met. The results indicate that species density changes with both altitude and distance, and that there is an interaction between these components. The squares in which the peak densities of the four species occur are not the same above and below the transect. There are also significant differences between squares when the components due to distance, altitude and their interaction have been extracted.

Two main points emerge from the analysis. First, the species are not homogeneously distributed, but appear to follow definite patterns. Secondly, in the early stages, this pattern is broadly consistent between species. It is possibly created by areas where suitable oviposition sites exist, where egg viability is high, or where adult survival was high in the previous season.

The overall effect of altitude above sea level in the west Cotswolds is fairly obvious. The season in spring tends to be more advanced in the Vale of Berkeley, which runs from the Severn to the foot of the Cotswolds Scarp. On top of the Scarp, the season is noticeably later. My sampling area on the scarp slope ran from approximately 100 m to 200 m in altitude above sea level. Consequently, height on the slope might be expected to create variation in the growth rates of individual grasshoppers. Figure 3.3 summarises the effect of altitude in terms of the proportion of individuals caught below the base line, for each species, and illustrates the change in this proportion with time. Since the base-line transect was marked out with canes, there is very little error in assigning an individual to a catch above or below. I have included the standard errors of these points although, since the sampling distributions are not random, these errors are not exact. The first three instars (the first two in the case of *C. brunneus*) have been included because the low density and spread of the later instars makes it impossible to produce a meaningful graph.

Figure 3.3 *a* indicates that in *O. viridulus*, altitude has a very obvious effect. The proportion of individuals taken in the lower half of the area falls with time. This reduction is greatest in Instar I. In mid-June, 85% of individuals are caught in the lower area. In just over a month, this proportion drops to 25%. It therefore appears that individuals hatch earlier in the lower area than in the upper. This discrepancy in the hatching rate is still evident in the second and third instars, but the reduction with time is not as marked. It is not possible to say whether the reductions in Instars II and III are entirely due to differences in the hatching rate, or whether altitude is producing differences in moulting rates. If a difference in development rates does exist, the gradients of Figure 3.3*a* would become steeper with each succeeding instar. This does not occur. The results of *C. parallelus* (Fig. 3.3*b*) show that altitude has some effect in this species. There is a significant drop in the proportion of Instar I individuals caught below the transect from mid-June to early July. There is no significant drop in either Instar II or III.

Just as *O. viridulus* exhibits a consistent drop in all three instars, *S. lineatus* (Fig. 3.3*c*) exhibits a consistent constant proportion below the line in each instar. The majority of points fall within the 0.5 to 0.8 region. There is no evidence of any reduction in these proportions with time.

For *C. brunneus* there are fewer points and wider errors than for the previous species (Fig. 3.3*d*). There is no consistent evidence of any drop in the proportions caught below the line in the first instar, and the two points plotted for Instar II indicate the opposite trend.

The altitude effect is very evident in Instars I, II and III of *O. viridulus*. This species is also the earliest to hatch. It is possible that its early development and consequent exposure to lower daily mean temperature make it more susceptible to the temperature differential which will exist with the changes in altitude.

This hypothesis tends to be reinforced by *C. parallelus* and *C. brunneus*. The former, which hatches later than *O. viridulus*, shows an altitude effect, but over the first three instars this is much less marked. The latest species to hatch, *C. brunneus*, does not appear to show an altitude effect.

In *S. lineatus*, the proportion hatching below the line remains constant throughout all three instars. This species has a hatching period and moulting rates very similar to those of *C. parallelus*, and ought to show a similar pattern in hatching proportions. It may be significant that, whereas the other species oviposit in soil, the egg-pods of *S. lineatus* are deposited on grass stems close to the ground. They may, therefore, be exposed to different temperature regimes.

Sampling distributions of the grasshoppers

The distribution (= dispersion) of individuals over the space occupied by the population is of considerable ecological significance in that it reflects the conditions of the population and its environment. Changes in the dispersal of a population may reflect changes in these conditions, as Taylor (1981) points out.

The observed sampling distribution of a population will depend upon, among other parameters, its density; therefore comparisons of such distributions must be made using short sampling intervals before large changes in density can intervene. The density of a particular instar will change over several weeks. Since, even at peak densities, the mean number of individuals per quadrat remains low for each instar, a single day's sample is not really sufficient to present a precise description of the sampling distribution. If, however, all the sampling occasions on which the instar was sampled were used to describe the sampling distribution, the results would be ambiguous as they would reflect a systematic, and large, change in the mean density with time. The sampling intervals used to investigate distribution in each instar are those where the appropriate life table for the species (as discussed later) estimates that the density of the instar is at a maximum.

The coefficient of dispersion (the ratio of the sample variance over the sample mean) is a good index of the randomness of a population (Greig-Smith, 1964), since it measures the extent to which the data fit the Poisson distribution. Significant deviations from a value of 1 indicate either an aggregated distribution (CD > 1), or an over-dispersed distribution (CD < 1). Table 3.2 presents values of this and other distribution parameters for each instar; obviously, many instars exhibit an aggregated or contagious distribution. The Negative Binomial distribution is widely used in the analysis of contagious distributions of insects, and consequently I also obtained distribution parameters for the instars using this model. The Negative Binomial distribution is a function of two parameters, the mean, μ, and K, which has no real biological meaning in this context but is an index of clumping. A discussion of the method of estimating the Negative Binomial parameters is given in Southwood (1978).

The coefficient of dispersion, when multiplied by the sampling degrees of freedom, behaves as a χ^2. Therefore, $CD \times (N\text{-}1)$ is distributed as a χ^2 with N-1 degrees of freedom. Since, however, in every case in Table 3.2, N is greater than 100, we can find an approximate normal deviate from the χ^2 value. The term $\sqrt{2\chi^2} - \sqrt{2(N\text{-}1)}$ is distributed as a standard normal deviate as N becomes larger. Therefore, $d = \sqrt{2(N\text{-}1)}(CD\text{-}1)$ approximates to a normal deviate. Values of d are given in Table 3.2, those outside the 95% confidence interval being marked with an asterisk. Changes in K with change in $\bar{x}$ have also been analysed to determine whether significant changes in degree of aggregation have occurred (Bliss & Owen, 1958). The details are presented in Bradley (1975).

In *C. parallelus*, the Negative Binomial model presents a better fit to

Table 3.2 The sampling distributions of each instar in each species. The mean $(\bar{x})$, variance (s^2) and the coefficient of dispersion (CD) of the observed distributions are shown, as well as the approximated normal deviate (d) of the coefficient of dispersion, the χ^2 goodness-of-fit values to the Poisson (a) and Negative Binomial (b) distributions and the parameter (K) of the Negative Binomial. Generally, the Negative Binomial provides a better fit. $P < 0.001$ is indicated by ***; $0.01 > P > 0.001$ by **, and $0.05 > P > 0.01$ by *.

Species and stage	$\bar{x}$	s^2	d	CD	χ_a^2	K	χ_b^2
C. parallelus							
I	0.282	0.781	12.6***	2.77	2.6×10^5***	0.156	5.38
II	0.327	0.990	10.1***	3.02	1.6×10^5***	0.195	8.68*
III	0.279	0.351	1.9	1.26	4.9	0.903	0.85
IV	0.148	0.314	6.7***	2.12	554.5***	0.122	2.18
A	0.165	0.187	1.1	1.13	2.9	1.12	0.94
S. lineatus							
I	0.277	0.548	7.7***	1.97	655.4***	0.32	4.83
II	0.272	0.412	3.5***	1.52	54.7***	0.49	3.08
III	0.223	0.229	0.19	1.03	0.5	11.18	0.4
IV	0.248	0.244	—	0.98	0.3	—	—
A	0.256	0.327	2.3*	1.28	9.2*	0.89	0.9
C. brunneus							
I	0.330	0.760	8.1***	2.30	6.5×10^3***	0.30	5.9
II	0.095	0.196	5.3***	2.08	108.0***	0.06	1.7
III	0.068	0.064	—	0.94	0.4	—	—
IV	0.167	0.233	3.2**	1.40	13.7**	0.35	0.58
A	0.098	0.119	2.3*	1.40	24.8***	0.55	2.5
O. viridulus							
I	0.098	0.138	4.74***	1.41	32.2***	0.20	0.6
II	0.038	0.037	—	0.97	0.2	—	—
III	0.032	0.037	—	0.97	0.1	—	—

the data than the Poisson and there is considerable aggregation. In Instars I and II, the coefficients of dispersion are significantly greater than 1, and K is small. In the third instar, the coefficient of dispersion is closer to 1, and d only just reaches the 0.5 probability level. K is also larger than in the first two instars.

Instar IV, like Instars I and II, exhibits a clumped distribution, with the Poisson model presenting a poor fit to the data and K taking a low value. The adult instar resembles Instar III, in that K is large, and the Poisson model is a reasonable fit.

Individuals of *C. parallelus* appear to hatch in aggregations since Instar I is clumped. The eggs are laid in pods with, according to Richards & Waloff (1954), approximately seven eggs per pod. Richards & Waloff also point out that *C. parallelus* shows a strong preference for oviposition in bare areas of ground, which would probably result in a clumping of the pods in broken ground on the common. The clumping in the early instars is, therefore, likely to be produced by the oviposition behaviour and biology of the adult female, rather than by any behaviour of the hatching individual.

The relaxation of this clumping effect in Instar III suggests that movement on the part of the individuals of Instars I and II has broken down the hatching aggregation. It is feasible that selective predation of dense groups of individuals would have this effect, but the mortality in Instars I and II appears insufficient for this mechanism.

If movement on the part of young individuals breaks down initial aggregation, then the clumping that occurs in Instar IV cannot be due to the selection of oviposition sites by the previous generation's females. The two alternative mechanisms which will produce reaggregation are selective mortality and behavioural effects. Mortality in Instar IV is high, but it would have to be very localised to produce a contagious distribution. Behavioural aggregational mechanisms are certainly well known in other Acrididae, even among species that do not exhibit swarming behaviour (see, for example, Uvarov (1966). Aikman & Hewitt (1972), in the course of a movement experiment on *C. parallelus*, mention apparent temporary aggregations of individuals which occurred as the animals migrated outwards from an initial release point.

In the adult, the intense clumping of fourth instar individuals is no longer evident, and the dispersion is more nearly random. The reproductive behaviour of the Acrididae involves movement of the females towards stridulating males and searching for suitable oviposition sites, with, possibly, movement on the part of males searching for females. There is evidence of territorial behaviour in some species of Acrididae, and it is possible that the males disperse themselves by territorial interaction.

Overriding these 'normal' movements will be the 'escape' movements of disturbed grasshoppers, usually a series of long jumps, depending on the strength of the disturbance. This factor may be greater in the larger, adult grasshoppers, because their ability to jump is greater. This movement may result in the less dense aggregations of Instar IV, but the observed distribution does not imply that such movement is random.

A final process which will have some effect is the rate of development of individuals. Differential rates of development will produce increasing asynchrony in moulting dates, and this will be greatest in the adult. Unless environmental factors tend to synchronise development, the variation in duration of each instar will successively add to the overall variation in life history. Although individuals may remain aggregated throughout this process, if sampling distributions are compared between instars, aggregations will become successively smaller as fewer individuals are in the same instar at the same time.

Overall, the results of *S. lineatus* exhibit a similar pattern to those of

C. parallelus. None of the changes in K were found to be significant, however. I have not fitted a Negative Binomial model to the observations of Instar IV because the value of K arrived at indicates a regular dispersion, for which the Negative Binomial is not an appropriate model. For the same reason, the coefficient of dispersion of less than 1 is not given.

As in *C. parallelus*, Instars I and II exhibit contagious distributions, with high coefficients of dispersion and low K values, although these values are not as extreme as in the case of *C. parallelus*. Instar III also follows the trend in that species, although this time the distribution is more nearly random. The Poisson model fits the data as well as the Negative Binomial, K is large and the coefficient of dispersion is close to unity.

The Adult instar is not as randomly distributed as III and IV, and there appears to be an increase in the level of aggregation. There is always less aggregation in *S. lineatus* than in *C. parallelus*. This may be a reflection of the fact that its pods contain fewer eggs (Ragge, 1966), or that the conditions for oviposition are less stringent. This species lays in the roots of grass rather than in bare soil.

The pattern of distribution in *C. brunneus* is like that of *C. parallelus* in that, over the first three instars, there is a decrease from the initial high level of aggregation which occurs in Instar I. Later in development, aggregation occurs again, probably by a behavioural mechanism. In *S. lineatus* this reaggregation is delayed until the adult, but occurs earlier in *C. parallelus*. The Negative Binomial has not been fitted to Instar III of *C. brunneus* because a large value of 58.4 for K suggests that the model is not appropriate.

The overall pattern of distribution in this species is very similar to that of the previous two species. The first two instars are highly aggregated. Both have high coefficients of dispersion and Instar II exhibits a low K value. Instar III exhibits very low aggregation. Instar IV and the adult instar are moderately aggregated, significantly more clumped than Instar III but less so than Instars I and II.

Because of the low density of *O. viridulus*, I have not presented parameters of the sampling distributions of Instar IV or the adult stage. The first three instars follow the pattern of the previous species. There is some aggregation in the first instar, though this is not as evident as in the other species. The coefficient of dispersion is close to 1 in Instars II and III, which indicates the breakdown of the clumping evident in Instar I.

The two *Chorthippus* species are very similar, both in the level of aggregation and in the fact that reaggregation occurs in the fourth instar. The similarities are unlikely to result from a common environment. Figure 3.2 indicates that they hatch and develop at different periods, and they are distributed differently on the Common. This favours the hypothesis that reaggregation is a behavioural phenomenon rather than an environmental effect.

The fact that individuals of all species appear to spend a proportion of their life histories in aggregations also affects considerations of competition. Unless individuals of one species tend to aggregate with those of another, clumping is unlikely to lead to interspecific competition, but it may lead to, or reinforce, intraspecific competition.

Estimating the population dynamics

Sequential sampling versus capture–recapture

An investigation of population dynamics has to be designed with a particular form of analysis in mind. Generally the choice lies between a sequential random-sampling programme using some form of quadrat, or individual captures for a capture–recapture programme.

Capture–recapture models, as the name implies, deal with situations where animals are removed from a population and are marked and released, and a further sample, containing marked and unmarked animals, is taken. Various studies, allowing for different dynamic processes in populations, have resulted in a series of statistical models. Cormack (1968) discusses the statistical philosophy of these models, and Seber (1973) describes their uses and abuses.

Two trends are evident in the development of these techniques. The first is that statisticians have regarded population numbers as the single most important parameter to be estimated, so that loss and dilution rates are regarded only as factors affecting numbers. For example, the models of Jolly (1965), Seber (1965) and Manly & Parr (1968) are all concerned with estimating the number of marked animals available for capture. Population size is derived directly from the estimator, but loss and dilution estimates are derived afterwards from two such estimators. In contrast, the earlier models of Leslie & Chitty (1951) and Fisher & Ford (1947) estimate loss rates initially, and derive estimates of numbers from these. In studies of natural selection, birth and death are, generally, as important as population size (see, for example, Bishop & Sheppard, 1973). The second trend is the development of more general models, which involve fewer limiting assumptions. As a result, the choice of models applicable to a specific biological situation must be made on a very narrow basis. Cormack concludes that there is '. . . in general, no advantage in using any restricted model, when the elegance and simplicity of the results of Jolly (1965) and Seber (1965) are available'. From the statistical viewpoint, this is certainly true. However, it does mean that a uniform approach is likely to be made to populations which vary widely in their ecology, without considering the special characteristics of the population. In addition, population biologists may not consider the adequacy of their data, or may not be able to obtain data in sufficient quantities for analysis by Jolly's method. Begon (1983) discusses in detail how the use of Jolly's method has been abused.

Deficiencies of standard capture–recapture models can be shown by taking an example. It has been the experience of those involved in the ecology field courses run by the Universities of Manchester and Liverpool that the grasshopper population of Selsley Common is excellent material for capture–recapture estimates, and fairly consistent results for total population sizes have been obtained. On the face of it, therefore, a capture–recapture sampling programme should have provided an adequate estimate of population size and mortality for the construction of a life table.

Table 3.3 shows the results of a capture–recapture experiment which I performed on a Selsley site from 4 to 10 June 1971. I analysed the data using Jolly's stochastic model. Since I considered each instar separately, these data presented a problem in that they included a loss of marks due to moulting, as well as death. Obviously such a population cannot be expected to have a loss rate even approximately constant over the period of the experiment.

However, information on loss due to death is available from the number of 'births' into the next instar. Table 3.3 shows loss and gain (calculated as numbers of animals) between each instar. The standard errors of the estimates of probability of daily survival (ϕ) vary between 0.2 and 0.6. The real daily loss due to death must be very small if any animals are to survive to become adults.

I sampled the population intensively to obtain those data. My results tend to show that Jolly's method is unsuitable for the study of this population of grasshoppers, where moulting occurs frequently, because the Jolly estimates of loss and dilution are insufficiently accurate.

A sequential sampling programme does not utilise data as efficiently as capture–recapture, in that it does not build up a 'history' of marked individuals. However, in the case of the Selsley grasshoppers, such a programme had two strong advantages:

(a) A large area of Selsley would be sampled, and a general picture provided, rather than the restricted area required for a capture-recapture experiment with a high sampling intensity.

(b) A method of life-table analysis was available for sequentially sampled data which provided estimates of mortality within each instar independent of moulting rates.

Table 3.3 Estimates of the population size (N), daily survival rate, and numbers lost and gained in Instars II, III, IV of the Selsley population of *S. lineatus*. The estimates were obtained using Jolly's (1965) stochastic model, and are presented with standard errors. Also shown are the differences in moults; that is, the difference between the numbers recruited into an instar and the numbers lost from the previous instar. This figure should indicate the true losses, as opposed to moulting individuals. The table indicates that this form of analysis cannot be used to separate out moults and deaths.

	Instar II				Instar III					Instar IV	
Day	Numbers N	Survival ϕ	Loss	Differences in moult	Gain	Numbers N	Survival ϕ	Loss	Differences in moult	Gain	Numbers N
2	25±24	1.1±0.66	−1.5	−26.6	25±15	25±13	0.64±0.25	8.8	2.8	7±4	5.0
3	102±106	0.76±0.36	24.6	−16.5	41±34	42±17	0.95±0.40	2.3	−6.7	9±9	10±4
4	80±48	0.76±0.31	19.1	23.4	−4±21	81±43	0.58±0.29	34.5	34.3	0±6	21±10
5	81±42	0.79±0.36	16.6	−13.1	30±25	43±21	0.66±0.31	14.8	−1.7	17±15	14±4
Totals	—	—	58.8	−32.8	91.6	—	—	60.4	28.7	32.5	—

Consequently, I used the less efficient but biologically more appropriate technique of sequential sampling rather than capture–recapture. The details of the model used for analysis, and the degree to which it fits the biology of the grasshoppers is discussed in the following sections.

Estimating the life tables

A number of approaches have been proposed for dealing with stage-structured populations, where estimates can be provided of the absolute density in each stage. Richards & Waloff (1954) estimated these numbers using a regression technique. Since the numbers in each instar exhibit a well-marked peak, these authors plotted the logarithm of numbers occurring after the peak against time. The use of logarithms presented the fall in numbers as a straight line, and a regression line was then fitted and extrapolated to the number of animals available when the stage first appeared in the population. If it is assumed that losses from the instars occur at a constant rate, this method estimates the total number of animals entering that stage. Unfortunately, if the loss is due to moulting, it can hardly be expected to remain constant throughout the instar.

Dempster (1961) describes a method of estimating mortality and natality in a population where the same stages of successive generations do not overlap, as with grasshoppers. Southwood (1978) states that this method is not robust; it requires a large number of samples in order to give accurate estimates. It also has a practical disadvantage in that it requires estimates of the numbers hatching from day to day over the sampling period.

Richards & Waloff (1954) describe how they estimated the hatch in the Silwood Park colonies using 'emergence tubs, which give a direct count of the numbers hatching from a known area of ground. Unfortunately, this method was not suitable for the Selsley population as it occupies common land much frequented by the public, where equipment could not be left unguarded. Another approach has been developed, initially by MacDonald (1957). This assumes that a population has a constant death rate and a constant age of transition from one stage to the next; the total of the time survived before transition, summed for all individuals and expressed as a proportion of the total time survived by all individuals, is equal to the proportion of individuals that fail to achieve the transition. Thus, in a situation where sampling is regular and uniform, and where it begins before the birth of the first individual and ends after the death of the last, the total incidence of each stage in the catch, summed over all samples, will be directly proportional to the total time survived in each stage. These two relationships give a method of estimating the survival rate from the following equation suggested by Hokyo & Kiritani (1967):

$$\frac{F_1}{F_1 + F_2} = 1 - S^{t_1}$$

where F_1 is the total incidence of stage 1 in the catch, F_2 is the total incidence of stage 2, S is the finite survival rate, and t_1 is the mean duration of stage 1.

Kiritani & Nakasuji (1967) elaborated this method to deal with more than two stages, and Manly (1976) extended it to deal with an irregular sampling schedule and to provide estimates of the numbers entering, and the mean duration of, each stage. Manly (1977) also provides a jack-knife technique for estimating variances.

An independent technique was developed by Manly (1976), similar in principle to that of Richards & Waloff, in that it fits a regression line through a decay function once most of the individuals have entered the stage in question. Like Richards & Waloff's technique, it demands a clear peak in numbers to be used successfully.

Read & Ashford (1968) also describe a system of models which are applicable to an organism passing through a series of stages in its life history. These models differ from those discussed above in that they are stochastic. They are concerned with fitting theoretical distributions to mortality and moulting rates, and treat the lengths of time spent in a stage by an individual before it exits, either by death or by moulting, as continuous random variables governed by specific types of probability density functions. Thus a probability of being at any stage at any time can be assigned to any individual. Similarly, there is a probability of dying or moulting during a fixed time interval. These probabilities can then be estimated by maximum likelihood. Like the previous models, they provide estimates of mortality at each stage; they also provide estimates of the numbers hatching and the mean time spent in each instar. Ashford *et al.* (1970) describe the analysis of data from a population of *C. parallelus*, using the models derived by Read & Ashford, and deduce which model is most appropriate.

The models predict the probability that an insect is in a particular instar and occupying the area sampled at any given time. Since the numbers of insects in each instar in the samples are known with a fair degree of accuracy if extraction has been efficient, a likelihood function of the probability of the observations can be constructed. The maximum of the function can be found by using an iterative optimisation technique, and the values of the parameters at the maximum represent the maximum likelihood solution.

The joint probability of observations, X_i, where $i = 1 \ldots n$, regarded as a function of an unknown parameter θ, is called the likelihood function (l) and is given by:

$$l(x|\theta) = f(x_1|\theta) \times f(x_2|\theta) \ldots f(x_n|\theta)$$

The maximum likelihood estimator of θ is that value $(\bar{\theta})$ where $l(x|\theta)$ attains its maximum value, i.e. where it gives the highest probability of the observations x occurring at any value of θ. In practice it is usual to work in terms of the logarithm of the likelihood, rather than in terms of the likelihood itself. This generally leads to a more simple and more readily computable function. The maximum value of the log-likelihood occurs at the same value of θ as the maximum of the likelihood.

Suppose we sample a population of grasshoppers which occupies an area (A) and our sample on day (i) captures grasshoppers from an area A_i which is included in A. The population is limited to those individuals that can be sampled by our field techniques and excludes eggs. The population, therefore, began at time (t_0) with the hatching of the first egg-pods, and a total of N individuals have hatched (or will hatch, depending on when our sample is taken) into the population.

Read (1966) showed that the log-likelihood of obtaining r_{ij} individuals of states $j = 1 \ldots k$ in a series of samples t taken on days $i = 1 \ldots n$, on dates t_1 to t_n onwards (in other words, a season's data) is a function of the N, r_{ij}, A_i and p_j (t_i) values, where $p_j(t_i)$ is the probability of any insect being in instar j at time t_i.

This function assumes that the site is uniform, and that insects are independently distributed, so that the probability of any individual being included in the ith sample is $p_j(t_i) \times \left(\dfrac{A_i}{A} \right)$. A third assumption is that the decline in numbers due to destructive sampling is negligible. This is reasonable since A_i/A is always a very small ratio in Selsley populations.

The unknowns in the expression are N and the $p_j(t_i)$. Since we have as many $p_j(t_i)$ as we have r_{ij} observations, and we have the value of N to estimate, a maximum likelihood solution cannot be found.

Read (1966) demonstrated that, by describing the process of hatching, moulting and death with uncomplicated distributions, all the $p_j(t_i)$ could be generated from a further limited set of parameters, and that a maximum likelihood solution existed for those parameters. Any grasshopper moulting into any instar (j) would spend a period Y_j in that instar before moulting into the next, or a period Z_j in that instar before dying. Y_j and Z_j are random variables, and therefore X_j, where $X_j = \text{minimum } (Y_j, Z_j)$, will also be a random variable. The process of hatching can be considered as a special form of moulting, and treated in exactly the same way. The final instar, the adult phase, presents problems in that it is terminated by death for all individuals. However, Read considered mortality in the adult to be of two types:

(a) death due to a random event, such as predation, which is generally identical to death in any earlier instar;

(b) death due to the physiological process of ageing or senility, which can be considered, like moulting, to be an age-dependent phenomenon and treated similarly.

Read & Ashford (1968) demonstrated that the $p_j(t_i)$ depend upon the governing distributions of the Y_i, Z_i and t for their values. They suggest that the governing distributions of the Z_j and Y_j are best selected from the special Erlangian class of functions, for which:

$$f(y) = \frac{\lambda^a(y^{a-1}e^{-\lambda y})}{(a-1)!}$$

for positive integer values of the order a.

The reasons for using this type of distribution are as follows. The occurrence of death in each instar (with the exception of death due to ageing in the adult) is assumed to be a random event, governed by a Poisson process. The distribution of the Z_i, where survival in j is terminated by death, will follow a negative exponential distribution:

$$f(Z) = \mu e^{-\mu Z}$$

where μ is the death rate. The negative exponential is itself an Erlangian function of order 1.

In some respects, the assumption that death is independent of time is biologically unrealistic. For example, the mortality of freshly moulted individuals with softened uncoloured cuticles is likely to be different from that of an individual whose cuticle has hardened up and whose epidermis is pigmented. However, this assumption is implicit in all population models except those where the death rate is estimated over short intervals. If variation in death rate is known to be systematic and significant, the model can be adjusted to take this into account. For example, the instar can be treated as two stages, a freshly moulted stage where individuals have soft cuticles, and a later stage where they do not. If sufficient freshly moulted individuals can be included in samples, mortality and duration can be estimated for both stages. In the case of grasshoppers, this will require considerably more sampling effort, since the cuticle usually requires less than 24 h to harden, and the juvenile instars last between 1 and 3 weeks. The selection of distributions to govern the Y_j (survival in the stadium until a moult occurs) is a more complex problem.

The distribution which seems most appropriate from biological insight is the log-normal, which is traditionally used when dealing with rate-dependent phenomena. Mathematically, however, it is not very suitable. It is a function of two parameters, the mean and the variance, both of which must be estimated, and it does not lead to a directly computable solution to the $p_j(t_i)$.

Erlangian functions of the lower orders provide computable solutions to the $p_i(t_i)$, and are functions of only one parameter. Like the log-normal, they are similar in shape to skewed normal distributions. The following section will consider how well they fit the biological assumptions.

The $p_i(t_i)$, and hence the r_{ij} individuals in each sample i, can be calculated, in the case of grasshoppers, from 13 parameters. These are:

N	the total number of individuals emerging into the population;
t_0	the date on which the hatch begins;
λ	the rate parameter of the hatch;
$\lambda_{I...IV}$	the rate parameters of moulting in the four juvenile stadia;
$\mu_{I...IV}$	the death rate in each juvenile stadium;
λ_A	the rate parameter of physiological death in the adult;
μ_A	the rate parameter of 'random death' in the adult.

The biological meaning of N and t_0 are obvious. The death rate μ represents the probability that an individual in a particular stadium will die in it; alternatively, it represents the proportion of individuals dying in that stadium. The rate parameter has no direct biological meaning, but the mean duration of each stadium (l) can be calculated from it.

This is given by:

$$\bar{l} = \frac{a\lambda}{(2+\mu)^2} + \frac{\mu^2}{(\lambda+\mu)^3}$$

where a is the order of the Erlangian function whose governing parameter is λ.

The model therefore describes the population in terms of a mean individual, and estimates the period the individual spends in each state, and, consequently, the dates on which it would hatch or moult, and the probability of death in each state. Read & Ashford (1968) apply a series of models to a population of *C. parallelus*. From inspections of the fit between the predicted r_{ij} and the observed r_{ij}, they conclude that an Erlangian function of order 3 describes the moulting rate more accurately than a function of order 2.

Biological assumptions of the maximum likelihood model

In the previous section, several deviations from the assumptions of Read's model have been considered. In the real world, where organisms are variable, idiosyncratic and interesting, imperfect agreement has to be accepted if any estimates are to be obtained. The extent of the agreement is therefore considered in more detail here. A fundamental assumption of the model is that hatching, moulting and senescent death can be adequately described by Erlangian functions.

Moulting is known to be an age-dependent process in insects, and is initiated by the prothoracic glands, which, in turn, are the target of a neurohormone secreted by the corpora cardiaca of the supra-oesophageal ganglia, the insect 'brain'. The stimulus which triggers the system varies from species to species. Wigglesworth (1963) has shown that, in the bug *Rhodnius*, the stretching of the larval abdomen after a meal of blood provides the stimulus; in grasshoppers, the action of chewing and swallowing may achieve the same effect. Moulting is probably a rate-dependent process in the grasshopper, and variation in the duration of stadia will arise from variations in the rate of eating or growth, or in the efficiency of the secretory cells of the corpora cardiaca and corpora allata, and in the threshold levels of the target cells involved in the moulting process.

Bernays (1972) describes the hatching process in the locust *Schistocerca gregaria* (Forskal). He determined that serosal cuticle digestion, size increase, and the development of a co-ordinated movement pattern of serial contractions are necessary to the embryo before it can hatch. All these phenomena depend upon the size and development of the embryo, and hatching, like moulting, would appear to be a rate-dependent process. However, Bernays found that hatching activity could be promoted by many stimuli. These included mechanical disturbance and rise in temperature.

Hatching in the natural habitat is therefore not an independent event. Stimuli, such as temperature drops, may cause individuals, in variable states of readiness, to hatch out together. It is likely that moulting is also affected to some extent by external stimuli; as in the case of hatching, the log-normal distribution may not be as good a fit as it appears at first sight.

Figures 3.4 and 3.5 are histograms of the numbers of grasshoppers hatching, with the appropriate Erlangian functions of orders 2, 3 and 4 superimposed. Figures 3.4 *a* and *b* are results taken from a culture of *C. parallelus* and *O. viridulus*.

All Acrididae indigenous to Britain have an obligate egg diapause; the eggs require a sufficient number of day-degrees at low temperature before normal embryonic development occurs. The egg-pods were collected from captured adult individuals in 1972. The pods were then placed in petri dishes filled with sand containing approximately 10% moisture by volume, and the dishes were sealed by means of paraffin wax. The dishes contained up to 20 pods and were filled over a period of several days as pods were laid. Each dish was stored at room temperature until the end of the season. When the most recently laid pod had been held at room temperature for a period of 4 weeks, the dishes were placed in a refrigerator and held at a temperature which varied between 4 and 8°C for a period of some 12 weeks. The sand was

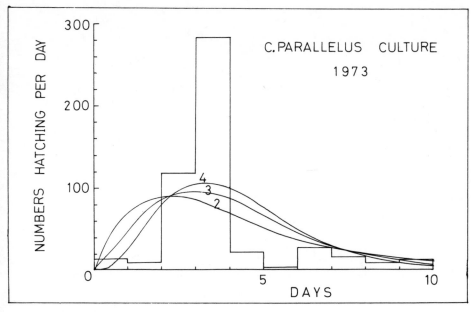

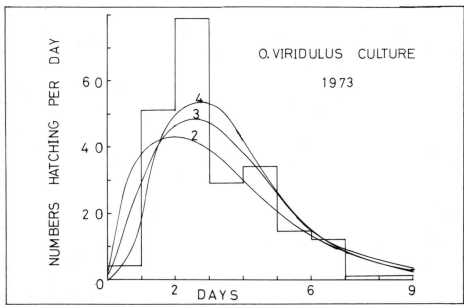

Fig. 3.4 The fit of Erlangian functions of orders 2, 3 and 4 to the numbers of *O. viridulus* and *C. parallelus* hatching in a culture.

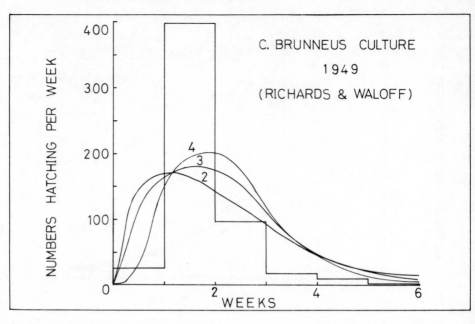

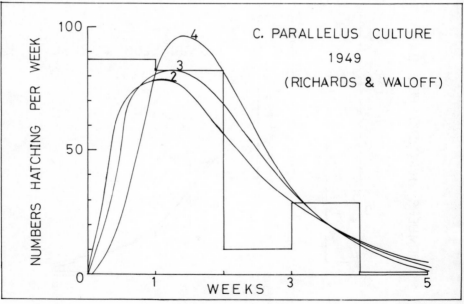

Fig. 3.5   The fit of Erlangian functions of orders 2, 3 and 4 to the numbers of *C. parallelus* and *C. brunneus* hatching in a culture. The histograms are drawn from data published in Richards & Waloff (1954).

periodically remoistened to prevent excess drying out in the dry environment of the refrigerator.

The petri dishes were kept at room temperature for a further 10 days. At the end of this period, the pods were redistributed, since the purpose of the experiment was to gain genetic information, pods from the same cross being grouped together. Small plastic pots were placed over each group of pods and the sand was moistened at regular intervals. The pots were checked twice daily for hatched individuals, which were then transferred to cages.

The short time period over which the hatch took place, 10 days in the *C. parallelus* culture and 9 days in the case of *O. viridulus*, reflects the synchronisation of their development. In both species, however, the distribution of hatching is clearly asymmetric, and the modes occur at the same point as the peaks in the three Erlangian functions which are superimposed on the histograms.

Figure 3.5 is constructed from data presented in Richards & Waloff (1954) that represent hatches from the pods of captive individuals. These pods were kept throughout in an unheated shed, and therefore show a much larger spread in the hatching period. The hatch of *C. parallelus* occurred over a period of 5 weeks, in contrast to the 10

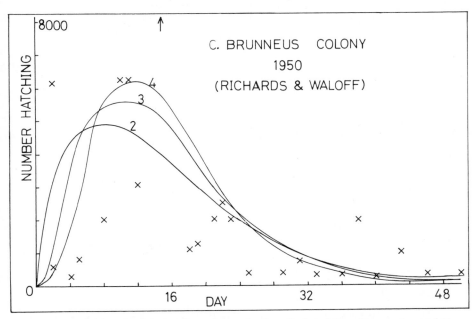

Fig. 3.6 The fit of Erlangian functions of orders 2, 3 and 4 to the numbers of *C. brunneus* hatching in the field, estimated by the use of 'emergence tubs'. The figure is drawn from data published in Richards & Waloff (1954).

days it took in my culture. Figure 3.5 is, therefore, much closer to the field situation. The histograms are again asymmetric, and the mode is in the same position as the peaks of the functions in the *C. brunneus* culture, and distorted to the left in the *C. parallelus* culture. Richards & Waloff recorded the hatching from individual pods, and in the case of *C. parallelus* demonstrated that pods which were laid early tended to hatch early. This is one source of variation that would tend to spread the hatch.

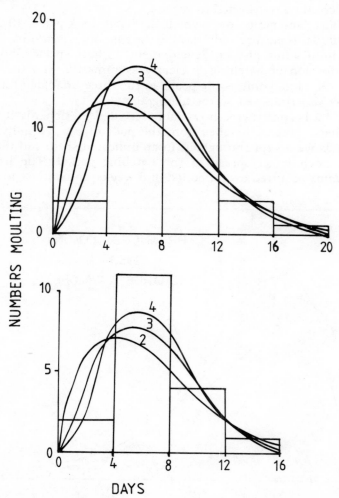

Fig. 3.7 The fit of Erlangian functions of orders 2, 3 and 4 to the duration of the first two instars occurring in a culture of *C. parallelus*. The upper histogram represents the duration of the first instar, the lower the second instar.

Figure 3.6 shows the estimated numbers of *C. brunneus* hatching into one of the Silwood Park colonies. Richards & Waloff estimated the numbers hatching by placing 'emergence tubs' on ground cleared of nymphs, and counting the numbers emerging at regular intervals; the spread of the hatch is slightly larger in the field than in the culture, but not significantly so. Again, there is good agreement between the mode of the hatch and the peak of the Erlangian functions. Although the Erlangian functions cannot precisely fit the distributions, they do appear to follow the histograms approximately, showing the correct type of skew, and agree remarkably well with the mode of the hatch. Although Read & Ashford selected the functions on mathematical grounds, I believe that their choice is justified on biological considerations also, at least for the hatching process.

Figure 3.7 shows histograms of the time spent in Instars I and II by *C. parallelus*. Although some difficulties of culture were experienced, there is good agreement for both skewness and the mode between the histograms and the functions. This indicates that the functions may be reasonable descriptions of moulting as well as hatching.

The maximum likelihood life table

All four species occurred at sufficiently high density to make Read's method feasible. The data used were obtained from the whole sampling area over the total 1972 season. I have not attempted to analyse data from restricted portions of the sampling area, despite the differences in observed densities described in a previous section. It is probable that the overall populations are not strictly homogeneous, but subdividing them would lead to low sampling densities and, consequently, increase the sampling variance.

The estimated hatching population of *O. viridulus* (see Table 3.4) is 23 000, a density of one grasshopper to approximately 4 m² over the sampling area. This species began hatching early in May and the highest intensity of hatching occurred near the end of the month. The average length of time spent in each juvenile instar declined from 20.6 days in Instar to 14.5 days in Instar IV, and the average longevity of the adult was 28.3 days.

The daily mortality was high in the first instar, at 0.03 deaths per individual per day. The death rate was reduced by a factor of 10 over Instars II, III and IV, to an average mortality of 0.003. In the adult, daily mortality was increased to 0.017.

Table 3.5 presents the analysis of *S. lineatus* population data. The total hatching population is 54 000 or about double the hatching density of *O. viridulus*. The hatch began in this species in mid-May, but the peak hatching period was not achieved until a month later, in

Table 3.4 The life table of *O. viridulus* obtained from fitting sampling data to Read's third-order maximum-likelihood model. Parameter estimates and the transition dates for a 'mean individual' are included. Moult and death rates are per individual per day. The duration of stage is in days. An explanation of the method is given in the text. (Starting population (N) = 23 059; starting date (t_0) = 5 May.)

| | Rate parameters | | Duration of | Transition |
	Moult (λ)	Death (μ)	stage (l)	date
Hatch	0.147	—	20.36	25.9 May
Instar I	0.147	0.0334	20.58	15.5 June
Instar II	0.163	0.0042	18.45	3.9 July
Instar III	0.173	0.0021	17.38	21.3 July
Instar IV	0.207	0.0036	14.51	4.8 August
Adult	0.107	0.0165	28.27	2.1 September

Table 3.5 The life table of *S. lineatus* obtained from fitting sampling data to Read's third-order maximum-likelihood model. Parameter estimates and the transition dates for a 'mean individual' are included. (Starting population (N) = 54 234; starting date (t_0) = 19 May.)

| | Rate parameters | | Duration of | Transition |
	Moult (λ)	Death (μ)	stage (l)	date
Hatch	0.092	—	32.74	20.8 June
Instar I	0.147	0.0020	20.36	11.2 July
Instar II	0.165	0.0020	18.14	29.3 July
Instar III	0.192	0.0021	15.59	13.9 August
Instar IV	0.168	0.0149	17.84	0.8 September
Adult	0.0105	0.0035	28.47	29.2 September

mid-June. The duration of each instar follows a similar pattern to that exhibited by *O. viridulus*, a first instar duration of 20 days, and a gradual reduction in instar duration over the juvenile instars although, in this case, Instar III is shorter than IV. The adult duration is 4 weeks as in *O. viridulus*.

Daily mortality was low in the first three instars, highest in Instar IV, and low again in the adult, unlike *O. viridulus*, where mortality in the adult was high.

The analysis of *C. parallelus* is summarised in Table 3.6. This species has a higher density of hatch than *O. viridulus*, at approximately 44 000. The starting date falls close to that of *S. lineatus* in mid-May and, again, the time taken to the peak density of hatching is approximately one month, in mid-June. The duration of each instar follows a similar pattern to that of *S. lineatus*, i.e. a reduction in instar length of the juvenile instars after Instar I, the

Table 3.6 The life table of *C. parallelus* obtained from fitting sampling data to Read's third-order maximum-likelihood model. Parameter estimates and the transition dates for a 'mean individual' are included. (Starting population (N) = 44 978; starting date (t_0) = 24 May.)

	Rate parameters		Duration of	Transition
	Moult (λ)	Death (μ)	stage ($\bar{l}$)	date
Hatch	0.110	—	27.26	20.52 June
Instar I	0.127	0.0021	23.61	14.1 July
Instar II	0.198	0.0042	15.16	29.3 July
Instar III	0.226	0.0022	13.29	11.6 August
Instar IV	0.181	0.0364	16.68	28.3 August
Adult	0.089	0.0105	33.85	1.1 October

shortest duration occurring in Instar III. Apart from Instar I, the duration of the juvenile instars in *C. parallelus* is shorter than in *S. lineatus*. The adults appear to survive slightly longer, however. Overall, the total length of life in *C. parallelus* and the peak hatching date are very similar to those of *S. lineatus*.

The mortality rates follow the trend of *O. viridulus* and *S. lineatus*, in being low in the first Instars I, II and III, and higher in later life. Unlike *S. lineatus*, however, the adult mortality remains high.

The analysis of *C. brunneus* is summarised in Table 3.7. The hatching population of approximately 23 000 is less than that of *S. lineatus* and *C. parallelus*, and close to that of *O. viridulus*. The hatch begins in early June, later than in many other species, and peak hatching occurs in early July. The duration of the instars follows the pattern of *S. lineatus* and *C. parallelus*, decreasing from first to third instar. The mean duration of the third instar is very short, at 10 days, in contrast to the fourth instar, which has a mean duration of 20 days.

Table 3.7 The life table of *C. brunneus* obtained from fitting sampling data to Read's third-order maximum-likelihood model. Parameter estimates and the transition dates for a 'mean individual' are included. (Starting population (N) = 22 614; starting date (t_0) = 3 June.)

	Rate parameters		Duration of	Transition
	Moult (λ)	Death (μ)	stage ($\bar{l}$)	date
Hatch	0.101	—	29.82	3.7 July
Instar I	0.145	0.0021	20.74	24.5 July
Instar II	0.213	0.0021	14.08	7.5 August
Instar III	0.283	0.0040	10.60	18.1 August
Instar IV	0.145	0.0268	20.70	7.9 September
Adult	0.061	0.0021	48.91	26.8 October

The adults appear to be long lived, with a mean duration of 48 days. This is considerably longer than any other species, and appreciable numbers of this grasshopper were still present in mid-October, when the final sample was taken. The estimate of adult longevity is, however imprecise because the final sample of the season was taken before the majority of adults had died. Variances were calculated for these parameters, but are not given here. In general, the variance of mortality was greatest and sometimes exceeded that for growth rate and for duration of instar by a factor of ten.

Conclusions

Comparison of temporal distributions of the four species

Figure 3.8 illustrates the life history of the 'mean individual' of each of the four species in 1972. On average, *O. viridulus* individuals hatch first, with a mean hatching date of 26 May. The mean hatching date of both *C. parallelus* and *S. lineatus* occurs on 20 June, some 24 days later. The mean hatching date of *C. brunneus* occurs 14 days thereafter, on 4 July.

The duration of the juvenile phases of *O. viridulus*, *C. parallelus* and *S. lineatus* are very similar, at approximately 70 days. Since *O. viridulus* hatches early, the majority of these individuals will be at least one instar ahead in development. As Fig. 3.8 shows, *C. parallelus* and *S. lineatus* are closer together in their development. These two species are also the most abundant on the Common. The individuals of both tend to be in the same instar at the same time and, hence, there is a possibility that they will be in competition. However, their distribution on the Common is very different, and this may be in order to avoid competition. This reasoning does not account for the fact that the life histories are so synchronised despite the differences in distribution and, hence, in micro-environment. It seems to be more likely that the similarity arises from adaptations by the two species to coincidental optimum durations of their life histories. Under this hypothesis, if populations of the two species from the Common were kept in controlled identical conditions, they would exhibit unsynchronised life histories.

Chorthippus brunneus has the latest hatching date, and the fastest rate of development in the juvenile phase, taking only 64 days to reach adulthood. This condition may be a result of its later hatching since, on average, temperatures are higher in July and August than in May or June, and the earlier instars of *C. brunneus* are subjected to warmer conditions.

Differences between species in the average height at which they are located on the scarp slope might also produce temporal variation between species. The data presented in Fig. 3.8 certainly indicate that this factor has an effect on the early instars *within* species. *Omocestus viridulus* is found predominantly in the lower half of the common; 68% of the individuals caught occurred in quadrats below my base line, and none of the other species bettered this proportion. However, *S. lineatus* and *C. brunneus*, with proportions of 63% and 60%, respectively, and which are hence also predominantly lower-slope species, ran considerably behind *O. viridulus* and are fairly synchronous with *C. parallelus*, which at 41% is predominantly an upper-slope species. Consequently, although individuals of each species probably do respond to microclimatic differences arising from the effect of height

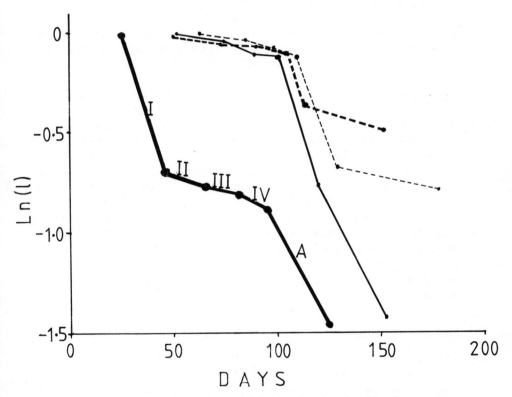

Fig. 3.8 Survivorship curves of mean individuals of each of the four species. The natural log of the probability of the mean individual surviving (l) is plotted against time. The graph is constructed from the parameter estimates presented in Tables 3.4–7. The heavy solid line represents *O. viridulus*, the heavy broken line *S. lineatus*, the light solid line *C. parallelus*, and the light broken line *C. brunneus*.

on the slope, this factor alone cannot determine the differences in hatching dates between the species.

Comparison of the mortality patterns within the four species

Figure 3.8 shows that the pattern of mortality in *C. parallelus*, *S. lineatus* and *C. brunneus* is similar. The death rate in the first three juvenile instars is very low, and then increases drastically in Instar IV. In *C. parallelus*, heavy non-senescent mortality continues in the adults; in the other two species, adult mortality is lower, although, in fact, the lifespan of the average adult is not much greater in the case of *C. brunneus*, and about the same in the case of *S. lineatus*. This perhaps suggests that the model is not differentiating clearly between random mortality and death due to ageing in the adults.

In *O. viridulus* there is a different mortality pattern from that of the other species in that heavy mortality occurs in the first instar. Thereafter the pattern follows that of the other species, with the exception that mortality in Instar IV is light. Mortality in the adult is identical with that of *C. parallelus*.

The graph strongly suggests that all four species are subjected to the same cause of mortality at the same time, irrespective of which instar the majority of individuals have reached, and that there was a substantial increase in mortality in July, when *O. viridulus* individuals are, in the main, adult, and Instar IV predominates in the other species.

The mortality exhibited on this graph can therefore be split into three phases. First, there is an early phase of high mortality in late April and May, to which only first instar individuals of *O. viridulus* are subject. Presumably this is because none but a few early-hatching individuals of the other species were present at this time. Secondly, there is a phase of very light mortality from mid-May to early July. All species, irrespective of instar, exhibit a very low death rate over this period. Finally, there is a third phase of heavy mortality from July onwards.

Possible environmental effects on the demography of the species

The first major constraint for all four species must be microclimate. The four species are all seasonal, with an obligate diapause, which allows fairly precise control of the timing of the embryonic development and hatching. The newly hatched insect must be able to maintain sufficient body temperatures over a sufficient period to allow the ingestion of adequate amounts of food. The hatch must be delayed for this purpose after the egg has overwintered. The insect then has to develop through its series of moults and become a sexually mature adult. The fecundity of the female strongly correlates with the body weight (Richards & Waloff, 1954), and consequently the efficiency of feeding at optimum ambient temperatures is of great adaptive significance. However, at the other end of the season, microclimate constrains the reproductive period of the adult. There is therefore a 'window' for the hatch of each species: individuals hatching too early do not survive, and those hatching too late have a curtailed reproductive period.

The window for *O. viridulus* would appear to be earlier than that for the other species. On Selsley, this species hatched some 4 weeks before the others but the first instar was subjected to a much higher mortality than the other species. Two possible factors may cause this. The first is that, in April, when this species was hatching, the climate was still sufficiently poor to lower the survival rate markedly. The second is that there was insufficient food available to the newly hatched grasshoppers. Bernays & Chapman (1970*a*, *b*) demonstrate that, in *C. parallelus*, first-instar individuals are limited in the type of grass they can consume by the lamina thickness and hairs on the blade. It is feasible that in all species, survival in the first instar could depend upon the probability of the individual finding adequate small soft shoots. In April, new grass is going to be less dense and more widely dispersed than it is in May, and consequently first-instar individuals of *O. viridulus* may be much more at risk of failing to find sufficient quantities than later-hatching species.

During the period of low mortality which occurs in all species from May onwards, there are plenty of fresh growing tips of grass available. The climate is mild, with frequent warm sunny days. Spiders and other invertebrate predators do not seem to occur at particularly high densities over the slope, and at this period avian predators are not obvious on the Common. The initial aggregated distributions of the grasshoppers become more random.

Later in the season, avian predators are much more in evidence, and this coincides with the third phase of heavy mortality in the fourth instar and adult individuals. During my sampling programme, at this period the Common was the regular haunt of kestrels (*Falco tinnunculus* L.), and was searched by rooks (*Corvus frugilegus* L.) from nearby woods practically on a daily basis. The rooks hunted in small groups, forming a line across the gradient and walking steadily up the slope. Through binoculars it was possible to observe them taking grasshoppers.

I suggest that this phase of mortality is primarily caused by bird predation, and that it occurs when it does because the fourth instar and adult grasshoppers provide sufficient energy returns on hunting effort for birds the size of rooks and kestrels, whereas the earlier instars, although at higher densities, do not. M.C. Calver (pers. comm.) has found exactly this situation in the grasshopper *Acrida conica* (Forskal), in Western Australia, where an important predator is the Australian magpie (*Gymnorhina dorsalis* Campbell). Calver has demonstrated that the optimum return of biomass per unit time for the predator occurs with the later instars, and that a population of *A. conica* which he investigated shows a similar increase in mortality in the pre-adult and adult instars due to predation by the magpie.

It is interesting that the very obvious colour polymorphisms exhibited by all four species are not well developed until the third instar onwards (Richards & Waloff, 1954; Bradley, 1975). This suggests that, if the polymorphism is associated with protection from predators by crypsis, it does not become important until the later instars. The 'reaggregation' behaviour noted earlier in this chapter may also have a role in predator avoidance since it may provide 'predator swamping' in the later instars. Gillet *et al.* (1979) described an example of this effect in locust nymphs. Consequently, all these species may be adapted to a phase of heavy avian predation which generally occurs from the third or fourth instar onwards.

The life history of *O. viridulus* is interesting, because in the season studied its fourth instar was not subject to heavy mortality. Since they developed ahead of the other species, the majority of *O. viridulus* individuals were in the fourth instar when very few of the others were so advanced. This means that the fourth-instar individuals are a low proportion of the total number of grasshoppers, and are therefore not necessarily a very cost-effective meal for a hunting rook, since the time the bird spends finding them would be high. Schultz (1981), for example, demonstrates that avian predators will not always take the larger instar of a grasshopper if search and handling costs are too high. The *O. viridulus* individual completes more of its development before the heavy predation phase begins, but to counterbalance this, suffers a heavier mortality in the first instar because of its earlier emergence.

To test these ideas, it would be necessary to partition mortality throughout the life history of the species, and to see if avian predation really increased substantially around July and August. It would also be necessary to determine the biomass returns per unit handling time by predators for grasshoppers of different sizes. Such an approach would begin to provide a comparative picture of life-history strategies in grasshoppers, and to suggest the types of selective forces that act upon timing rates of development and fecundity in these species. The purpose of this chapter has been to demonstrate that only by the use of comprehensive life-table models can such a comparative approach be adequately developed, and that the extra sampling and computational effort necessary to generate results from such models is worth while in the light of the detailed life-history information that they provide.

References

Aikman, D. & Hewitt, G. (1972) An experimental investigation of the rate and form of dispersal in grasshoppers. *Journal of Applied Ecology*, **9**, 807–17.

Ashford, J.R., Read, K.L.Q. & Vickers, C.G. (1970) A system of stochastic models applicable to studies in animal population dynamics. *Journal of Animal Ecology*, **39**, 29–50.

Begon, M. (1983) Abuses of mathematical methods in ecology: applications of Jolly's capture–recapture method. *Oikos*, **40**, 155–8.

Bernays, E.A. (1972) Hatching in *Schistocerca gregoria* (Forskal) (Orthoptera, Acrididae). *Acrida*, **1**, 41–60.

Bernays, E.A. & Chapman, R.F. (1970a) Food selection by *Chorthippus parallelus* (Zetterstedt) (Orthoptera: Acrididae) in the field. *Journal of Animal Ecology*, **39**, 383–94.

Bernays, E.A. & Chapman, R.F. (1970b) Experiments to determine the basis of food selection by *Chorthippus parallelus* (Zetterstedt) (Orthoptera:Acrididae) in the field. *Journal of Animal Ecology*, **39**, 761–75.

Bishop, J.A. & Sheppard, P.M. (1973) An evaluation of two populations using the technique of computer simulation, in *Mathematical Theory of the Dynamics of Biological Populations*, Bartlett, M.S. and Hiorns, R.W. eds. London and New York: Academic Press.

Bliss, C.I. & Owen, A.R.G. (1958) Negative binomial distributions with a common *k*. *Biometrika*, **45**, 37–58.

Bradley, J.S. (1975) *Population Dynamics and Natural Selection in a Mixed Colony of Grasshoppers*. Unpublished Ph. D. thesis, University of Liverpool.

Broughton, W.B. (1972) The grasshopper and the taxonomer. Part II. Acoustic aspects and the interpretation of results. *Journal of Biological Education*, **6**, 333–40.

Clarke, E.J. (1948) Studies in the ecology of British grasshoppers. *Transactions of the Royal Entomological Society, Lond* on 99, 173-222.

Cormack, R.M. (1968) The statistics of capture–recapture methods. *Oceanography and Marine Biology Annual Review*, **6**, 592–32.

Dempster, J.P. (1961) The analysis of data obtained by regular sampling of an insect population. *Journal of Animal Ecology*, **30**, 429–32.

Fisher, R.A. & Ford, E.B. (1947) The spread of a gene in natural conditions in a colony of the moth *Panaxia dominula* (L.) *Heredity, London*, **1**, 143–74.

Gillett, S.D., Hogarth, P.J. & Noble, F.E.J. (1979) The response of predators to varying densities of gregarious locust nymphs. *Animal Behaviour*, **27**, 592–6.

Grieg-Smith, P. (1964) *Quantitative Plant Ecology*. London: Butterworth.

Harper, J.L. (1977) *Population Biology of Plants*. London: Academic Press.

Hokyo, N. & Kiritani, K. (1967) A method for estimating natural survival rate and mean fecundity of an adult insect population by dissecting the female reproductive organs. *Researches on Population Ecology*, **9**, 130–52.

Hubbard, C.E. (1968) *Grasses*, 2nd edn. Harmondsworth: Penguin.

Kiritani, K. & Nakasuji, F. (1967) Estimation of the stage specific survival rate in insect populations with overlapping stages. *Researches on Population Ecology*, **9**, 143–52.

Jolly, G.M. (1965) Explicit estimates from capture–recapture data with both death and immigration — stochastic model. *Biometrika*, **52**, 225–47.

Leslie, P.H. & Chitty, D. (1951) The estimation of population parameters from data obtained by means of the capture–recapture method. I. The maximum likelihood equations for estimating the death-rate. *Biometrika*, **38**, 269–92.

MacDonald, G. (1957) *The Epidemiology and Control of Malaria*. London: Oxford University Press.

Manly, B.F.J. (1974) Estimation of stage-specific survival rates and other parameters for insect populations developing through several stages. *Oecologia*, **15**, 277–85.

Manly. B.F.J. (1976) Extensions to Kiritani and Nakasuji's method for analysing insect stage frequency data. *Researches on Population Ecology*, **17**, 191–9.

Manly, B.F.J. (1977) A further note on Kiritani and Nakasuji's model for stage-frequency data including comments on the use of Tukey's jack-knife technique for estimation of variances. *Researches on Population Ecology*, **18**, 177–86.

Manly, B.F. & Parr, M.J. (1968) A new method of estimating population size, survivorship and birth-rate from capture–recapture data. *Transactions of the Society British Entomology*, **18**, 81–9.

Ragge, D.R. (1966) *Grasshoppers, Crickets and Cockroaches of the British Isles*. London: Warne.

Read, K.L.Q. (1966) *Some Problems in Applied Statistical Estimation*. Unpublished Ph.D. thesis, University of Exeter.

Read, K.L.Q. & Ashford, J.R. (1968) A system of models for the life-cycle of a biological organism. *Biometrika*, **55**, 211–21.

Richards, O.W. & Waloff, N. (1954) Studies on the biology and population dynamics of British grasshoppers. *Anti-Locust Bulletin*, **17**.

Schultz, C. (1981) Adaptive changes in the antipredator behaviour of a grasshopper during development. *Evolution*, **35**, 175–9.

Seber, G.A.F. (1965) A note on the multiple-recapture census. *Biometrika*, **52**, 249.

Seber, G.A.F. (1973) *Estimation of Animal Abundance and Related Parameters*. London: Griffin.

Sokal, R.R. & Rohlf, F.J. (1969) *Biometry. The Principles and Practice of Statistics in Biological Research*. San Francisco: Freeman, 776 pp.

Southwood, T.R.E. (1978) *Ecological Methods with Particular Reference to the Study of Insect Populations*, 2nd edn. London: Chapman & Hall.

Taylor, R.A.J. (1981) The behavioural basis of redistribution. 1. The △-model concept. *Journal of Animal Ecology*, **50**, 573–86.

Uvarov, B.P. (1966) *Grasshoppers and Locusts*, vol. 1. London: Cambridge University Press.

Wigglesworth, V.B. (1963) The juvenile hormone effect of farnesol and some related components: quantitative experiments. *Journal of Insect Physiology*, **9**, 105–19.

4   M.V. Hounsome

Bird population studies

Introduction

Estimates of the number of birds using the spring area of the valley (SO 81200152) have been made in every year since 1971 on the zoology course at the end of June, and since 1976 on the biology course at the beginning of July. Birds, being large and obvious, can be censused, and various attempts have been made to use Common Bird Census (CBC) methods to estimate the number of territories, not just at the spring site, but for the whole valley. Unfortunately, these field courses take place more than a month too late for these methods to be effective, although comparative results from year to year may be valid. Also, even a month's censusing does not give a sufficient time-spread of observations to be compatible with the national CBC figures.

Mark, release, recapture (MRR) methods have been a central theme of the field courses since 1960, so it was natural to use these methods in estimating the number of birds at the spring site. Unlike the estimates for other animal groups, those for birds are based on year-to-year retraps rather than day-to-day ones. In 1978 a new method, using retraps within the year, was instigated (duFeu et al., 1983), and this has been used in every year since then.

In the early years, trapping was also carried out in a less systematic way in the Cottage orchard (SO 81200115), but since 1980, serious attempts have been made to trap at the two sites simultaneously, both in order to compare the catch and estimates between two sites 370 m apart, and to assess the mobility of the populations by examining retraps between the sites.

As well as participating in the general projects (of which the bird project is one), the students carry out special projects on their own or in pairs. Since 1971 there have been more than thirty special projects connected with birds, the most important of which have been concerned with flocking, diversity in different habitats, and thrush anvils.

The primary object of all these studies has been to introduce the students to real-life ecology, methods of analysis, and the practical problems to be overcome in the field. Nevertheless, the bird general project is not entirely realistic, as one would seldom seriously attempt to estimate the numbers of a very mixed population of birds at such a site over so many years. One of the lessons which it is hoped that the students learn is that all methods of analysis have premises and limitations, and that a major part of the ecologist's job is to assess the suitability of the various methods to a particular problem, and to interpret the results realistically.

The site and its birds

The site

The spring site is a strip of Alder/Willow carr running approximately east–west, bounded on its north side by a Larch plantation and on its south by a pasture. At the western end there is the spring, which flows immediately into a wide and shallow gravelly pool which is used by birds for drinking and bathing. The site is a silted-up pond (Brick-kiln Pond) which had been produced by damming the stream. Some of the trees on the margins of this pond are still present; these are mostly Oak, Ash and Cherry.

The bird species recorded in or over Woodchester Park in June and July are listed in Appendex 1. The attractions of the site for birds are thus water, and food from the Alder/Willow/Oak/Ash/Cherry woodland. The attraction for the bird ringer is that, as well as drawing the birds, the site is linear and presents good opportunities for the siting of mist nets. The island nature of the site has diminished over the years as the Larch on the north side has grown from about 1–2 m in height in 1971 to as much as 10 m in 1983. Much of the bird activity now takes place in this high canopy, and fewer birds are travelling at mist-net height (up to 3 m). Birds using the spring still have to come down to mist-net height, as do those using the Willow, but it is now possible for birds to forage in the canopy well above the nets. In spite of this there has been no discernible *systematic* change in the array of species of adult birds caught, or their relative numbers. Although a G-test on the twenty most common species shows that the species array is highly heterogeneous with regard to year (G = 15 585, df = 240, $P \rightarrow 0$), few species have shown any consistent trends over the years.

Twenty-nine different net positions have been tried over the years, but there are seldom more than ten nets in operation at any one time

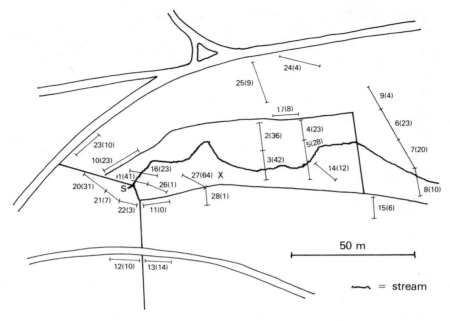

Fig. 4.1 The spring site, showing net positions, numbers and mean number of captures per year (in parentheses). S = spring, X = UK Grid SO 1200152.

(Fig. 4.1). Nine of the net positions (1,1A,2,3,4,5,7,8,10) have been used every year since 1972, so that only one or two other positions are tried each year. This means that the site is almost a 'constant effort' one, so that changes in the catch from one year to another reflect either real changes in the number or behaviour of the birds, or chance fluctuations. One of the major sources of differences between years is liable to be the earliness or lateness of the season. The field courses take place at approximately the same time of year, but the birds may be in different phases of their annual cycle; this factor may be particularly important when assessing the relative numbers of adults and juveniles.

Numbers of birds captured, and their relationships

A total of 3370 handlings have been recorded at the spring site, involving 2625 different birds of 39 species. Same-day retraps were not recorded before 1978, but since then they have been noted and used in duFeu's population estimate (duFeu *et al.*, 1983). Table 4.1 lists the number of adults captured in each year; this is repeated in Table 4.2 for juveniles.

Table 4.1   Captures of adult birds caught at the spring.

Species	1971	1972	1973	1974	1975	1976	1977	1978	1979	1980	1981	1982	1983	1971–1983
Blackbird	9	18	11	10	18	31	18	20	16	8	9	6	13	187
Blackcap	14	13	7	5	6	16	26	18	7	13	12	12	12	161
Blue Tit	0	2	2	3	2	3	7	5	6	8	3	1	15	57
Bullfinch	4	7	15	9	21	25	19	12	22	9	6	3	12	164
Chaffinch	12	2	6	1	8	13	6	2	9	9	1	4	8	81
Chiffchaff	4	5	2	1	0	11	8	9	7	2	2	3	2	56
Coal Tit	0	1	0	2	3	2	6	3	0	2	1	0	3	23
Dunnock	2	3	6	2	2	5	3	2	4	2	3	0	1	35
Garden Warbler	1	3	5	1	0	4	1	3	1	0	1	0	4	24
Greenfinch	0	0	0	0	0	0	0	0	0	0	0	0	1	1
Green Woodpecker	0	0	0	0	0	0	1	0	0	1	0	0	0	2
Goldcrest	0	3	1	3	4	2	2	0	4	2	1	1	2	25
Great Tit	4	8	3	2	9	6	14	8	6	12	7	3	15	97
Grey Wagtail	0	0	0	0	0	0	1	2	0	1	0	0	0	4
Grasshopper Warbler	0	1	0	0	0	0	0	0	0	0	0	0	0	1
Great Spotted Woodpecker	0	0	0	0	1	1	1	1	2	0	0	0	0	6
Jay	0	1	2	1	6	6	4	8	12	9	3	0	3	55
Kingfisher	0	1	0	0	1	0	0	0	0	0	0	0	0	2
Lesser Whitethroat	0	0	0	1	0	0	0	0	0	0	0	0	0	1
Long-tailed Tit	2	4	2	0	1	1	5	6	6	9	2	2	4	44
Marsh Tit	2	2	2	3	4	2	6	3	6	3	3	1	5	42
Mistle Thrush	0	0	0	0	3	0	1	0	0	0	2	0	0	6
Nuthatch	2	0	0	1	0	2	2	2	0	1	1	0	3	14
Redstart	0	0	1	0	0	1	0	0	0	0	0	0	0	2
Robin	2	5	7	8	7	10	4	8	9	7	8	3	5	83
Sparrowhawk	0	1	0	0	1	2	0	0	0	2	0	0	0	6
Stock Dove	0	0	0	0	1	0	0	3	0	0	0	0	0	4
Spotted Flycatcher	0	0	1	1	0	1	1	1	1	0	0	0	2	8
Song Thrush	8	6	5	5	4	12	8	10	6	5	1	2	7	79
Treecreeper	0	1	0	4	2	6	1	3	4	0	1	0	4	26
Turtle Dove	0	0	0	0	0	0	0	1	1	0	0	0	0	2
Tawny Owl	0	0	0	0	0	0	0	0	0	0	0	0	1	1
Whitethroat	0	2	0	0	0	2	2	0	1	0	0	0	0	7
Willow Tit	4	0	4	2	2	6	4	1	0	2	0	1	2	28
Willow Warbler	4	12	3	2	3	5	4	1	0	0	2	0	0	36
Woodpigeon	0	0	0	0	1	6	5	2	1	5	1	0	0	21
Wren	2	4	11	5	3	9	6	14	3	5	6	2	6	76

   Attempts have been made to intercorrelate the captures and relative
abundances of each species with: the valley census, national CBC (for
woodland, farmland, and 'other species', as appropriate), the total
number of adults captured, the total number of juveniles captured, and
the Jolly and duFeu population estimates of the numbers of adults and
juveniles. The number of each species captured often correlates with
the Jolly estimate of the total number of birds, but apart from this
there are very few significant correlations: the CBC woodland and
farmland indices for Coal Tits are positively correlated with their
captures and their relative abundance at the spring; and the CBC
woodland and farmland indices for Great Tits are positively correlated

Table 4.2 Captures of juvenile birds caught at the spring.

Species	1971	1972	1973	1974	1975	1976	1977	1978	1979	1980	1981	1982	1983	1971–1983
Blackbird	1	0	2	0	3	6	3	11	4	0	5	0	2	37
Blackcap	5	0	2	3	0	7	1	12	17	10	5	6	13	81
Blue Tit	2	25	6	14	2	37	9	17	79	20	7	6	35	259
Bullfinch	0	0	1	1	0	2	0	0	2	0	0	0	0	6
Carrion Crow	0	0	0	0	0	0	0	0	1	0	0	0	0	1
Chaffinch	1	0	1	0	1	1	0	6	9	4	2	1	0	26
Chiffchaff	8	0	1	1	0	2	1	4	11	1	2	1	7	39
Coal Tit	3	8	3	4	15	9	21	21	26	10	3	4	11	138
Dunnock	3	0	3	5	3	9	3	3	4	0	2	0	2	37
Garden Warbler	0	0	1	0	0	0	0	2	2	0	0	0	4	9
Goldcrest	2	2	0	2	1	1	2	12	9	2	1	3	4	41
Great Tit	7	14	1	10	3	13	15	11	47	58	15	18	34	246
Grey Wagtail	0	0	0	0	0	0	2	0	0	0	0	0	0	2
Grasshopper Warbler	1	0	0	0	0	0	0	0	0	0	0	0	0	1
Great Spotted Woodpecker	0	0	0	0	0	2	0	0	3	0	0	0	0	5
Jay	0	0	0	0	0	0	0	0	0	1	0	0	0	1
Kingfisher	0	0	0	0	0	0	0	0	0	1	0	0	0	1
Long-tailed Tit	4	8	2	0	0	7	0	0	0	2	0	1	4	28
Magpie	0	0	0	0	0	0	0	0	0	1	0	0	0	1
Marsh Tit	5	8	4	3	12	9	0	10	23	17	6	5	6	108
Mistle Thrush	0	0	0	0	1	2	0	0	0	0	0	0	0	3
Nuthatch	0	0	0	0	0	0	0	1	4	0	1	0	1	7
Redstart	0	1	3	0	0	1	0	0	0	0	0	0	0	5
Robin	10	8	8	2	6	10	5	7	20	10	9	4	11	110
Song Thrush	1	3	0	1	2	1	1	2	3	0	1	0	2	17
Treecreeper	0	4	3	3	2	10	1	6	2	3	7	4	7	52
Whitethroat	0	2	0	0	0	1	0	0	0	0	0	0	0	3
Willow Tit	1	1	0	3	5	3	0	5	5	0	1	1	0	25
Willow Warbler	1	3	3	1	2	8	2	9	4	8	0	0	2	29
Wren	0	3	3	1	2	8	2	9	4	8	5	6	5	56

with their relative abundance; but the Long-tailed Tit CBC farmland index is *negatively* correlated with their relative abundance. Song Thrush, Robin and Wren woodland CBC indices are all *nearly* significantly positively correlated with their relative abundances, as is the valley census of Dunnocks.

Fourteen species show varying degrees of population trend with time over the period 1971–1983 (to 1982 for CBC), but for nine of the species it is only the CBC figures that do so — not the field-course figures. At the spring the only positive correlations with time are for captures of juvenile Blackcaps, and both captures and relative abundance of juvenile Great Tits. Negative correlations are found for the relative abundances of juvenile Dunnocks, adult Song Thrushes and Willow Warblers, and for captures of adult Willow Warblers.

Over the period 1971–1982, taking the published indices as parametric values with no variance (an assumption which increases the chances of demonstrating correlations with time), positive correlations with respect to time are found in the woodland CBC index for Willow Warbler and Great Tit, and in the farmland index for Blackcap; the Chaffinch shows positive correlations in both farmland and woodland indices. Negative correlations are found for Goldcrest in the woodland index, and for Treecreeper, Robin, Garden Warbler and Chiffchaff in the farmland index. Both indices show a negative correlation with time for Dunnock, Song Thrush, Blackbird and Bullfinch.

Significant correlations show that there is almost certainly a relationship, but lack of significance does not neccessarily mean that there is a lack of one. This is shown in the case of the Wren (Fig. 4.2), where there were no significant correlations. It is clear that since 1976

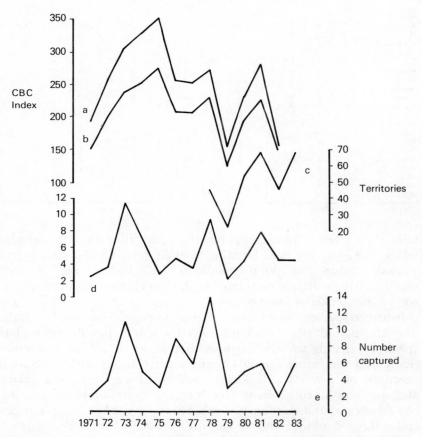

Fig. 4.2 Adult wrens. *a*, CBC farmland; *b*, CBC woodland; *c*, valley census; *d*, relative abundance (%); *e*, numbers captured.

all the Wren indices and estimates have been moving very nearly in phase. Juvenile captures and relative abundance in the last three years have spoilt a perfect concordance. Further analysis may demonstrate such relationships in other species; preliminary examination suggests that the various indices are more in phase after 1976 than before.

Diversity

The species diversity of the catch of adult birds shows very little variation (Fig. 4.3) over the years; with the exception of 1971 and 1982, all the Shannon indices (Hutcheson, 1970; Pielou, 1975) are between 2.72 and 2.91 (i.e. approximately 2.8 ± 0.1). The values for 1971 and 1982 are lower than that for 1973, the lowest value for the other years. At present it is not possible to offer any explanation for these low values, although the first year of the series has also produced anomalous population estimates. It is possible that the first year produced an atypical catch because the catching techniques had not been standardised, but there is no such convenient explanation for the low diversity in 1982. In some ways it is not the exceptions that are of interest, but the fact that, despite changes in the species composition of the catch, the diversity index varies by only 0.1.

It should perhaps be noted that, as usual, Shannon's index is positively correlated with the number of species recorded ($r = 0.769$, $P = 0.0013$), and that 1982 and 1971 had the lowest and third lowest

Fig. 4.3 Species diversity (H') of adult birds captured at the spring, 1971–1983.

number of captures of the series. It is possible that the low diversity
index in these years is simply the result of inadequate samples, but
captures in 1974 and 1981 were as low and did not have markedly low
indices. It must be concluded that constancy of diversity index is a real
feature of the bird population at the spring. It is tempting to speculate
that this constancy is indicative of the carrying capacity of the site, in
terms of the available niches. As one species declines, another close
ecological replacement increases, preserving the overall diversity. A
cluster analysis of the correlation matrix for the relative abundance of
each species shows that there are two groups of species which
fluctuate out of phase with each other, and that several pairs of close
congeners are split between the two groups (Fig. 4.4). These include
Willow Warbler and Chiffchaff, Blackcap and Garden Warbler,
Blackbird and Song Thrush; Chaffinch and Bullfinch are similarly

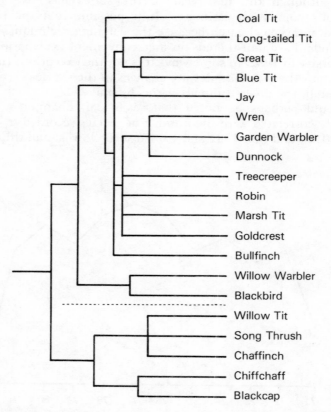

Fig. 4.4 Dendrogram based on the correlation matrix of the relative
abundance of the 20 species most often captured at the spring. Species above
the dashed line are negatively correlated with those below.

split. But all the tits (except Willow Tit) fluctuate in phase. The evidence from this study is not sufficient to confirm the theory of ecological replacement leading to stable diversity, but it is indicative and might encourage others to examine data from other sites.

Mark, release, recapture estimates at the spring

Methods Used

One of the aims of the mark–recapture analysis was to assess the value of the different methods. The estimates for adult birds of all species at the spring are shown in Table 4.3 and Fig. 4.5. Six different methods have been used during the whole period, duFeu's method being started in 1978 (duFeu, *et al.*, 1983). This last method was developed to give population estimates on the basis of a single capture session rather

Table 4.3 Jolly, duFeu, and Fisher & Ford estimates for adult birds at the spring.

	Fisher & Ford	Jolly				duFeu	
Year	Population	Population	Standard error	Survival rate	Ingress	Population	Standard error
1971	—	—	—		—	—	—
				0.2487	—		
1972	934	526	335			—	—
				0.4934	132		
1973	394	391	143			—	—
				0.7032	289		
1974	419	564	239			—	—
				0.2208	104		
1975	353	229	68			—	—
				0.6660	691		
1976	617	843	287			—	—
				0.3692	385		
1977	813	696	215			—	—
				0.4117	303		
1978	695	589	119			537	96
				0.4420	251		
1979	552	511	187			390	62
				0.6193	1066		
1980	1036	1383	613			602	155
				0.5972	10		
1981	612	836	585			136	17
				0.1248	193		
1982	977	297	166			125	34
				—	—		
1983	530	—	—			366	56

Overall survival rate: Fisher & Ford = 0.4638; Jolly = 0.3977.

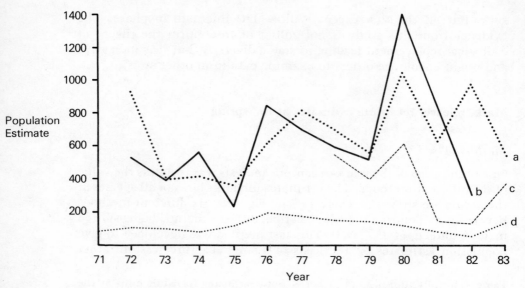

Fig. 4.5   Estimates of the number of adult birds at the spring. *a*, Fisher & Ford; *b*, Jolly; *c*, duFeu; *d*, numbers captured.

than a series of sessions. Each year's field course can be regarded as a single session independent of any previous year's ringing. The method does not give rates of survival and ingress; indeed it assumes that these do not occur during the session, although it does give indications when they do occur. The total number of captures new to a session and the total number of recaptures within the session are recorded, and the population estimate is looked up in the table (see Appendix 2) derived from duFeu's expression. The method hence has the great advantage of extreme simplicity, and has the capability of producing running estimates as the session progresses, as every animal captured enables another estimate to be made.

Of the six methods using year-to-year recaptures, those of Lincoln (1930), Bailey (1951), Manly & Parr (1968) and Jackson (1933,1939, 1944,1948) have been discarded in favour of Jolly's (1965), which is widely considered to be more theoretically sound. Nevertheless, this method suffers from its need for extensive retrap histories and intensive sampling. By considering all adults of all species as a single population, it has been possible to provide enough data to use Jolly's method, but it must be borne in mind that this increases the heterogeneity of the sample, and that this can invalidate some of the assumptions inherent in the model. In fact, it can be argued that there is more difference in behaviour between a male and female of the same species (or between a territory holder and a non-territory holder, or between an old or young bird) than between males of different species. All samples are heterogeneous in some respects, and it is hard to assess the consequences of the various groupings that can be made.

If the assumption can be made that the survival rate is relatively constant over the years, then Fisher & Ford's method (1947) may be justified; this might be desirable because this method can cope with 'thinner' data than can Jolly's (because of this rather drastic assumption). Jolly has pointed out (1982) that if this assumption can be made, then his method can be modified to give statistically more respectable estimates than Fisher & Ford's. In any case, it is quite clear that birds suffer different degrees of mortality, or emigration, in each year, so that the assumption of constant survival cannot be made. It thus seems that Jolly's method A, with Bailey's correction for small numbers of recaptures, is the most suitable for estimating the yearly population at the spring and its rates of survival and ingress.

The Estimates

As can be seen from Fig. 4.5, there are no long-term trends in the population estimates. As there are more falls from year to year than rises, it must mean that the rises are steeper; i.e. if the annual fluctuations truly reflect changes in the population size, then recoveries from lows are more rapid than falls from highs. This is not what one might expect, as it is often assumed that bird populations are drastically affected by, for example, bad winters or drought in the winter quarters, and that they slowly recover from these lows. Such steep rises might indicate immigration rather than internal recruitment.

A graph of the population estimates made by the three methods most likely to give reasonable results (Fig. 4.5) shows that Fisher & Ford's and Jolly's methods are tolerably close to each other, although there is no significant correlation ($r = 0.462$, df $= 9$, $P = 0.152$). The last two estimates for either method are liable to be changed by future years' captures (see Tables 4.4–6), so that over the period 1972–1980 the two series of estimates are significantly positively correlated ($r = 0.733$, df $= 7$, $P = 0.025$). The duFeu estimate is consistently lower than the other two; there is, as yet, no evidence to support the speculation (duFeu *et al.*, 1983) that this is because duFeu's method estimates the number of birds actually available for recapture on each occasion, whereas Jolly's method (and presumably the others) estimates the numbers theoretically available, whether they were there or not. In discussions during the field courses this has been called 'the Z problem'; mark–recapture data are recorded as a Manly & Parr table (Manly & Parr, 1968) where an animal known to be alive (because of a

Table 4.4 Jolly adult population estimates (spring).

Year of estimate	Year in which estimates were made										
	1973	1974	1975	1976	1977	1978	1979	1980	1981	1982	1983
1972	537	601	526	526	526	526	526	526	526	526	526
1973		488	410	391	391	391	391	391	391	391	391
1974			716	564	564	564	564	564	564	564	564
1975				294	257	233	229	229	229	229	229
1976					572	850	843	843	843	843	843
1977						635	797	718	718	718	696
1978							473	612	589	589	589
1979								397	368	350	511
1980									908	961	1383
1981										532	836
1982											297

Table 4.5 Jolly adult survival estimates (spring).

	1973	1974	1975	1976	1977	1978	1979	1980	1981	1982	1983
1971–1972	0.254	0.286	0.249	0.249	0.249	0.249	0.249	0.249	0.249	0.249	0.249
1972–1973		0.603	0.517	0.493	0.493	0.493	0.493	0.493	0.493	0.493	0.493
1973–1974			0.877	0.703	0.703	0.703	0.703	0.703	0.703	0.703	0.703
1974–1975				0.285	0.249	0.226	0.221	0.221	0.221	0.221	0.221
1975–1976					0.434	0.667	0.666	0.666	0.666	0.666	0.666
1976–1977						0.335	0.423	0.381	0.381	0.381	0.369
1977–1978							0.312	0.423	0.407	0.407	0.412
1978–1979								0.336	0.317	0.301	0.442
1979–1980									0.468	0.505	0.619
1980–1981										0.455	0.597
1981–1982											0.125
Overall survival	0.254	0.415	0.483	0.396	0.393	0.404	0.401	0.402	0.405	0.411	0.398

Table 4.6 Jolly adult ingress estimates (spring).

	1973	1974	1975	1976	1977	1978	1979	1980	1981	1982
1972–1973	126	138	132	132	132	132	132	132	132	132
1973–1974		357	289	289	289	289	289	289	289	289
1974–1975			133	117	106	104	104	104	104	104
1975–1976				460	694	691	691	691	691	691
1976–1977					350	441	397	397	397	385
1977–1978						225	309	297	297	303
1978–1979							191	181	173	251
1979–1980								763	784	1066
1980–1981									95	10
1981–1982										193

subsequent recapture) but not captured on a particular occasion is recorded as a 'Z'. All the methods implicitly, and Jolly's and Manly & Parr's explicitly, assume that it was not caught, *but could have been*, i.e. it was a part of the population, and its non-capture reflects the trapping efficiency. It is likely, particularly with birds, that some of these 'Z' animals are not actually there on that occasion, and hence could not have been caught, however high the trapping efficiency. Thus, whereas duFeu's method can only estimate the numbers present on a certain occasion, the others estimate the wider population from which the sample present is drawn, and will give higher estimates as a consequence.

It has been suggested (duFeu *et al.*, 1983) that as the spring was a major factor in drawing the birds to the site, one might expect a larger difference between the duFeu estimate and the others in wet years, when a smaller proportion was drawn to the water because of the presence of alternative water sources. Preliminary testing of this hypothesis by correlating the percentage difference in the estimates with various measures of wetness (collected both locally and regionally) have proved fruitless, with no significant correlations being found.

Jolly's estimate for a particular year will be altered in future years if animals are later caught which could have been alive in that year, i.e. if last 'Xs' are turned into 'Ys', and blanks are turned into 'Zs' (in Manly & Parr's terminology). This means that one cannot regard a Jolly estimate for a particular year as final until all hope of recapturing animals which were alive in that year has been lost. For small birds with an average adult life expectancy of 1½ years, this means that the last two Jolly estimates almost certainly will change with future trapping occasions, and that *small* changes may occur for up to about 7 years. Table 4.4 shows the population estimates for each year made in

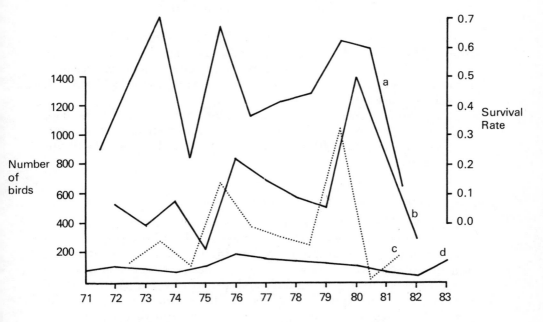

Fig. 4.6 Estimates for adult birds at the spring by Jolly's method. *a*, Survival rate; *b*, population; *c*, recruitment; *d*, numbers captured.

each year from 1973. Tables 4.5 and 4.6 show the survival rates and ingress respectively, and Fig. 4.6 illustrates the estimates made in 1983.

The only species for which there have been sufficient data for a separate population estimate to be made is the Blackbird. Survival rates derived from mark–recapture analyses refer to survival *in the population*, and hence represent survival from both death and emigration, i.e. $1 - S$ does not equal the mortality rate. Survival rates calculated nationally from recoveries of dead ringed birds, on the other hand, are true survival rates from death. The difference between the two estimates for a certain species should, therefore, reflect the emigration rate from the mark–recapture site. This would only be so if the true survival rate (from mortality) of the local population is the same as that for the species nationally. In this case, the estimates for adult Blackbird survival at the spring and the Cottage sites combined are 0.489 (Jolly) and 0.497 (Fisher & Ford). The national figure is hard to determine, but it has been estimated variously as 0.628 for males (calculated from data in Greenwood & Harvey, 1976), and 0.654 for both sexes between 1961 and 1970 (Batten, 1978). There is evidence that it has been increasing in recent years, and that this is due to increasing winter survival (Batten, 1978). If the valley birds have an average mortality rate, then their rate of emigration from the valley is between 10 and 16% per year.

The capture in 1983 of one bird from 1976, two from 1977, and two from 1978 upsets the pattern whereby estimates are not usually affected by captures more than three years later. These exceptional recaptures had a retrospective effect on the estimates for 1977 to 1979, as well as those for the last two years.

In very broad terms, we have an adult bird population of about 650, with an annual survival of about 0.4 and an annual ingress of about 345; we capture about 20% of the population, and about 12% of our captures are *re*captures.

The area occupied by the estimated population

Estimates of the area from which birds come to the trapping site can be made by taking the population estimate for the whole adult population, multiplying by a figure representing the average territory size, and dividing by two (to convert to pairs). The sources of error in such a crude calculation are enormous, and are so obvious as to need no explanation. Nevertheless, the above calculation, and that for individual species, gives estimates over a fairly limited range of areas encompassed by circles of radius 150 m and 500 m; most estimates are between 200 m and 350 m. A circle centred on the spring having a radius of 350 m passes through the Cottage site. It must be emphasised that these estimates are little better than guesses, but they serve to illustrate the point that the hundreds of birds caught at the spring *could* all be resident in what might appear to be a rather small area. There are likely to be large differences between the use of space by various species, so that, for example, one might expect most of the adult Wrens to be from the immediate vicinity, whereas the Great Spotted Woodpeckers might range over the entire valley, and perhaps beyond.

As the area from which the captured birds come is not known, it is open to speculation that it may vary from year to year. In dry seasons, when there is little standing water elsewhere, birds may visit the spring from larger distances than in wet seasons. The fluctuations in population estimate might, therefore, be due entirely to this phenomenon rather than to true changes in the population density. As with the difference between the Jolly and duFeu estimates, it has not been possible to demonstrate a correlation between population estimate and any measure of wetness, so this hypothesis is unsupported.

By making Jolly population estimates for the spring and Cottage sites, and for the two sites combined, it is possible to calculate the probable number of birds common to both; this turns out to be about 27% (varying from year to year between 17 and 49%). On the other hand, only 52 birds have been captured at both sites, and this amounts to only 1.5%. These have mostly been flock birds such as tits, Chiffchaffs, and Treecreepers (Chiffchaffs, especially juveniles, are common in tit flocks at this time of year), although wide-rangers such as Blackbirds and Great Spotted Woodpeckers and other species such as Blackcaps, Bullfinches, Robins, and Song Thrushes also feature. The only firm conclusion that can be made is that some individuals have been caught at both sites. It is not known from what area the birds come to the spring, and even though there is likely to be a declining probability of capture with distance from the spring, it is liable to vary from species to species, and even from individual to individual.

Differences between captures at the spring and at the Cottage

Comparison of the numbers of tits (parids) and non-parids and of adult and juvenile birds captured at the two sites shows that they are different in their use by the birds. The differences may be summarised by considering the following ratios. There is a lower frequency of parids at the Cottage than at the spring (32% of 802, compared with 39% of 2841). There is a lower frequency of adults at the Cottage than at the spring. Among parids, 14% of 258 are adult at the Cottage, 27% of 1095 at the spring. Among non-parids, 42% of 544 are adult at the Cottage and 67% of 1746 at the spring.

All these differences are highly significant ($P < 0.001$), and demonstrate that the Cottage orchard is used more by juveniles and non-parids than is the spring. The preponderance of juvenile parids at the Cottage is evident for all species (Fig. 4.7) except the Coal Tit, which is uncommon at the Cottage, and the Willow Tit, which has never been caught at the Cottage. At this time of year the main avian attraction of the Cottage orchard is the ripening cherries. Tits are unlikely to feed directly on these, whereas Starlings, Blackbirds, Blackcaps, thrushes, Bullfinches, and woodpeckers are undoubtedly attracted. It is not as easy to explain the preponderance of juvenile birds. It may be that, in common with some gulls (Spencer & Welch, 1956; Lloyd, 1969), the juvenile birds are exploiting an easy but temporary resource (such as

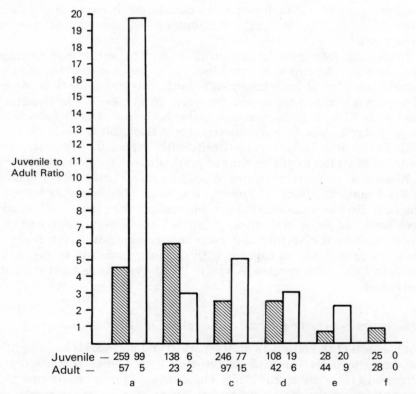

Juvenile —   259 99   138 6   246 77   108 19   28 20   25 0
Adult   —   57 5   23 2   97 15   42 6   44 9   28 0
                a   b   c   d   e   f

Fig. 4.7 Juvenile to adult ratio of tits captured at the spring (hatched) and the Cottage, all years combined. *a*, Blue Tit; *b*, Coal Tit; *c*, Great Tit; *d*, Marsh Tit; *e*, Long-tailed Tit; *f*, Willow Tit.

aphids on the cherry trees) and are excluding the adults; or it may be that the juveniles are moving around more than the adults and are hence more liable to be captured at the boundary of the wooded part of the valley, which is the Cottage's position, than at the centre.

It is usual for ringers to catch most birds around dawn and dusk, and fewest in the afternoon. At the spring site it soon became apparent that most birds were caught between 0800 and 1500 (Fig. 4.8), and that fewest were caught at dawn (between 0330 and 0400). This presumably reflects the site's use as a resource rather than a place to live; most birds caught at the spring are visiting: few have territories there. At the Cottage site, on the other hand, there is a decided morning 'rush' (Fig. 4.9) and a smaller evening peak, making it more of a conventional site. The morning peak occurs between 0700 and 0900, so that even here there is no dawn 'rush'. The lack of birds at both sites at dawn means that the bird general project team can stay in bed until

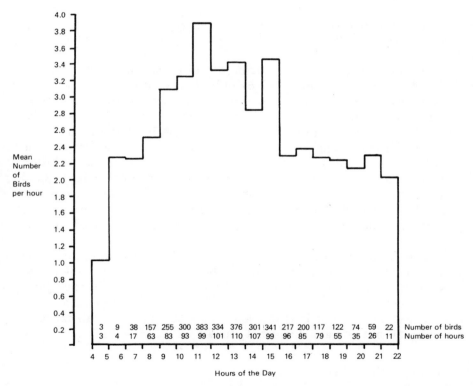

Fig. 4.8 Hourly captures of birds at the spring, all years combined. Total number of birds is 3370; total number of hours, 1166; mean birds per hour, 2.89.

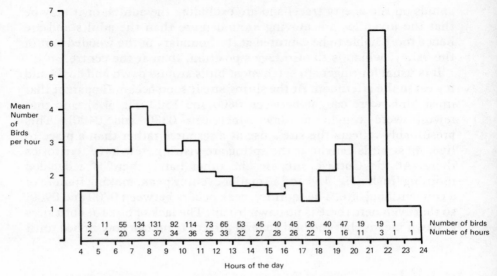

Fig. 4.9 Hourly captures of birds at the Cottage, all years combined. Total number of birds is 1015; total number of hours, 418; mean birds per hour, 2.43.

0600, so that the nets are set before 0700. Occasionally the students suggest a dawn start, and the lack of birds is confirmed.

Captures at the Cottage are at a maximum between 0700 and 0800, and those at the spring peak between 1000 and 1100. It is likely, therefore, that more birds roost in the region of the Cottage than at the bottom of the valley. A special project in 1976 examined the movements of birds between the two sites, both by direct observation and by recording the side of the net in which birds were caught (and hence the direction in which they were going). The conclusion was that birds moved from the edge of the valley to the centre as the morning progressed, and that the process was reversed in the afternoon.

There is no significant correlation, positive or negative, between the rate of capture at the two sites in each hour of the day, but there is also no significant difference between the rates of capture in each hour (R × 2 contingency table, G = 5.52, df = 17, P = 0.995). This may seem anomalous, but it is probably the result of the small range of values (all but one are between 1 and 4).

Census of the valley

Since 1978, Common Bird Census methods have been used to estimate the number of bird territories in the valley, but coverage has been uneven in all but the last two years. Late June is not a good time to carry out a CBC, and many species must be omitted because they have fledged their young, so only sixteen species have been regularly recorded. As the censusing is carreid out by different students, of differing abilities, each year, it is difficult to place much reliance on the results. The figures in Table 4.7 do not correlate with either the woodland or farmland national CBC results; nevertheless, some of the changes are worthy of note. The large number of Chaffinch territories counted in 1983 agrees with the large number ringed; the peak of 13 Whitethroat territories coincides with the most suitable stage of growth of a recently cleared area on the north side of the valley (where most of the territories were recorded); the falls in Wren numbers in 1979 and 1982 follow cold winters. Other changes are not so explicable, and may be the result of the differing abilities of the recorders; these include the large number of Chiffchaff, Goldcrest, and Willow Warbler territories recorded in 1983. Low numbers such as those for Blackbirds, Woodpigeons and Yellowhammers in 1981 may be due to the season being advanced, so that the birds had stopped singing.

The results from censusing are unsatisfactory for the above reasons, and must be regarded as subordinate to the students' learning of a new technique and to their practical experience of the difficulties, and joys, of fieldwork.

Table 4.7 Territory census.

Species	1978	1979	1980	1981	1982	1983
Blackbird	13	17	15	1	21	18
Blackcap	1	17	19	10	20	24
Bullfinch	2	4	8	2	0	0
Chaffinch	2	8	3	0	7	21
Chiffchaff	29	28	2	14	19	43
Dunnock	8	2	0	0	1	1
Garden Warbler	5	1	1	1	1	2
Goldcrest	?	8	7	6	8	24
Robin	?	8	16	11	11	13
Stock Dove	?	?	4	1	2	3
Song Thrush	9	7	7	7	7	15
Whitethroat	7	5	13	5	5	5
Willow Warbler	3	8	4	3	6	15
Wren	45	22	53	68	45	68
Woodpigeon	?[a]	?[a]	15	7	24	19
Yellowhammer	11	10	11	4	11	14

[a] ? = Not recorded, possibly absent.

Ringing recoveries

It is remarkable that having ringed over 2500 birds there are only seven recoveries, one control in, and one control out of the valley, i.e. there is only a 0.3% recovery rate (Table 4.8). Nationally, about 1–2% of resident birds and 0.3–0.5% of migrants are recovered, so some explanation is required for the low recovery rate of birds ringed in the valley. Tits and Blackbirds are the most commonly ringed birds in the valley, followed closely by Blackcaps (see Tables 4.1 and 4.2), and these have approximate national recovery rates of 1%, 3.8%, and 0.5%, respectively (Spencer & Hudson, 1982). There are two possible reasons for the low recovery rate of valley birds: (a) they do not leave the valley, and as public access is denied they do not get reported when dead; (b) they leave the valley, but seek out other relatively uninhabited areas. These are not mutually exclusive explanations, as the valley birds may well be less inclined than average to make excursions out of the valley, but when they do, they may visit equally secluded locations.

Most of the recoveries are local (Table 4.8), the adult Blackcap in Portugal and the Treecreeper in Surrey being the only 'distant' birds. The Treecreeper was controlled (recaptured by another ringer), and holds the record for the furthest travelled British Treecreeper; they are normally very sedentary.

A total of 219 birds have been recaptured in years subsequent to their initial capture; 103 after one year, 56 after two years, and 60 after three or more years (Table 4.9). Only one of these birds is remarkable for its longevity, and that is Marsh Tit KC78733, which was first captured as a juvenile in 1975 and has been recaptured in 1976, 1977, 1978 and 1983. The recapture in 1983 was 2937 days after the first capture, and is only a matter of days short of the British Trust for Ornithology record (Mead, 1974).

These 219 birds represent 8.3% of the birds captured; in other words,

Table 4.8 Ringing recoveries and controls.

Species	Ring		Age	Sex	Date	Recovered	
Ringed on field course, recovered or controlled elsewhere:							
Blackbird	XC	01333	3J	F	23 June 1977	Amberley, Stroud; found dead	5 July 1979
Blackcap	KK	65868	4	M	23 June 1977	Beira Baixa, Portugal	10 October 1977
Blue Tit	A	397665	3J	?	15 July 1979	Rodborough, Stroud; hit window	4 May 1980
Goldcrest	PP	1822	3J	?	26 June 1972	Amberley, Stroud; cat	10 September 1982
Mistle Thrush	CJ	69075	3	?	30 June 1975	Uley, Dursley; found dead	1 July 1976
Treecreeper	OA	9415	3	?	13 July 1978	Farnham, Surrey; controlled	7 October 1978
Sparrowhawk	DA	31310	5	M	26 June 1976	Local; hit window	21 February 1982
Woodpigeon	SS	71757	4	?	27 June 1976	Owlpen, Dursley; shot	4 August 1979
Ringed elsewhere, controlled on field course:							
Kingfisher	SE34779		1		23 June 1979	Frampton, Gloucestershire	1 July 1979

Table 4.9 Numbers of birds recaptured more than 2 years after first capture.

Species	Number of years after first capture					
	3	4	5	6	7	8
Blackbird	15	9	4	0	0	0
Blackcap	2	1	0	0	0	0
Blue Tit	1	0	0	1	0	0
Bullfinch	4	2	0	0	0	0
Chaffinch	1	0	0	0	0	0
Coal Tit	1	0	0	0	0	0
Great Tit	3	0	0	0	0	0
Green Woodpecker	1	0	0	0	0	0
Jay	2	0	0	0	0	0
Long-tailed Tit	1	0	0	0	0	0
Marsh Tit	4	1	0	0	0	1
Song Thrush	1	0	1	0	0	0
Treecreeper	1	1	0	0	0	0
Willow Tit	1	1	0	0	0	0
Total	38	15	5	1	0	1

one in twelve of all the birds ringed in the valley are recaptured in subsequent years. This seems to be a high proportion, but in the absence of comparable data from elsewhere, it is not possible to confirm this feeling.

Conclusions

The bird general project has proved valuable in giving the students practical experience both of catching birds and of seeing them in the hand, and of the concepts and problems of mark–recapture methods. Little of scientific value has been discovered, but the problems illustrated by the attempts to estimate the size of the bird population at the spring have played a significant part in the development of ideas on the utility and limitations of the various methods.

The fact that over 300 different birds can be captured in such a small area of woodland has been a revelation to many members of the field courses. That only a dozen or so birds can ever be *seen* at the site on any one occasion gives little indication of its *usage*. If the population estimates are right, then about 2000 birds, adults and juveniles, might be using the site at one time or another. The great mobility of animals, even of acknowledged travellers such as birds, is a concept yet to be incorporated into most zoologists' understanding of the natural world.

Mark–recapture methods are the only ones likely to be able to produce estimates of usage of a resource, and hence assume an importance in conservation studies. The students' work in the valley has been a valuable step in our understanding of the methods, their limitations and their usefulness.

Knowledge of the bird fauna of the valley may prove valuable in future years, as the habitat changes, both naturally and as a consequences of forestry and agricultural activities; we now have a fairly precise knowledge of the birds of this splendidly isolated, undisturbed valley. Already, the gradual replacement of the native (if not natural) trees by conifers is having an effect; so far, there is no strong evidence that this has affected the birds, but the information gathered between 1971 and 1983 will be a useful base line from which to judge the effects of these changes.

Acknowledgements

Many students have contributed to this study, and their generally cheerful response to the requests of an apparently demented ornithologist is gratefully acknowledged. Particular thanks must go to the students who have come back in subseqent years to help, or to take charge in my absence, namely Steve Hunter, Martin Jones, Paul Tatner and Andy Swash, all now professional ornithologists.

Reference

Bailey, N.T.J. (1951) On estimating the size of mobile animal populations from recapture data. *Biometrika*, **38**, 293–306.

Batten, L.A. (1978) The seasonal distribution of recoveries and causes of Blackbird mortality. *Bird Study*, **25**(1), 23–32.

duFeu, C.R., Hounsome, M.V. & Spence, I.M. (1983) A single-session mark/recapture method of population estimation. *Ringing and Migration*, **4**(4), 211–26.

Fisher, R.A. & Ford, E.B. (1947) The spread of a gene in natural conditions in a colony of the moth *Panaxia dominula* (L). *Heredity, London*, **1**, 143–74.

Greenwood, P.J. & Harvey, P.H. (1976) Differential mortality and dispersal of male Blackbirds. *Ringing and Migration*, **1**(2), 75–7.

Hutcheson, K. (1970) A test for comparing diversities based on the Shannon formula. *Journal of Theoretical Biology*, **29**, 151–4.

Jackson, C.H.N. (1933) On the true density of Tsetse Flies. *Journal of Animal Ecology* **3**, 204–9.

Jackson, C.H.N. (1939) The analysis of an animal population. *Journal of Animal Ecology*, **8**, 238–46.

Jackson, C.H.N. (1944) The analysis of a Tsetse-fly population II. *Annals of Eugenics, Cambridge*, **10**, 332–69.

Jackson, C.H.N. (1948) The analysis of a Tsetse-fly population III. *Annals of Eugenics, Cambridge*, **14**, 91–108.

Jolly, G.M. (1965) Explicit estimates from capture–recapture data with both deaths and immigration — stochastic model. *Biometrika*, **52**, 225–47.

Jolly, G.M. (1982) Mark–recapture models with parameters constant in time. *Biometrics*, **38** 301–21.

Lincoln, F.C. (1930) Calculating waterfowl abundance on the basis of banding returns. *Circular of the US Department of Agriculture* No. 18.

Lloyd, D.E.B. (1969) *The Use of Inland Habitats by Gulls Larus sp. in the Ythan Valley, Aberdeenshire*. Unpublished M.Sc. thesis, Aberdeen University.

Manly, B.F.J. & Parr, M.J. (1968) A simulation study of animal population estimation using the capture–recapture method. *Journal of Applied Ecology*, 7, 13–40.

Mead, C. (1974) *Bird Ringing*. BTO Guide 16.

Pielou, E.C. (1975) *Ecological Diversity*. New York: Wiley.

Spencer, K.G. & Welch, A. (1956) Immature–adult proportions and behaviour in Black-headed Gull flocks. *The Naturalist*, **858**, 114.

Spencer, R. & Hudson, R. (1982) Report on bird ringing for 1981. *Ringing and Migration*, **4**(2), 65–128.

Appendix 1   Bird species recorded in or over Woodchester Park in June and July

Little Grebe: *Tachybaptus ruficollis*
Great Crested Grebe: *Podiceps cristatus*
Cormorant: *Phalacrocorax carbo*
Grey Heron: *Ardea cinerea*
Mute Swan: *Cygnus olor*
Mandarin: *Aix galericulata*
Mallard: *Anas platyrhynchos*
Tufted Duck: *Athya fuligula*
Ruddy Duck: *Oxyura jamaicensis*
Sparrowhawk: *Accipiter nisus*
Buzzard: *Buteo buteo*
Osprey: *Pandion haliaetus*
Kestrel: *Falco tinnunculus*
Hobby: *Falco subbuteo*
Partridge: *Perdix perdix*
Quail: *Coturnix coturnix*
Pheasant: *Phasianus colchicus*
Moorhen: *Gallinula chloropus*
Coot: *Fulica atra*
Lapwing: *Vanellus vanellus*
Woodcock: *Scolopax rusticola*
Curlew: *Numenius arquata*
Redshank: *Tringa totanus*
Common Sandpiper: *Actitis hypoleucos*
Black-headed Gull: *Larus ridibundus*
Lesser Black-backed Gull: *Larus fuscus*

Herring Gull: *Larus argentatus*
Great Black-backed Gull: *Larus marinus*
Stock Dove: *Columba oenas*
Woodpigeon: *Columba palumbus*
Collared Dove: *Steptopelia decaocto*
Turtle Dove: *Streptopelia turtur*
Cuckoo: *Cuculus canorus*
Little Owl: *Athene noctua*
Tawny Owl: *Strix aluco*
Swift: *Apus apus*
Kingfisher: *Alcedo atthis*
Green Woodpecker: *Picus viridis*
Great Spotted Woodpecker: *Dendrocopus major*
Wood Lark: *Lullula arborea*
Skylark: *Alauda arvensis*
Sand Martin: *Riparia riparia*
Swallow: *Hirundo rustica*
House Martin: *Delichon urbica*
Tree Pipit: *Anthus trivialis*
Meadow Pipit: *Anthus pratensis*
Yellow Wagtail: *Motacilla flava*
Grey Wagtail: *Motacilla cinerea*
Pied Wagtail: *Motacilla alba*
Wren: *Troglodytes troglodytes*
Dunnock: *Prunella modularis*
Robin: *Erithacus rubecula*
Nightingale: *Luscinia megarhynchos*

Redstart: *Phoenicurus phoenicurus*
Blackbird: *Turdus merula*
Song Thrush: *Turdus philomelos*
Mistle Thrush: *Turdus viscivorus*
Grasshopper Warbler: *Locustella naevia*
Sedge Warbler: *Acrocephalus schoenobaenus*
Lesser Whitethroat: *Sylvia carruca*
Whitethroat: *Sylvia communis*
Garden Warbler: *Sylvia borin*
Blackcap: *Sylvia atricapilla*
Chiffchaff: *Phylloscopus collybita*
Willow Warbler: *Phylloscopus trochilus*
Goldcrest: *Regulus regulus*
Spotted Flycatcher: *Muscicapa striata*
Long-tailed Tit: *Aegithalus caudatus*
Marsh Tit: *Parus palustris*
Willow Tit: *Parus montanus*
Coal Tit: *Parus ater*
Blue Tit: *Parus caeruleus*

Great Tit: *Parus major*
Nuthatch: *Sitta europaea*
Treecreeper: *Certhia familiaris*
Jay: *Garrulus glandarius*
Magpie: *Pica pica*
Jackdaw: *Corvus monedula*
Rook: *Corvus frugilegus*
Carrion Crow: *Corvus corone*
Starling: *Sturnus vulgaris*
House Sparrow: *Passer domesticus*
Tree Sparrow: *Passer montanus*
Chaffinch: *Fringilla coelebs*
Greenfinch: *Carduelis chloris*
Goldfinch: *Carduelis carduelis*
Linnet: *Carduelis cannabina*
Redpoll: *Carduelis flammea*
Bullfinch: *Pyrrhula pyrrhula*
Hawfinch: *Coccothraustes coccothraustes*
Yellowhammer: *Emberiza citrinella*
Corn Bunting: *Miliaria calandra*

Appendix 2 Population estimation by duFeu method. Values of N from five to 70 in steps of five, and R from one to 50 are tabulated; this is a section of a more extensive table (up to $N = 1050$ and $R = 110$) which is available from the author on receipt of a large stamped addressed envelope (U.K. only) A Texas Ti58/59 program is appended to the full table.

No. of recaptures ↓	Number of New Animals Captured													
	5	10	15	20	25	30	35	40	45	50	55	60	65	70
1	14	52	115	204	317	455	619	807	1020	1259	1522	1810	2124	2462
2	9	30	63	109	167	238	321	417	525	646	780	925	1084	1255
3	7	22	45	77	117	165	222	287	360	442	532	630	737	852
4	6	19	37	61	92	129	173	222	278	340	409	483	564	651
5	6	16	32	52	77	108	143	183	229	279	334	395	460	530
6	6	15	28	46	67	93	123	157	196	238	285	336	391	450
7	6	14	26	41	60	83	109	139	172	209	250	294	341	393
8	5	13	24	38	55	75	99	125	155	187	223	262	304	350
9	5	13	23	36	51	69	91	114	141	171	203	238	276	316
10	5	12	22	33	48	65	84	106	130	157	186	218	253	289
11	5	12	21	32	45	61	79	99	121	146	173	202	234	268
12	5	12	20	30	43	58	74	93	114	137	162	189	218	249
13	5	11	19	29	41	55	71	88	108	129	152	178	205	234
14	5	11	19	28	40	53	67	84	102	122	144	168	194	221
15	5	11	19	28	38	51	65	80	98	117	137	160	184	209
16	5	11	18	27	37	49	62	77	94	112	131	152	175	199
17	5	11	18	26	36	47	60	74	90	107	126	146	168	191
18	5	11	18	26	35	46	58	72	87	103	121	140	161	183
19	5	11	17	25	34	45	57	70	84	100	117	135	155	176
20	5	11	17	25	34	44	55	68	82	97	113	131	150	170
21	5	10	17	24	33	43	54	66	79	94	110	127	145	164
22	5	10	17	24	32	42	53	64	77	91	107	123	140	159
23	5	10	17	24	32	41	52	63	75	89	104	119	136	154
24	5	10	16	23	31	41	51	62	74	87	101	116	133	150
25	5	10	16	23	31	40	50	60	72	85	99	113	129	146
26	5	10	16	23	31	39	49	59	71	83	97	111	126	142
27	5	10	16	23	30	39	48	58	69	82	94	108	123	139
28	5	10	16	23	30	38	47	57	68	80	93	106	121	136
29	5	10	16	22	30	38	47	56	67	79	91	104	118	133
30	5	10	16	22	29	37	46	56	66	77	89	102	116	130
31	5	10	16	22	29	37	45	55	65	76	88	100	114	128
32	5	10	16	22	29	37	45	54	64	75	86	99	112	125
33	5	10	16	22	29	36	44	53	63	74	85	97	110	123
34	5	10	16	22	28	36	44	53	62	73	84	96	108	121
35	5	10	16	22	28	36	44	52	62	72	83	94	106	119
36	5	10	16	22	28	35	43	52	61	71	82	93	105	117
37	5	10	16	21	28	35	43	51	60	70	80	92	103	116
38	5	10	15	21	28	35	42	51	60	69	79	90	102	114
39	5	10	15	21	28	35	42	50	59	69	79	89	101	113
40	5	10	15	21	27	34	42	50	59	68	78	88	99	111
41	5	10	15	21	27	34	42	49	58	67	77	87	98	110
42	5	10	15	21	27	34	41	49	57	67	76	86	97	108
43	5	10	15	21	27	34	41	49	57	66	75	85	96	107
44	5	10	15	21	27	34	41	48	57	65	75	85	95	106
45	5	10	15	21	27	33	40	48	56	65	74	84	94	105
46	5	10	15	21	27	33	40	48	56	64	73	83	93	104
47	5	10	15	21	27	33	40	47	55	64	73	82	92	103
48	5	10	15	21	27	33	40	47	55	63	72	81	91	102
49	5	10	15	21	27	33	40	47	55	63	72	81	91	101
50	5	10	15	21	26	33	39	47	54	62	71	80	90	100

Interspecific competition and the comparative ecology of two congeneric species of mice

Introduction

The genus *Apodemus* (Kaup, 1829) contains somewhat primitive mice distributed from Ireland to Japan, extending northwards into Iceland and southwards into North Africa. Throughout this extensive range, two or more congeners may be present in the same geographical area, so that *Apodemus* species have attracted the attention of mammalogists interested in comparative ecology and interspecific competition. For example, in Japan, *A. argenteus* and *A. speciosus* are ubiquitous in natural forests. Doi & Iwamoto (1982) demonstrated that *A. speciosus* declines in density with altitude whereas *A. argenteus* increases in abundance relative to *A. speciosus* with increase in age of the habitat. At the western end of the range of the genus, the distributions of the Wood Mouse, *A. sylvaticus*, and the Yellow-necked Mouse, *A. flavicollis*, overlap in much of Europe including Britain (Corbet, 1966; Brink, 1967; Arnold, 1978). In eastern Europe these species are morphologically very similar (Hedges, 1969) but occupy clearly defined habitats; *A. flavicollis* is more restricted to mature or high forest whereas *A. sylvaticus* may thrive in scrub or shelter-belt habitats (Vereschchagin, 1959; Hamar *et al.*, 1966; Zedja, 1966; Haitlinger, 1969; Aulak, 1970). Such is the degree of morphological similarity in these regions that introgression between *A. sylvaticus* and *A. flavicollis* has been claimed for populations in West Germany (Bothschafter, 1963; Amtmann, 1965), Yugoslavia (Witte, 1964), Bulgaria (Peshev & Georgiev, 1961) and the Crimea (Heptner, 1959), although interbreeding in the wild has not been substantiated (Niethammer, 1969). In central Europe, Heinrich (1951), Matthews (1952), Muller (1972) and Saint Girons (1973) proposed a less discrete spatial separation based on altitude, with *A. flavicollis* restricted to forests of montane regions. In western and north-western Europe, however, both *A. sylvaticus* and *A. flavicollis* are often found in the same habitat. Curry-Lindahl (1959) captured both species equally in all habitats in central Sweden except swampy forests, where *A. flavicollis* predominated. In southern Sweden, Bergstedt (1965) also found both species in mixed deciduous woodland though Hansson (1968) and later Hoffmeyer & Hansson (1974) reported that whereas both *A. sylvaticus* and *A. flavicollis* are found in forest, only *A. sylvaticus* regularly enters and survives in old field habitats. This pattern of habitat use is similar to that apparent in *Apodemus* populations in Britain.

On mainland Britain, adult *A. flavicollis* are on average 50% heavier than adult *A. sylvaticus* (Corke, 1977a), are more brightly coloured, with a complete band of pigmentation across the pectoral region, and when handled, squeal and bite more than *A. sylvaticus*. The latter is found in many diverse habitats throughout Britain and the surrounding offshore islands (Flowerdew, 1977); *A. flavicollis* is restricted both in range and habitat, being rare outside the south and south-east of England, the eastern counties of Wales and the adjacent western counties of England (Arnold, 1978). Corke (1977a) suggested that British *A. flavicollis* are found more frequently in woodland than its smaller congener. Montgomery (1978a) provided some evidence linking the distribution of *A. flavicollis* to long-established deciduous woodland in drier areas of southern Britain. Unlike the situation that exists in Sweden, however, wherever *A. flavicollis* is found, it is generally in low numbers and *A. sylvaticus* is always present (Corke, 1977a). Hedges (1966), for example, caught *A. flavicollis* and *A. sylvaticus* in the ratio 1 : 70 in the New Forest, and Corke & Harris (1974) found 20–25% of *Apodemus* captured in Essex to be the larger species. The coexistence of closely related species with similar ecologies, such as *A. sylvaticus* and *A. flavicollis* in Britain and much of western Europe, is often regarded as paradoxical, apparently contradicting that most revered dogma of community ecology, the Principle of Competitive Exclusion. Several authors have suggested differences in the ecologies of these *Apodemus* species that might explain their coexistence, at least at habitat level. Corbet (1966), Hedges (1966) and Corke (1974) proposed that *A. flavicollis* makes greater use of arboreal runways than *A. sylvaticus*. Corke (1974, 1977b), working in woodland interspersed with arable fields in Essex, suggested that *A. sylvaticus* migrated to fields to breed, resulting in habitat separation during the breeding season. It is also said that *A. flavicollis* enters houses and stores more frequently than does *A. sylvaticus* and in some areas of Britain is known as the 'apple mouse'. Miller (1967) proposed an interesting model of species coexistence where the niche of a more aggressive species is included within that of a subordinate species. He suggested that the relationship of *A. sylvaticus*, a species with a broad range of habitats and an opportunistic feeder, and *A. flavicollis*, the supposedly more restricted and more aggressive species, may be described by his included niche model. The low densities at which *A. flavicollis* is found in the rodent communities of southern Britain have frustrated attempts to test these hypotheses. Neither has it been possible to explore the generality of local differences in ecology such as that reported for the breeding season in woodland close to arable farmland in Essex (Corke, 1974, 1977*b*).

During early summer, starting in 1967, estimation of small mammal populations has been carried out as part of a field course at Woodchester Park. Yalden (1971) reported the unusually high proportion of *A. flavicollis* among captures of *Apodemus* as a whole. In many places this fraction exceeded 50%, and on a grid first trapped in 1968 the density of *A. flavicollis* was twice that of *A. sylvaticus* in each of three years. Later, Montgomery (1976) summarised data from seven successive summers, concluding that, contrary to the anticipated negative relationship between closely related species, fluctuations in numbers of *A. sylvaticus* and *A. flavicollis* were positively correlated. Further, densities of both species were comparable with those recorded in allopatric studies. Clearly some woodland in Woodchester Park affords a unique opportunity to study the comparative ecology of *Apodemus* species. This study has continued during summer field courses from its inception in 1968 to the present. Annual dynamics, population parameters, spatial relationships and behaviour were analysed more intensively between 1974 and 1976 (Montgomery, 1977).

Two main lines of investigation have been pursued. First, the ecologies of *A. sylvaticus* and *A. flavicollis* have been compared with respect to abundance and dynamics, reproduction, age structure and use of space within and between habitats. Species differences, whether or not they result from competition between species, may elucidate the structure of biological communities by highlighting how competition may be avoided, hence promoting species diversity. The second aspect of the study examined the hypothesis that *A. sylvaticus* and *A. flavicollis* compete for resources such as space and food. Although both species undoubtedly coexist within some areas of woodland, the possibility that competition between *A. sylvaticus* and *A. flavicollis* occurs may not be discounted, as the interaction may be insufficiently strong to establish single-species domination at any one place or be intermittent and confined to periods of food shortage. Alternatively, division of space within a given habitat may involve domination of very limited areas, with frequent excursions into adjacent areas which are normally the reserve of the competing species. By virtue of their close spatial relationship within woodland, *Apodemus* species are particularly interesting, as most studies of competition in rodent communities have concentrated on species occupying different habitats. For example, Grant (1969) and Morris & Grant (1971) carried out a series of experiments on the relationship between the woodland species *Peromyscus maniculatus* and *Clethrionomys gapperi* and the grassland species *Microtus pennsylvanicus*. Competitive relationships between species within habitats present greater problems in the design and interpretation of experiments. It is possible only through experimental manipulation to assess the role of competition as a dynamic process in the relationship between species and to determine whether inter-specific differences in ecology are intrinsic to the species or result from interspecific competition. The aim of the present report is to re-view and integrate the 16-year study of the relationship between *A. sylvaticus* and *A. flavicollis* carried out at Woodchester Park with studies elsewhere in Britain and Europe. Particular attention will be given to the importance of methodology in comparing population parameters in two species.

Study area and methods

The ecological and geological setting of Woodchester Park valley has been reviewed in Chapter 1. During the 16 years of investigations into the ecology of small mammals, almost every part and every habitat in the valley have been surveyed. Here, only the location, history and noteworthy topographical and vegetational features of those sites of greatest trapping effort will be presented. Specific and common names of plants are listed in Appendix 1. Greater detail may be found in Montgomery (1977, 1980a). In all, eight grids have been trapped on the southern slopes of the valley towards its western end (Fig. 5.1). Some of these have been trapped infrequently whereas others have been intensively surveyed in long-term studies of rodent abundance.

Grid M. Leaze Wood, the steep bank of dense, heterogeneous woodland in front of the field station, was trapped first in 1968 and has been surveyed every June during the University of Manchester field course. It has become known as the main grid, M (Fig. 5.1). Although methodology and the precise area under study varied somewhat in early years (Yalden, 1971), data are sufficient to allow comparison of the relative abundance of rodents over a prolonged period. In 1972, C.J. Roberts (formerly Department of Biology, University of Southamp-ton) marked out the grid which has continued in use to the present. This consisted or eight rows of twelve points at 10-m intervals. This grid was trapped for five consecutive nights at approximately 2-month intervals between January 1974 and June 1976 (Montgomery, 1977, 1980a). Grid M has also been trapped for five consecutive nights during June in 1967 to 1983. Leaze Wood is dominated by a particularly dense

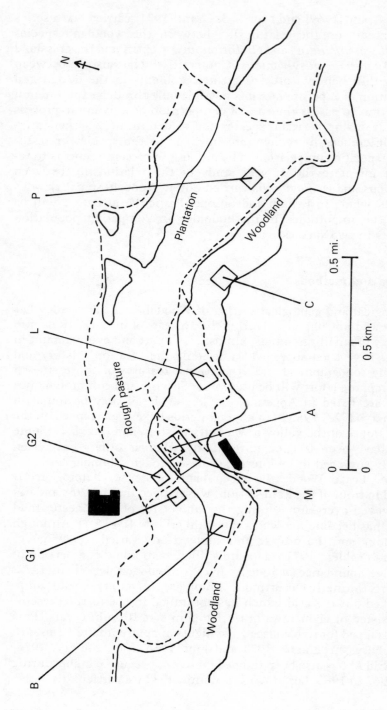

Fig. 5.1 Location of grids on the north-facing slope of Woodchester Park valley. The area of the main grid, M, was trapped from 1968 to 1983; between 1975 and 1976, grids A, B and C were trapped at regular intervals as part of a removal experiment. The Liverpool grid, L, was established in 1969 and trapped intermittently in the 1970s.

stand of *Taxus, Fagus, Ulmus* (mostly diseased or deceased by the mid 1970s), *Fraxinus, Prunus* spp., *Sambucus, Buxus, Mercurialis, Allium* and *Urtica*.

Grid A. This was a portion (seven rows of seven points) of grid M used as a control in the removal experiment carried out between January 1975 and July 1976 (Montgomery, 1981). Populations on grid A were not disturbed but merely surveyed at bimonthly intervals for four consecutive nights. Montgomery (1977) found no significant inconsistencies in the use of grid A data in association with that of the whole of the main grid (M) such that monthly changes in abundance and other population parameters were available for comparison with the experimental grids B and C.

Grid B. The dimensions of this grid, set on the steep, earthy slopes of the appropriately named Mouse Wood, were identical to those of grid A. Grid B was trapped for four nights at monthly intervals throughout 1975. From January to July 1976, all *A. sylvaticus* were removed, leaving a rodent community of just one *Apodemus* species, *A. flavicollis*. The vegetation of Mouse Wood is dominated by *Taxus, Fagus, Ulmus, Fraxinus, Acer, Buxus, Sambucus* and extensive areas of *Allium* and *Mercurialis*.

Grid C. Grid C was set in Stoneshard Wood and trapped from January 1975 to July 1976. The dimensions of the grid were identical to those of grids A and B. Grid C was trapped every month for four consecutive nights. From January to July 1976, all *A. flavicollis* were removed to leave an isolated population of *A. sylvaticus*. Stoneshard Wood, standing on steep slopes with thin soils, consists of a fine stand of *Taxus, Fagus*, and *Fraxinus*, and a peripheral plantation of *Larix, Corylus, Sambucus, Rubus, Urtica* and *Mercurialis*.

Grids A, B and C were involved in the removal experiment, the design and interpretation of which was discussed by Montgomery (1981). They were chosen for the similarity of their plant communities. Like the main grid, all three form part of the continuous strip of deciduous woodland interspersed with compact stands of *Taxus*, on the north-facing slopes of Woodchester Park (Fig. 5.1).

Grid L. This grid was established first by the Department of Zoology, University of Liverpool, in September 1969 (Fig. 5.1). Trapping regimes were somewhat irregular. Yalden (1971) noted that the proportion of *A. flavicollis* in this area at the end of the summer was much lower than on the main grid some 200 m to the west in June. Grid L lies in a shallow-sided gully with a dense, scrubby undergrowth. Predominant tree species are *Fraxinus, Corylus, Crataegus, Fagus* and *Acer*. Although part of the belt of woodland on the southern side of the valley, the vegetation of grid L contrasts with that of grids M, A, B and C (Fig. 5.1).

Grid G. In 1967 and 1969 two adjacent areas of the rough pasture of Mansion Meadow were trapped during the June field course. At this time the grassland was broken up by patches of *Rubus* and *Urtica*. Subsequently and throughout most of the 1970s, the meadow was grazed by cattle throughout the year.

Grid P. This grid was trapped several times during the early summer in the 1970s. It was set in a plantation of *Populus* standing on a gentle slope leading down to Middle Pond (Fig. 5.1). Beneath the open canopy of the trees, the dominant plants are grasses, *Urtica*, *Rubus* and *Epilobium*. Trapping regimes varied between years.

Grids G and P contrast markedly with M, A, B, C and L as they lie below the woodland strip on the gentler slopes of the valley (Fig. 5.1). Both grids are interesting as they allow an evaluation of the impact of *Apodemus* species in habitats other than woodland. Unfortunately, data are available only for early summer.

All trapping was carried out using Longworth live traps (Chitty & Kempson, 1949). These were provided with dry hay as bedding and wheat grain to sustain the captives. Gurnell (1976) demonstrated that the presence of food in traps increases significantly the captures of both marked and unmarked *A. sylvaticus*. On grid M between 1974 and 1976, and on grids A, B and C, two traps were set at each grid point. Mice captured on grids M to P were marked individually by a combination of toe clipping and ear punching. Fullagar & Jewell (1965) examined several methods of marking small mammals. They concluded that toe clipping combined with ear punching is a more durable technique than ear tagging or leg ringing and that there is no evidence that these methods affect survival. The proposition that these methods of marking do affect rate of recapture is examined below. Rodents caught on the numerous traplines set in early summer were marked by clipping fur from the flank of newly captured individuals. After examination for pelage condition, sex and reproductive state, and weighing, all rodents were released at the point of capture. Full details of methodology are presented in Montgomery (1977).

During the course of the study, *C. glareolus* and *M. agrestis* were captured frequently. Results concerning these microtine species are not presented here unless they have some relevance to the relationship between *A. sylvaticus* and *A. flavicollis*. Other rodent species, *Rattus norvegicus*, *Mus musculus* and *Sciurus carolinensis*, are present in and around the valley though these were not taken in Longworth traps with the exception of one individual *Mus* caught on grid M. The shrews *Sorex araneus*, *S. minutus* and *Neomys fodiens* were present throughout, and locally, as on grid P, the first of these species was very common (Yalden, 1974).

Trappability of small mammals and the estimation of population parameters in comparative studies

Flowerdew (1976) considered three methods of estimating the absolute size of small mammal populations. Removal techniques, such as the Standard Minimum method (Grodzinski *et al.*, 1966), were unsuitable in the present study since the area of woodland, and hence population size, was limited. Moreover this restriction was more severe on *A. flavicollis* than *A. sylvaticus* and one would anticipate great bias in removal methods of population estimation. The second method, the Calendar of Captures (Petrusewicz & Andrzejewski, 1962), employs mark, release, recapture (MRR) data and is widely used in the study of the dynamics of small mammal populations. The Calendar of Captures is not an MRR method of estimation but rather assesses the number of individuals alive at a given time, including in the total count those which are absent but reappear during a subsequent sampling period. The accuracy of this method is closely related to intensity of trapping and the proportion of the population captured. Trapping must be regular and frequent; Flowerdew (1976) recommended trapping at least once a month. The Calendar of Captures was also inapplicable in the present long-term study of rodent dynamics at Woodchester Park and the more intensive sampling programme on grids M, A, B and C. Intervals between trapping sessions in the latter were variable and probably too great, and the 5 days of trapping in the former too short, to allow an accurate enumeration of the populations. More importantly, it was by no means certain that the sampled proportion of the populations of *A. sylvaticus* and *A. flavicollis* was sufficiently great and equitable to allow comparison of estimates between species. Further, estimation by Calendar of Captures suffers from major drawbacks. The estimates fall off towards the end of the trapping programme and there is no consideration of error, which may be critical in the evaluation of estimates as an indicator of true population size. Finally, Calendar of Captures always results in an underestimation of population size as the number of individuals not caught is not assessed and may well be variable.

The third group of methods, widely applied in the estimation of mammal populations, is based on the Lincoln Index (Lincoln, 1930). Southwood (1978) summarised the underlying assumptions of simple and more complex MRR methods. Most required that marked animals are not affected with respect to their behaviour or life expectancy. Marks of course, as in the case of the present study, must be permanent. Marked animals should mix freely with the rest of the population; the interval between samples must be sufficient to permit this and be large in proportion to the time required to conduct the sampling process. The probability of catching any individual in the population must be constant with respect to mark status, sex and age. This requirement extends to breeding condition and less tangible aspects of social behaviour as in dominance–subordinancy relationships. In addition, further assumptions are made in the use of the simple Lincoln Index. The population should be closed, i.e. there should be neither immigrations nor births, emigration nor deaths, unless these can be evaluated and taken into consideration in the population estimate. More sophisticated MRR models permit estimation of open populations where ingress and/or egress occur. These methods require that capture of an individual does not affect its future chance of capture, and may require that every marked animal has an equal probability of survival through the sampling period; i.e. if animals of different ages are marked, then mortality must be independent of age. Bishop & Hartley (1976), for example, applied the Jolly–Seber method of estimation to a population study on rats after verifying that mortality was independent of age. Their technique could not be applied here as the age structure of *Apodemus* populations may change quickly and is not always adequately determined by weight.

It is highly unlikely that any population satisfies all the criteria assumed in MRR methods. Begon (1979) discussed this point with regard to the compromise between statistical propriety, biological reality and collection of sufficient data to maximise the precision of estimates. He concluded that it is unwise to apply any MRR method uncritically. Although it may not be possible to fulfil the assumptions outlined above, the ecologist may at least be able to state whether his estimate is likely to be above or below the true value through awareness of the shortcomings of his methodology or non-randomness in the behaviour of the animals under study. He often does not do so (Begon, 1983). Southwood (1978), Begon (1979) and Blower *et al.* (1981) present a number of tests of the assumptions inherent in MRR models. Choice of test and its application depend on the aim of the study. Here we are primarily interested in the comparative abundance of two species so it is pertinent to concentrate on interspecific disparities in trappability and response to marking and handling. Population estimation during the June census, 1968 to 1983, was based on 5 days' data. In keeping with this precedent and to avoid anomalies introduced by the variable and rather long intervals between sampling, MRR estimates over a short period of 5 days were employed during the intensive work on annual dynamics, 1974 to 1976. Data from the latter study are presented here. Seasonal differences in trappability have not been investigated.

The effect of marking

The criterion that marking does not affect the chances of recapture is central to all MRR methods of population estimation. After January 1974, two classes of mice were captured on day 1 of each sampling period on grid M: first, those that had been marked before the current month, and secondly those unmarked, which were newly marked before release. The effect of marking, i.e. initial restraint and handling, toe clipping and ear punching, may be assessed using data for recapture of these two groups. The effect of marking male and female *A. sylvaticus* and *A. flavicollis* was investigated in relation to recapture over 24 h, 4 days and at any time after release, using a χ^2 test of homogeneity (Blower *et al.*, 1981). Data were lumped for 16 trapping periods on grid M. There were no differences between male and female conspecifics. Neither were there any differences in recapture rates of *A. sylvaticus* and *A. flavicollis* (Table 5.1). However, an inhibition of recapture rate of freshly marked mice was apparent within both species. This effect persisted throughout the trapping period but was significant only for *A. sylvaticus* and only during the first 24 h after release. The majority of mice were recaptured within the same trapping period (Table 5.1). Only a few were not recaptured either during the next sampling session or at a later date. If data for these

Table 5.1 Recapture data for *A. sylvaticus* and *A. flavicollis* released on day 1 of a 5-day trapping period on grid M, January 1974 to June 1976. When released, mice were classed as newly marked, by toe clipping and ear punching, or marked during an earlier occasion. Recapture rate (% rec.) was determined within 24 h, at any time during the same trapping session, and at any time subsequent to the initial release.

	Within 24 h			Within 4 days			At any time		
	rec.	not	% rec.	rec.	not	% rec.	rec.	not	% rec.
A. sylvaticus									
newly marked	49	47	51	80	16	83	89	7	93
marked previously	88	42	68	120	10	92	123	7	95
χ_1^2	5.735; $P < 0.05$			3.531; $P < 0.1$			0.095; n.s.		
A. flavicollis									
newly marked	24	26	48	40	10	80	43	7	86
marked previously	40	29	59	60	9	87	63	6	91
χ_1^2	0.332; n.s.			0.591; n.s.			0.382; n.s.		
A. sylvaticus vs *A. flavicollis* χ_1^2									
newly marked	0.030; n.s.			0.073; n.s.			1.020; n.s.		
newly marked + marked previously	1.231; n.s.			1.003; n.s.			1.806; n.s.		

subsequent sampling periods are included, then the detrimental effect of marking on recapture rate disappears (Table 5.1). Smal & Fairley (1982) and Fairley (1982) reported a similar impact of marking (in their case just toe clipping) on the recapture rate of *A. sylvaticus* in Ireland. Fairley (1982) concluded that MRR population estimates may be inaccurate whenever a large proportion of individuals are newly marked. In the present study this occurred during the annual June census on grid M and periods of influx of new animals during the annual cycles of abundance revealed between 1974 and 1976 (Montgomery, 1980a). Marking effects inflate Lincoln Index based estimates such that numbers of individuals handled tend to fall short of the estimated population size. However, the proportion of the estimated population actually handled was, in general, above 90%, in both long- and short-term trapping programmes (see below). This suggests that the impact of marking was offset by the high frequency of recaptures of previously marked and freshly marked mice over 5 days. Recapture rates over 24 h, for example (Table 5.1), were well above those documented by Fairley (1982), indicating that some aspect of the methodology or the habitat on grid M enhanced chances of recapture. Nevertheless, it should be borne in mind that estimates may be slight overestimates of abundance.

The present report is concerned primarily with interspecific comparisons. It is clear that the methods employed in marking mice had similar effects on the recapture of *A. sylvaticus* and *A. flavicollis*. Also the recapture rates of *A. sylvaticus* and *A. flavicollis* in general did not differ significantly (Table 5.1).

Trappability of A. sylvaticus *and* A. flavicollis

Mark, release, recapture estimates require that subgroups within populations are sampled in the proportion in which they occur, and that all individuals are equally available for capture irrespective of their position in the habitat (Southwood, 1978). Unfortunately, little can be said about the trappability of the untrapped portion of the population, but it is possible to examine variation in trappability between and within species using the data for that fraction of a population which is caught. Gurnell (1982) measured trappability of *A. sylvaticus* and *C. glareolus* using the night of initial capture and the frequency of captures during a sampling period. He found little difference in these evaluations of trap response. Here, the latter method, the number of captures during a 5-day period, is used to examine relative trappability between species, between males and females and between those animals making their first appearance and those caught in an earlier sampling period. Frequencies of captures are illustrated in Fig.

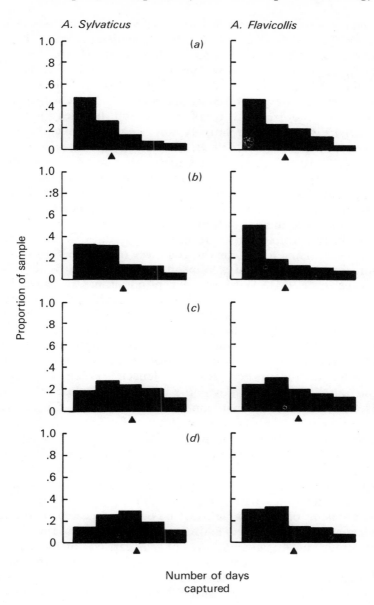

Fig. 5.2 Proportion of *A. sylvaticus* and *A. flavicollis* caught one, two, three, four or five times in a single sampling period. Data collated for all sampling periods on M, 1974 to 1976. (*a*) and (*b*): Male and female mice during the first month of capture; (*c*) and (*d*): male and female mice during their second and subsequent months of capture. Triangles indicate mean number of captures.

5.2. Data were collated for grid M in 16 sampling periods, 1974 to 1976, transformed as square root $(x + 0.5)$ and subjected to three-way analysis of variance (Sokal & Rohlf, 1981). As anticipated by analysis of the effect of marking, new individuals were less trappable than established ones ($F = 49.25$, df = 1,918, $P < 0.001$). This was evident in both *A. sylvaticus* and *A. flavicollis* (Fig. 5.2). There was no overall difference in the trappability of males and females, but female *A. sylvaticus* were caught relatively more frequently in comparison to male conspecifics than female *A. flavicollis* in comparison to male *A. flavicollis*. Although there was little difference in trappability of male *A. sylvaticus* and male *A. flavicollis*, the increased trap response of females of the former species was sufficient to produce an overall species effect ($F = 6.25$, df 1,918, $P < 0.025$), though this was small in comparison to the impact of trap experience (Fig. 5.2). Heterogeneity in trappability within each subgroup of the populations present on grid M was tested using a test for the goodness of fit to a zero truncated Poisson distribution (David & Johnson, 1952). This test is described in Blower *et al.* (1981). With the exception of newly captured and previously captured female *A. flavicollis*, significant heterogeneity was detected in all subgroups illustrated in Fig. 5.2. Homogeneity may result from random sampling or from the superimposition of two or more non-random distributions. These results suggest that sources of variation other than species, sex and experience were important in the trappability of rodents on grid M. Jensen (1975), for example, demonstrated that, in·*A. flavicollis* and *C. glareolus*, reproductive adults are more trappable than non-reproductive adults. Gurnell (1982) reported that trap response of juvenile *A. sylvaticus* and *C. glareolus* was a little less than that of unmarked adults. Breeding and age effects on the trappability of *Apodemus* species at Woodchester Park were not investigated, though both may be of importance, as it is already clear that in order to achieve the highest level of precision in estimation, many subgroups within a population must be considered separately. Division of the sample must be balanced against maintaining an adequate sample size. Estimation of the population size of *A. sylvaticus* and *A. flavicollis* was always carried out independently but no attempt was made to assess numbers using intraspecific subgroups. Not only was potential subgroup size, at times, less than 10, but, as in earlier reports (Gurnell, 1982), the variation in capture frequency within subgroups was so great that between-subgroup variation accounts for relatively little of the overall variation in capture data. This was clearly so among *Apodemus* species on grid M (Fig. 5.2), where individuals captured one, two, three, four or five times were found in all subgroup categories. Results of this analysis suggest that the trappable portion of the population of *A. flavicollis* was slightly less prone to capture than *A. sylvaticus*. If this interspecific difference extends to individuals not captured, then estimates of population size of *A. flavicollis* may be slight over-estimates relative to those of *A. sylvaticus*.

Pattern in captures and recaptures of A. sylvaticus *and* A. flavicollis *in sequential samples*

More sophisticated models of MRR require several successive samples from the population under study. Estimates may be influenced by the incidence of new individuals and the rate of recapture in the series of samples. As sampling progresses, the former might be expected to decline while the latter increases, provided a significant proportion of the population is captured. Also the sample size should remain fairly constant if there is no aversion to traps after initial capture and the population is sampled randomly. These propositions were examined with respect to interspecific differences. It has already been noted that there was wide variation in numbers of captures even within peer groups of a population. During the course of trapping it was evident that numbers of captures fluctuated from night to night. The annual dynamics of both *A. sylvaticus* and *A. flavicollis* were such that numbers handled varied by a factor of 10 between January 1974 and July 1976. To accommodate this large variation in rates of capture, a data set was constructed for number handled, number of new individuals (new to that sampling period) — both as a proportion of the total number of individuals handled in the sampling period — and the proportion of recaptures in daily samples, over the 5 days of each sampling period on grid M, 1974 to 1976. Data from some months in the same season were lumped to create daily sample sizes of 25 or more mice handled. Homogeneity within data for each day of the three data sets was checked using a test of independence based on the binomial expansion (Parker, 1979). Samples significantly at odds with results for any one day were eliminated from the whole data set. This reduced the number of samples but also reduced the variation in the data so that analyses would be more sensitive to differences between species and between days. Proportions were transformed using angular transformation and subjected to two-way analysis of variance in which data were the capture frequencies for each sample over 5 days for two species (Winer, 1971). This takes into account variation between sampling periods.

Between 30% and 60% of individuals known to be alive at the end of a trapping period were caught each day (Fig. 5.3a). There was no significant variation in the capture rate between *A. sylvaticus* and *A. flavicollis* but the level of capture increased slightly after day 1 such

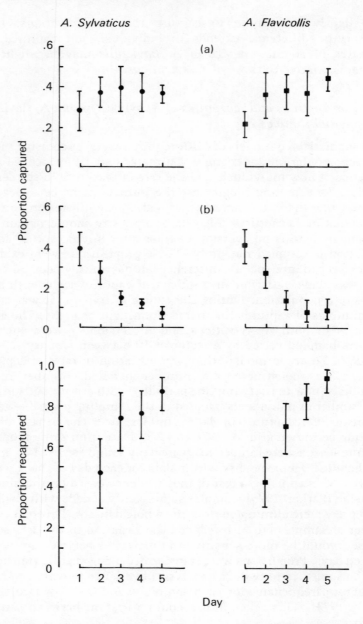

Fig. 5.3 Capture characteristics of *A. sylvaticus* and *A. flavicollis* over a 5-day period on grid M. (*a*) Proportion of all individuals caught on any day. (*b*) Proportion of all individuals initially caught on any day. (*c*) Recaptures as a proportion of the catch on days 2 to 5. Bars indicate 95% confidence limits of the mean calculated after arcsin transformation.

that variation over the 5-day trapping period was significant ($F = 8.11$, df 4, 48, $P < 0.01$). Fewer marks enter the population on day 1. This will not affect population estimates directly, but by reducing the number of marks liable to recapture may detract from the precision of Lincoln Index-based estimates. The appearance of new individuals over 5 days was remarkably similar in the two species (Fig. 5.3*b*). The proportion of mice caught for the first time during the trapping period declined steeply from days 1 to 3 but levelled off in days 4 and 5. Such a temporal pattern would, in removal estimations of rodent abundance, produce an asymptotic, 'cumulative catch curve' (Gebczynska, 1966; Grodzinski *et al.*, 1966). This rapidly declining catch of new individuals suggests that a very high proportion of the mice present in the sampling area were captured over the 5 days of trapping. This is also indicated by the increase in the proportion of recaptures in daily samples (Fig. 5.3*c*), which rose from 45% on day 2 to around 90% on day 5 in both *A. sylvaticus* and *A. flavicollis*. Again the pattern of recapture in the two species was very similar.

Annual samples of abundance, June 1968 to 1983, have not been analysed since numbers were frequently small. However, since many of these samples contained a high proportion of trap-naive mice, the slope of the 'cumulative catch curve', the inverse of the incidence of new captures, would be less steep. Recapture frequency would also increase less steeply. This too would detract from the precision of estimates since the proportion of the population handled may be less than in sampling periods at shorter intervals. However, it is possible that, over a 5-day sampling period, sufficient recaptures occur and sufficient of the population is handled to maintain accuracy in the estimation of numbers. Further it is clear that any effect would be equitable between *A. sylvaticus* and *A. flavicollis*.

Why are capture rates so variable?

The factors determining the numbers of captures of *Apodemus* species resulting from a given effort in sampling a population of constant size are poorly understood. Only the variability of trapping success during a sampling period is guaranteed. For example, the range in the proportion of a known number of *A. sylvaticus* captured on each day of a 5-day trapping period was 50% or more. Weather conditions and moonlight (Kikkawa, 1964) may affect capture rate. Catches are increased if weather is warm and overcast. Evans (1942) found that greatest numbers of *A. sylvaticus* were caught in abnormally wet weather and least in a period of drought. Gurnell (1975, 1976), on the other hand, suggested that catches of this species are reduced during cold, wet weather through reduced activity. Tanton (1965) noted that prolonged periods of severe weather do not affect capture rate unduly, presumably because of acclimatisation. He concluded that estimates of populations, and the calculation of their error, may be affected if the sampling period is short. This may be pertinent in evaluation of numbers on traplines (see later) as sampling periods on these were usually just 3 days. During the long- and short-term analyses of dynamics on grid M, large numbers of captures were associated with overcast, wet conditions, but sudden increases or decreases in catches occurred when weather changed suddenly. Presumably, even when conditions were adverse for rodent activity, requirements of diet, social interaction and so on were met by an increase in activity as the inclement weather continued.

A further source of variation in capture rates of rodents may lie in endogenous, synchronised activity patterns among the members of a population. Individual *A. sylvaticus* in small captive groups go through periods of social and asocial activity (Bovet, 1972) which, under field conditions, may create fluctuations in trapping success. Response to new sources of food, such as a windfall of ripe seed, may also lead to increased surface activity (Gurnell, 1975). Gurnell (1978a) proposed that mice are caught shortly after nightfall, so reducing the number of traps available to free mice. If different segments of the population are active at different times, as indicated by Garson (1975), it is important that sufficient traps are available to maintain a high ratio of traps to individuals during the later stages of their nocturnal activity. Southern (1973) suggested that at least 20% of traps should be unoccupied to ensure that less trappable individuals remain liable to capture throughout the sampling period. On grids M, A, B and C, the number of traps was always well in excess of the total number of rodents caught.

The importance of this surplus capacity cannot be overemphasised. It is becoming apparent that occupied traps take on the odour of their occupants and may become more or less attractive to others in the population. Stoddart (1982) demonstrated experimentally that less trappable individuals in a population of *M. agrestis* are deterred by the odours of conspecifics and that this effect leads to understimation of abundance. Biases, probably resulting from trap odour, occurred on grid M between 1974 and 1976 (Montgomery, 1979a) but these seemed less constrictive and more ephemeral than those described by Stoddart.

Both extrinsic and intrinsic factors influence trappability of rodents over any sampling period. Extrinsic factors, such as weather conditions or food availability, may cause similar responses in different species. Trap success, as indicated by the proportion of the total number handled that were caught on any day, was positively correlated between *A. sylvaticus* and *A. flavicollis* ($r = 0.662$, df 38, $P < 0.001$). Mice of these species actively avoid one another in small enclosures (Hoffmeyer, 1973) and it seems unlikely that their social activity was positively related. The probable foundation of this positive association in trapping success was that extrinsic factors had a similar impact on the activity of the two species. Hence some 43.9% of variation in trappability may be attributed to extrinsic influences and 56.1% to intraspecific sources. The effect of these intrinsic and extrinsic influences on population estimates is uncertain, though their impact would probably be most severe when numbers of traps were limited. Data from trapline analyses should be used cautiously.

Choice of population estimation

Choice of MRR method depends largely on the design of the sampling programme, the pattern of survival in the population and the sampling intensity (Blower *et al.*, 1981). All of these are functions of the biology of the species under investigation and the aims of the ecologist in estimating abundance. Programmes of trapping at Woodchester Park were intended to integrate long-term and shorter-duration changes in abundance of two species. Sampling at 1-month, 2-month or 12-month intervals presents difficulties in comparing the results of one survey with those of another. Therefore a sampling period of 5, or in some cases 4, days was used in both long- and short-term studies. There is evidence that, within 5-day sampling periods, the assumptions of constant trappability and neutral response to marking were unwarranted. To some extent these were offset by remarkably high recapture rates, indicating a high sampling intensity. High sampling intensity and the similarity of *A. sylvaticus* and *A. flavicollis* in their trappability characteristics suggest that MRR methods, though not ideal, offer the most precise and bias-free means of comparing abundance of these species.

The estimation of open populations by, for example, the Manly & Parr or the Jolly–Seber methods introduces lower limits on the number of marked individuals on the probably unfounded assertion that mortality is age independent. Numbers of both *Apodemus* species on all grids fell below 10 on occasions. Watts (1969), Flowerdew (1974) and Gurnell (1978*b*) suggest that juvenile survival in *A. sylvaticus* is lower than that of adults during early summer. Although they embody worthy biological ideals, such models of estimation as Manly & Parr and Jolly–Seber may, in practice, result in widely varying estimates of abundance. Less sophisticated but robust methods may actually perform better in application (Blower *et al.*, 1981; Jolly, 1982).

An alternative approach, again to be used with caution, is to treat the population as closed. Minimum survival rate per month fluctuated around 0.6 in populations of both *Apodemus* species on grid M. This is equivalent to less than 2% loss per day. Mortality of *A. sylvaticus* due to predators, the weasel and the Tawny Owl, both of which are present in Woodchester Park, may amount to some 30% per month, though this may vary with time of year and availability of other prey items (King, 1980; Southern & Lowe, 1982; Dunn, 1977). This is equivalent to a loss of just over 1% per day. Gains over a short period are also minimal. At maximum rates of growth, populations doubled in a month on grids M, A, B and C, which amounts to approximately 2% per day. In populations generally less than 50, and often less than 20, these small losses and gains amount to at most two or three individuals over a 5-day trapping period. This is in keeping with the adoption of an estimate assuming a closed population.

The method of population estimation used throughout the whole trapping programme was described by Schumacher & Eschmeyer (1943) and later applied to small mammals by Hayne (1949). In studies of small mammals it is often regarded as Hayne's modified Lincoln Index method (Flowerdew, 1976). The rationale of the method is that there is an increase in the fraction marked in a sequence of samples. The population is estimated from the slope of a line, passing through the origin, of the relationship between recaptures, as the proportion of a sample, and the cumulative number of marks in the population:

$$\hat{P} = \frac{\Sigma n_i x_i^2}{\Sigma m_i x_i}$$

where n_i is the number of animals in a sample on day i, m_i is the number of recaptures in a sample on day i, and x_i is the cumulative total of marks in the population before day i using the notation of Blower *et al.* (1981). This method requires that the population is closed, probability of capture is constant and the process of marking should not affect the chance of recapture. It cannot be applied to *Apodemus* population data without reservation. Marking of mice had some effect on recapture; trappability was heterogeneous within and between species, and intrapopulation subgroups and populations were not, strictly speaking, closed. However, these effects were either minimal, as in egress and ingress, or offset by high recapture rates on grids with high densities of traps. Also the profiles of trappability of *A. sylvaticus* and *A. flavicollis* were very similar, especially in incidence and rate of recapture and the appearance of new animals during the 5-day sampling periods (Table 5.1, Fig. 5.3). Nevertheless, population estimates are probably slightly below true population size.

The application of any MRR method also depends on the appropriateness of the model on which it is based to the population data. Hayne's method assumes that the relationship between y_i, the marked proportion in a sample on day i, and x_i, the cumulative number

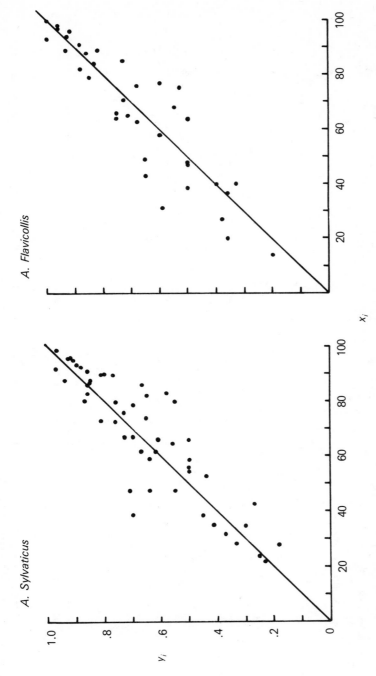

Fig. 5.4 The relationship between y_i and x_i from estimates of population size of *A. sylvaticus* and *A. flavicollis* on grid M. y_i is the marked proportion of a sample on day i, and x_i is the total number of mice marked previously, with the total number of individuals standardised as 100.

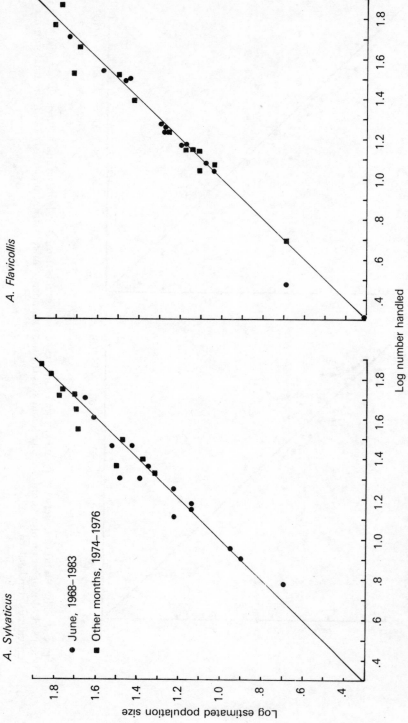

Fig. 5.5 Relationship between the numbers handled and population size, estimated after Hayne (1949) in *A. sylvaticus* and *A. flavicollis* on grid M. Lines have a slope of 1.

of marks before day *i*, is linear and passes through the origin. This was so for both *A. sylvaticus* and *A. flavicollis* on grid M in 1974, 1975 and 1976 (Fig. 5.4). This relationship will hold only if the assumption of equal catchability is not violated (Caughley, 1977). Once again this indicates that contraventions of assumptions underlying Hayne's method were cancelled out by high recapture rates and availability of traps. Throughout this section it has been maintained that a high proportion of the populations sampled was caught. The numbers handled and population estimates were closely related in both species in the June censuses, 1968 to 1983, and the more frequent sampling periods on grid M, 1974 to 1976 (Fig. 5.5). The increased number of trap-naive mice in the long-term study did not appear to alter this relationship.

What is the population being assessed?

Blower *et al.* (1981) defined a population as a collection of conspecifics of stated character inhabiting a delimited place during a given period of time. This utilitarian approach requires some biological qualification in considering the rodent communities of Woodchester Park. Both *A. sylvaticus* and *A. flavicollis* are' highly mobile species capable of traversing favourable and not so favourable habitats. It is likely that there is a great deal of movement of mice within, into and out of Woodchester Park valley. In short there are no readily apparent spatial limits, physical or biological, to the populations under study. Areas sampled in the surveys of dynamics and habitat use were small in relation to the mobility of the rodents. Grid sites were not chosen at random but for the constitution of their rodent communities. Therefore it may not be argued that dynamics on grid M, for example, were typical of some biologically reasonable population or even of Woodchester Park as a whole.

Dynamics of 'A. sylvaticus' and 'A. flavicollis' in sympatry and allopatry

One of the key parameters in the relationship between any two species is that of abundance. This is particularly true if interspecific competition is suspected. Reynoldson & Bellamy (1970) commented that although insufficient to establish competition on its own, relative abundance of potential competitors should be compatible with the ' competition hypothesis. The dynamics of *A. sylvaticus* and *A. flavicollis* have been studied in allopatric and sympatric populations throughout Europe. Here the dynamics of *Apodemus* species are reviewed, with particular reference to possible interspecific interaction.

Annual dynamics of Apodemus *species at Woodchester Park, 1974 to 1976*

In general the dynamics of *A. sylvaticus* on grid M followed the pattern described by Elton *et al.*, (1931) and Watts (1969) (Fig. 5.6). There was a characteristic spring decline in all years, though this was less severe in 1976 than in the previous years. In 1974, numbers were low throughout the summer months, rising only in autumn. In 1975, population size was small in summer but rose from June onwards. This was probably an artefact of the trapping regime as intervals between sampling periods were rather long. Data for grid A suggest that numbers were static in Leaze Wood during June and July 1975, just as in the previous year (Montgomery, 1980a). Numbers of *A. sylvaticus* were high in autumn and winter of all three years, though they were particularly high in the 1975–1976 winter. At this time, survival rates were also high and numbers declined slowly in spring 1976 to reach a June level three times greater than that in June 1975 and considerably more than that in June 1974.

In *A. flavicollis* on grid M in 1974, winter and spring population size was small, rising in June before declining slightly in August (Fig. 5.6). The main period of recruitment was from August to October and was followed by a slow decline throughout winter. A further decrease in numbers occurred between February and April 1975. This was somewhat earlier than the corresponding spring decline in *A. sylvaticus*. In 1975, recruitment of *A. flavicollis* was uninterrupted from April to October. During early winter, numbers decreased steadily, again some time before the corresponding decline in numbers of *A. sylvaticus*.

The dynamics of *A. sylvaticus* and *A. flavicollis* between 1974 and 1976 differed in two major respects. First, during early summer, numbers of *A. sylvaticus* were low and stable whereas those of *A. flavicollis* were increasing. This resulted in relative abundance in June, favouring the latter species. It was this feature that first attracted the attention of Yalden (1971). Later in the summer, recruitment of *A. sylvaticus* may overtake *A. flavicollis* so that by late summer the latter no longer has numerical dominance. This switch in relative abundance of *Apodemus* occurred on grids M, A, B and C (Montgomery, 1981). There is also some evidence that a similar change occurred on grid L in the early 1970s when the proportion of *A. flavicollis* among *Apodemus* fell from 39.3% on June/July traplines to 19.5% in September (χ^2 = 3.96, P < 0.05). However, elsewhere in

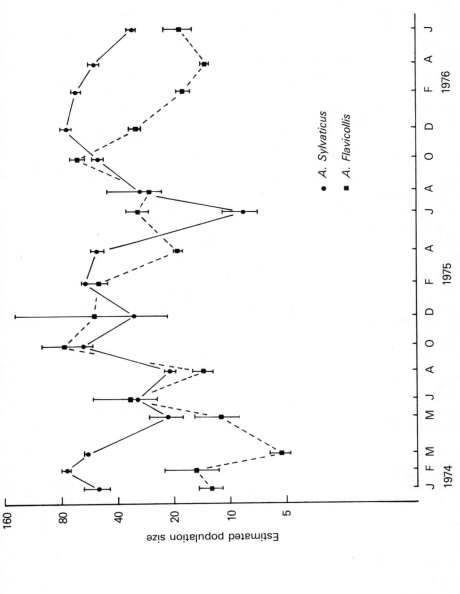

Fig. 5.6 Estimated population size of *A. sylvaticus* and *A. flavicollis* on grid M, 1974 to 1976. Vertical bars indicate 95% confidence limits of the estimate. (After Montgomery, 1980a.)

Woodchester Park, numerical superiority of *A. flavicollis* over *A. sylvaticus* in early summer did not occur (Montgomery, 1979*b*).

The second major difference in the annual cycles of *A. sylvaticus* and *A. flavicollis* on grid M was the earlier winter decline in numbers of the latter. This was evident in 1975 and 1976 but the low numbers at the start of the study also suggest that an early winter decrease in population size of *A. flavicollis* occurred in 1973–1974. Early winter decline was a much more general phenomenon, throughout Woodchester Park, as low numbers of *A. flavicollis* in the second half of winter were found in a number of habitats (Montgomery, 1979*b*). These periods of decline were associated with poor survival such that interspecific differences in survival mirrored those in numbers (Montgomery, 1977, 1980*a*). There was no significant relationship between population size ($r = 0.112$, df 15, ns) or survival rates ($r = 0.440$, df 14, $P < 0.1$) of *A. sylvaticus* and *A. flavicollis* on grid M. This suggests that the dynamics of *Apodemus* species progressed independently, although local or temporary changes in environmental conditions may have produced minor changes in survival or abundance of both species.

Both *A. sylvaticus* and *A. flavicollis* had pronounced annual breeding seasons in which males came into breeding condition some time before females (Fig. 5.7). This delay in the attainment of sexual maturity, in males and females, was less noticeable in *A. flavicollis*, possibly because testicular development in this species was underestimated; fully developed testes are relatively smaller than those of *A. sylvaticus* (Kratochivil, 1970). In the winters of 1974–1975 and 1975–1976, all females were non-reproductive, but in 1974–1975,

Table 5.2 Numbers of reproductive and non-reproductive female *A. sylvaticus* and *A. flavicollis* before and during the onset of the breeding seasons in 1974, 1975 and 1976. Data for all grids except B and C in 1976. (From Montgomery, 1980*a*.)

	Non-reproductive	Reproductive	χ_1^2
March, April 1974			
A. sylvaticus	44	6	$P = 0.004$
A. flavicollis	3	5	(Fisher Exact)
March 1975			
A. sylvaticus	21	12	11.28; $P < 0.001$
A. flavicollis	1	14	
February, March, April 1976			
A. sylvaticus	66	19	6.93; $P < 0.01$
A. flavicollis	9	11	

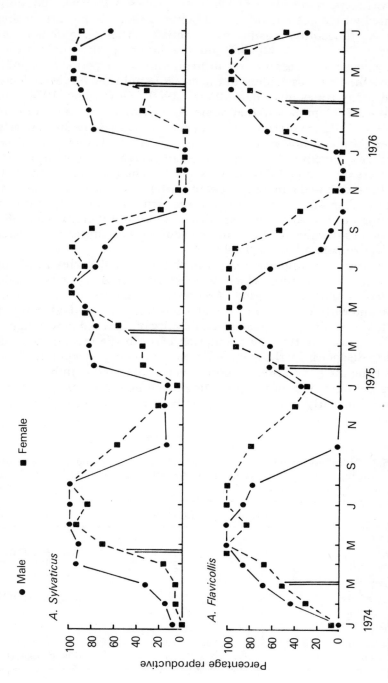

Fig. 5.7 Percentage of adult male and female *A. sylvaticus* and *A. flavicollis* in reproductive condition. Data for all grids and traplines in 1974 and 1975 and grids M and A in 1976. (From Montgomery, 1980*a*.)

152 *Case studies in population biology*

there was some winter breeding in both species, which was possibly associated with a heavy crop of seed (Smyth, 1966). In all three years, female *A. flavicollis* became reproductive earlier than female *A. sylvaticus* (Fig. 5.7, Table 5.2). In the latter species the start of breeding does not necessarily result in an immediate period of population growth. This was evident in the present study and has been documented many times elsewhere. Watts (1969), Flowerdew (1974) and Gurnell (1978b) proposed that male *A. sylvaticus* are antagonistic towards juveniles, which in consequence survive poorly during early summer. This did not appear to happen in *A. flavicollis*; the initial appearance of juveniles led to an immediate increase in population size in all years on M and 1975 on A, B and C. The early breeding of *A. flavicollis* facilitated a rapid turnabout in the slowly declining populations of late spring. As a result, the age structures of early summer populations of the *Apodemus* species were quite different (Fig. 5.8). The ratio of juveniles to overwintered adults was significantly greater in *A. flavicollis* in all years (Table 5.3).

There were two important aspects of the annual cycles in abundance and age structure which were similar in *A. sylvaticus* and *A. flavicollis*. The main period of recruitment in both species was in autumn and early winter when populations were largest (Figs. 5.6 and 5.8). This coincides with greatest availability of tree seed in woodland. Secondly, mice entering the population early in the breeding season tended to disappear by the start of the next breeding season (Fig. 5.8). At this time the populations of both species consisted mainly of mice born in the latter half of the preceding breeding season. This cohort, after breeding early in the season, finally disappeared in mid- to late summer.

Table 5.3 Numbers of adult and juvenile *A. sylvaticus* and *A. flavicollis* captured during June in three years. Data for all grids bar B and C in 1976. (From Montgomery, 1980a.)

	Adult	Juvenile	χ^2_1
June 1974			
A. sylvaticus	38	17	7.64; $P < 0.01$
A. flavicollis	13	22	
June 1975			
A. sylvaticus	24	6	15.12; $P < 0.001$
A. flavicollis	20	39	
June 1976			
A. sylvaticus	26	9	$P = 0.041$
A. flavicollis	14	13	(Fisher Exact)

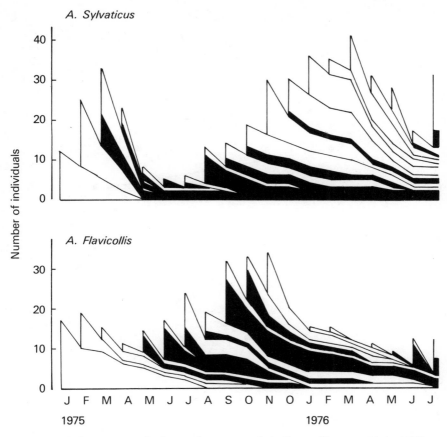

Fig. 5.8 Cohort survival of *A. sylvaticus* and *A. flavicollis* on grid A, 1975 to 1976. Shading indicates those individuals caught initially as juveniles. (From Montgomery, 1980*a*.)

Long-term changes in abundance of Apodemus *species*

Montgomery (1976) noted the positive association of June population size of *A. sylvaticus* and *A. flavicollis* on grid M between 1968 and 1974 and commented that it was not in keeping with a competitive interaction. Since the mid 1970s, this relationship has changed; during the first 8 years of the summer census, densities of *A. sylvaticus* and *A. flavicollis* were positively correlated (r_s = 0.714, P < 0.05) and numbers of the latter were greater than those of the former (Fig. 5.9). From 1976 onwards, numbers of *A. sylvaticus* were greater in every year except 1978. During this period, 1976 to 1983, and over the entire 16 years, numbers of *A. sylvaticus* and *A. flavicollis* fluctuated

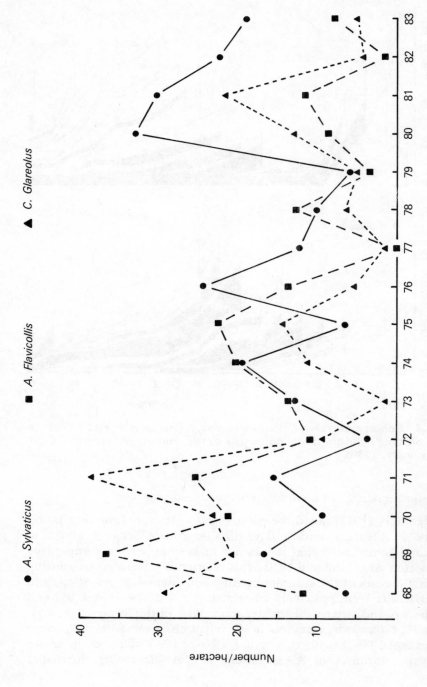

Fig. 5.9 Density of *A. sylvaticus*, *A. flavicollis* and *C. glareolus* on grid M, 1968 to 1983. Numbers were estimated in June and density calculated after Yalden (1971).

● *A. Sylvaticus*　　■ *A. Flavicollis*　　▲ *C. Glareolus*

Number/hectare

independently. June densities of *A. flavicollis* gradually declined from 1975 whereas whose of its congener increased erratically from the early 1970s onwards. This resulted in a marked change in the relative abundance of the two *Apodemus* species. The density of *C. glareolus* also underwent major fluctuations in the course of the study. In three of the first four summers, *C. glareolus* was the most common rodent on grid M. In 1972, numbers of this species were well down on previous years and densities remained low and erratic until the beginning of the 1980s. Throughout the survey of annual dynamics, 1974 to 1976, numbers of *C. glareolus* were low, with an increase in autumn followed by a decrease in early winter (Montgomery, 1977).

These changes in community composition are presented in Fig. 5.10. Relative abundance of the three rodent species changed significantly over the whole period (x^2 = 114, df 8, P < 0.001). During the first 6 years, proportions of all species were fairly consistent, but by 1974–1976, the percentage of *C. glareolus* fell and the percentage of *A. sylvaticus* rose. Between 1977–1979 and 1980–1983, the proportion of *A. flavicollis* on grid M fell consistently and was accompanied by further increases in the relative abundance of *A. sylvaticus*. These relative changes in abundance were embodied in changes in the average density of all three species. Mean numbers of *C. glareolus* were lower after 1971 (t = 5.392, df 9, P < 0.001); mean numbers of *A. flavicollis* were lower after 1975 (t = 3.033, df 9, P < 0.02); and mean numbers of *A. sylvaticus* were higher, though not significantly, after 1975 (t = 1.848, df 14, P < 0.1). It would be inappropriate to conclude that numbers of *A. sylvaticus* increased at the expense of *A. flavicollis* as the increase in the population size of the former was minimal and unsteady and commenced some years before the start of the decline of its congener.

The explanation for the change in fortune of the three rodent species in Leaze Wood is uncertain, though it is possible to speculate. Numbers of *A. flavicollis*, but not *A. sylvaticus*, were correlated with those of *C. glareolus* during the 16 years (r = 0.635, df 14, P < 0.01). Again the source of this relationship is obscure, as diets of these species, for example, have little in common (Drozdz, 1966). Spring populations of both species may be determined by overwinter survival. If spring population size determines numbers in early summer, as seemed to be the case in *A. flavicollis* from 1974 to 1976, then there may have been some common or linked determinant of overwinter success in *A. flavicollis* and *C. glareolus*. The decline in numbers of *C. glareolus* in the early 1970s coincided with the passage of Dutch Elm disease through Leaze Wood. Elm was a common species providing a good supply of palatable leaves on which *C. glareolus* no doubt fed during winter months (Watts, 1968). The loss of this potential food

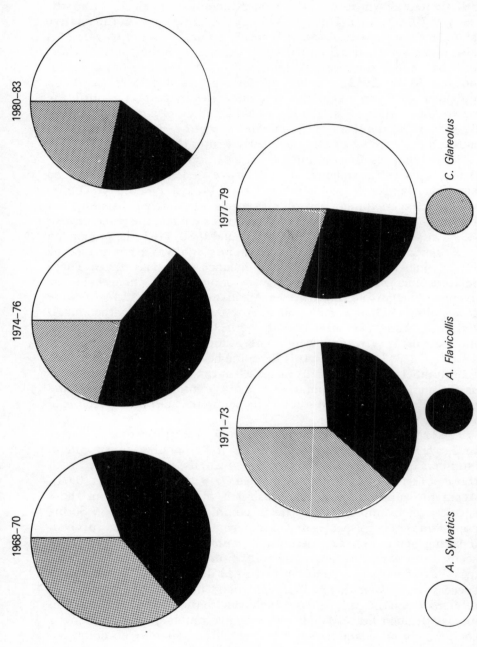

Fig. 5.10 Rodent community structure on grid M, 1968 to 1983.

1980–83

1977–79

1974–76

1971–73

1968–70

A. Sylvatics

A. Flavicollis

C. Glareolus

supply would have been detrimental to the chances of survival over winter such that numbers of *C. glareolus* dropped in the following spring and summer. Throughout much of the year *A. flavicollis* feeds on tree seed (Drozdz, 1966), so that it is unlikely that the demise of the Elm affected this species directly. However, the loss of the Elm from the erstwhile dense canopy over grid M left gaps which exposed trees, mainly Yew *Taxus baccata*, to high winds and heavy snowfalls in winter. Increased exposure probably resulted in decreases in seed crops, through loss of flowers, and increases in mortality in Yews, which have shallow roots on thin soils. Up to seven Yews were lost from grid M in one winter after the reduction of the protective canopy of Elm. Additional losses of Yew were incurred through commercial exploitation of timber. Yew seeds, which were eaten by both *Apodemus* species, have the highest calorific value recorded for any available seed (Smal & Fairley, 1980). Therefore the decline in numbers of *A. flavicollis* may have resulted from insufficient seed to maintain good survival through winter months. The differential impact of declining food supply on *A. sylvaticus* and *A. flavicollis*, despite both feeding on tree seed (Drozdz, 1966; Watts, 1968), may have resulted from the much greater tracts of woodland and other habitats inhabited by the former species (see below).

Changes in the composition of rodent communities occurred elsewhere in Woodchester Park during the 1970s. Trapline studies of numbers in early summer on three north-facing and three south-facing traplines before and after 1975 suggest that the decline in abundance of *A. flavicollis* occurred only on north-facing slopes (Table 5.4). It is probable that these underwent greater changes in the structure of habitats as the southern side of the valley has more deciduous woodland and a greater incidence of Yew, and is possibly more exposed to winter gales.

The 16-year study of rodent populations at Woodchester Park demonstrates that biological communities are vulnerable to catastrophic change. The loss of a single plant species through disease had unpredictable effects on all three rodent species. The overall impact of

Table 5.4 Numbers of *A. sylvaticus* and *A. flavicollis* on three north-facing and three south-facing traplines in June and July of the late 1960s–early 1970s or the late 1970s.

| | North facing | | South facing | |
	A. sylvaticus	*A. flavicollis*	*A. sylvaticus*	*A. flavicollis*
1967–1975	61	48	38	25
1976–1979	49	11	17	8
χ_1^2	10.149; $P < 0.01$		0.183; n.s.	

the events of the 1970s was to bring the composition of the rodent community into line with that of many other places in southern Britain.

Dynamics of Apodemus *species in allopatry and sympatry in Britain and Europe*

Annual changes in numbers of *A. flavicollis* and *A. sylvaticus* on grid M and in areas of similar woodland at Woodchester Park differed in their timing of recruitment and decline from peak, early winter, populations. These differences are also evident in allopatric populations. Watts (1969), for example, described the annual cycles of abundance of *A. sylvaticus* in woodland shared with *C. glareolus*. Cycles were characterised by spring decline and low, stable numbers in summer. Data for annual dynamics of *A. flavicollis* are scant, but Bobek (1973), working on *A. flavicollis* in Polish forest, recorded dynamics similar to those observed in the present investigation in three out of four years. Although methodology varies both in the field and in calculation of effective trap area, densities in allopatric and sympatric populations also appear similar. For example, Watts (1969) quotes the highest density of *A. sylvaticus* over a period of four years as 37.6 per hectare, whereas Ashby (1967), working in the north-east of England, recorded a density of 44.5 per hectare. Gebczynska's (1966) highest density of *A. flavicollis* was 58.0 per hectare. Densities calculated for grid M (Montgomery, 1980*a*) indicate that both *Apodemus* species attained densities comparable with those in allopatry. The highest density for both *A. sylvaticus* and *A. flavicollis* was, by coincidence, 52.8 per hectare. The combined densities of *Apodemus* species exceeded 60 per hectare in seven sampling periods. Comparison of dynamics and densities of *Apodemus* species on grid M, 1974 to 1976, with those of populations in allopatry reveals no evidence that a negative interaction between *A. sylvaticus* and *A. flavicollis* occurred in the main areas of study at Woodchester Park. Numbers of these species fluctuated independently in these areas of woodland, such that simultaneous high densities occurred only in autumn and early winter. This suggests that intrinsic differences in the population biology of *A. sylvaticus* and *A. flavicollis* ameliorate possible competition, which might otherwise lead to exclusion at least at the habitat level (Montgomery, 1977, 1980*a*).

Flowerdew (1974, 1978) and Gurnell (1978*b*) provided substantial evidence in support of Watt's contention (1969) that male aggression regulates numbers of *A. sylvaticus* in early summer. No comparable analysis of the regulation of populations of *A. flavicollis* has been attempted. However, Adamczewska (1961) submitted that

A. flavicollis numbers are governed by the intensity and duration of reproduction and the population size at the start of breeding. At Woodchester Park, numbers of *A. flavicollis* were more closely related to reproduction than numbers of *A. sylvaticus*. Numbers of *A. flavicollis* in June 1972 were higher than the previous year after larger numbers in April and an earlier start to breeding. In 1976, after an erratic start to breeding (Fig. 5.7), June numbers were down on both 1974 and 1975. This aspect of regulation in *A. flavicollis* remains to be investigated, though it is evident that intraspecific aggression did not operate in the same manner as in *A. sylvaticus*: the early winter decline occurred before the onset of breeding; during the late spring and early summer, when aggression may have reached a peak, numbers increased.

Food supply is known to influence population size of both *A. sylvaticus* and *A. flavicollis*. Watts (1969), Hansson (1971), Flowerdew (1972, 1973) and Flowerdew & Gardner (1978) indicated that improved food availability promotes survival of *A. sylvaticus* in winter. This leads to larger numbers in spring populations, which in turn govern numbers in early summer. The role of food supply in the dynamics of *A. flavicollis* is less well understood, but Adamczewska (1961) presented some evidence of a similar relationship between spring numbers and food. If this is so, then the positive association in numbers of *A. sylvaticus* and *A. flavicollis* in censuses in June from 1968 to 1975 was the direct result of overwinter survival dictated by a common food supply. Changes in the structure of Leaze Wood evidently disrupted this relationship.

The population biology of *A. sylvaticus* and *A. flavicollis* has been studied in Essex (Corke, 1974), in Hampshire (Hedges, 1966) and at Alice Holt Forest on the Surrey Hampshire border (Gurnell, 1981). In these studies, *C. glareolus* was also present and numbers of *A. flavicollis* were generally low. Dynamics of *Apodemus* in Gurnell's five-year study are illustrated in Fig. 5.11. Annual cycles of *A. sylvaticus* were rather irregular but this species predominated throughout; *A. flavicollis* went through three rather unspectacular cycles where the period of increase was initiated in late summer or autumn and the period of decline in early winter. Between these outbreaks, *A. flavicollis* was absent so that migration into the study area, a 9-ha oak wood, must have occurred during or just before periods of increasing abundance. Interestingly, these changes in abundance of *A. flavicollis* at Alice Holt Forest are not unlike those on several traplines set at Woodchester Park in woodland other than that of the north-facing slopes of the valley. Dynamics of *A. flavicollis* seem heavily dependent on habitat. The annual dynamics reported here and elsewhere (Montgomery, 1980a) are not typical of *A. flavicollis* in the valley as a

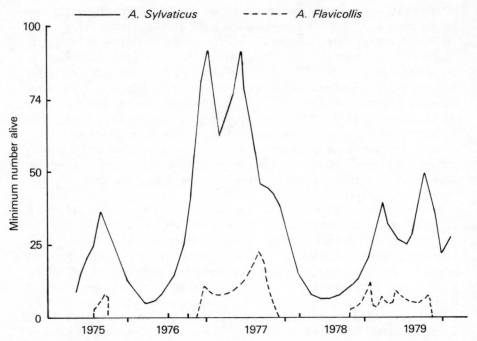

Fig. 5.11 Numbers of *A. sylvaticus* and *A. flavicollis* known to be alive on a 90 m × 80 m grid in oak woodland of Alice Holt Forest. (From Gurnell, 1981.)

whole, let alone British woodland in general. However, the relationship between *Apodemus* species on grids M, A, B and C exemplified the degree to which these species may coexist without any apparent interspecific effects on numbers of either species. Also it is clear that *A. flavicollis* and *A. sylvaticus* need not separate into different habitats during the breeding season, as proposed by Corke (1970, 1974); both reproduced while continuing to exploit the woodland of Woodchester Park.

Dynamics of sympatric populations of *Apodemus* species have attracted attention in continental Europe. Bergstedt (1965) in southern Sweden and Mermod (1969) in Switzerland examined the dynamics of *Apodemus* in association with *C. glareolus*. Von Judes (1979), working in north Germany near Kiel, described the changes in relative abundance of the two *Apodemus* species. The circumstances of these studies differ considerably from those in Woodchester Park. The Swedish study was set in a wooded valley surrounded by arable farmland, and the Swiss study was set in 80 ha of deciduous woodland at an altitude of 850 m and flanked by pastureland. Von Judes estimated relative abundance of *Apodemus* in woodland and field edges using trapline indices. Winters in all these studies were more severe than those experienced at Woodchester Park between 1974 and 1976; the Swiss area was subjected to prolonged periods of snow. In Bergstedt's study, the most numerous rodent was *C. glareolus*, and *Apodemus* populations were generally small. However, in two of five years, dynamics of *A. flavicollis* were similar to those described here and in allopatry (Bobek, 1973). The population size of *A. sylvaticus* was, except for a few months, less than that of its congener and had no regular cycles of abundance. In Mermod's study *A. flavicollis* was predominant. In three out of four years, numbers of *A. sylvaticus* were similar to and fluctuated closely with those of *A. flavicollis*. Neither species exhibited annual cycles which might be regarded as typical (Watts, 1969; Bobek, 1973), although in autumn, peaks followed by a decline occurred in both species during three years. Similarly, in north Germany, Von Judes found that numbers of both *Apodemus* species declined in winter. However, as in Gloucestershire, *A. flavicollis* commenced reproduction earlier in spring than *A. sylvaticus*.

In these continental and British studies, as at Woodchester Park, there is no indication of interference between *A. sylvaticus* and *A. flavicollis*. Numbers of one species are not necessarily high when numbers of the other are low. Dynamics of both species are very variable such that the ratio in which they coexist is also very variable both in space and time. The abundance of *A. sylvaticus* relative to *A. flavicollis* and the manner in which this relationship changes is probably dictated by environmental conditions in the habitat in which the populations coexist. This contention is supported by the changes in the abundance of rodent species on grid M between 1968 and 1983. Spatial variation in relative abundance of *A. sylvaticus* and *A. flavicollis* at Woodchester Park emphasises the often neglected relationship between dynamics over time and the spatial distribution of a population.

Habitat and microhabitat discrimination in *Apodemus* species at Woodchester Park

Spatial separation of potential competitors may occur at three levels: such species may have clearly defined, exclusive ranges; they may live in different habitats; or spatial separation may occur within a single habitat. Exclusive habitats are perhaps the most common form of spatial separation. For example, Lack (1944) found that of 39 pairs of closely related British passerines, geographical isolation is evident in 3 pairs, habitat separation in at least 18, differences in feeding habits in 4, size difference in 5, separate winter ranges in 2 and apparent ecological overlap in 5 to 7 pairs. *Apodemus sylvaticus* and *A. flavicollis* coexist within a single habitat at Woodchester Park but this woodland is very heterogeneous, as is the spatial distribution of both rodent species (Yalden, 1971). Here this spatial variation in abundance is considered in relation to dynamics over time through an investigation of the distribution of catches in different types of habitats, principally several kinds of woodland, and the spatial relationships within a limited area of woodland.

Habitat variation in relative numbers of four rodent species in early summer

Woodland rodents are mobile animals which may pass through a variety of habitats during their lifetime. Limited trapping may reveal their position at a given time but the extent to which capture data represent habitat use is unknown. Samples collected using small numbers of traps over a few nights may be biased towards more trappable individuals, or be susceptible to weather conditions, leading to underestimates of true abundance (see above). However, more intensive, repeated surveys indicate that a large proportion of rodent populations remain for some time in one place (Fig. 5.8), though this may be dependent on local food supply or other environmental conditions. Samples taken over a short period should, therefore, contain a high proportion of individuals resident in that habitat in the immediate future. It would be unwise to use trapline data to estimate absolute abundance, but the similar catch curves and susceptibility to capture of *A. sylvaticus* and *A. flavicollis* suggest that such data may be used confidently in determining their relative abundance. Analyses of trappability in *C. glareolus* at Woodchester Park (Montgomery, 1977) and elsewhere (Gurnell, 1982) suggest that it is more reluctant to enter traps. Therefore trapline data underestimate the proportion of *C. glareolus* in rodent communities. Stoddart (1982) demonstrated that differential trappability in *M. agrestis* may also result in under-estimates of population size of this species.

During the early summer field courses run by Manchester University, the small mammal communities of a large number of areas and habitats within Woodchester Park valley were surveyed using traplines. Early summer is a particularly important period in the dynamics of both *Apodemus* species. Numbers of *A. sylvaticus* are generally stable and those of *A. flavicollis* are increasing, resulting in the numerical superiority of the latter in the intensively sampled populations of grids M, A, B and C. Relative abundance of *Apodemus* species in June and July is, therefore, a good indication of numerical relationships throughout their annual cycles.

From the early 1970s onwards, the proportion and absolute density of *C. glareolus* and *A. flavicollis* on grid M and other north-facing areas of woodland declined (Table 5.4; Fig. 5.10). Traplines were set in several years between 1968 and 1983, often sampling the same areas of woodland. Data for 1975 or earlier on north-facing traplines and 1977 or earlier on south-facing traplines were collated to increase sample size and smooth out between-year variation in relative abundance, without the confounding influence of long-term changes in the rodent communities. Data for grids M, P, G1 and G2 have been included for comparison. G1 was set in 1967 and G2 in 1969 (Fig. 5.1). Sample size was rather variable, though most of 27 traplines and grids caught well over 25 rodents. Altogether, 1416 rodents of four species were captured; the distribution of these is illustrated in Fig. 5.12. Traplines and grids were grouped into four habitat categories;

(a) Mature woodland with a dense canopy of *Taxus* and *Fagus* over bare ground.
(b) Mixed secondary deciduous woodland with few *Taxus*. Most common trees were *Fagus*, *Fraxinus*, *Ulmus*, *Corylus*, *Crataegus* and *Sambucus*, often forming a dense scrub. Good cover at low level.
(c) Conifer plantations in the age range 15 to 25 years; chiefly *Larix* and *Picea*. Usually thick ground cover of *Rubus*.
(d) Rough grassland with patches of *Rubus*, *Urtica* and other herbaceous plants.

The distributions of *A. sylvaticus*, *A. flavicollis*, *C. glareolus* and *M. agrestis* were extremely heterogeneous with respect to the four habitat types ($\chi^2 = 970$, df 9, $P < 0.001$).

As expected (Evans, 1978), the field vole *M. agrestis* was caught only in grassland habitats, G1 and G2, and the Aspen plantation, P, where it was the predominant species (Table 5.5; Fig. 5.12). All three other rodent species also occurred in grassland. The incidence of

Table 5.5 Incidence of four species of rodent as a percentage of total individuals caught in four habitats. (a) Mature deciduous woodland in which Beech and Yew form a dense canopy. (b) Secondary mixed deciduous woodland with dense low cover. (c) Conifer plantations. (d) Grassland and Aspen plantation. For further details see text.

Habitat	A. sylvaticus	A. flavicollis	C. glareolus	M. agrestis	n
a	27.9	43.1	28.8	< 1	684
b	38.1	21.7	40.2	0	391
c	36.5	7.1	56.5	0	170
d	24.8	5.6	6.8	62.7	161

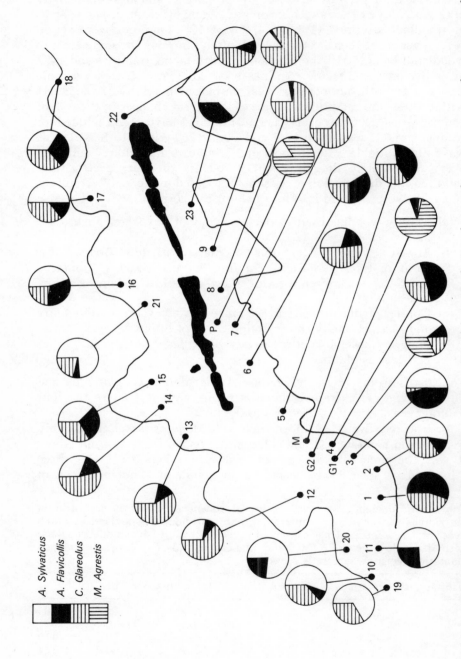

Fig. 5.12 The distribution of 1416 rodents at 27 sites in Woodchester Park. Data from early summer in several years; on north-facing slopes 1975 or earlier, on south-facing slopes 1977 or earlier.

A. Sylvaticus
A. Flavicollis
C. Glareolus
M. Agrestis

A. sylvaticus, A. flavicollis and *C. glareolus* in grassland adjacent to woodland, G1 and G2, was higher than in the more isolated grassland of grid P. There was great variation in the proportion of *C. glareolus* in rodent communities; a χ^2 test of association between the three woodland rodent species and the four habitat types indicated that *C. glareolus* was significantly less frequent than expected in mature woods (a) and grassland and more common than expected in plantations of conifers. In secondary woodland (b), *C. glareolus* constituted 40.2% of total rodents and was the most common species (Table 5.5). This distribution conforms with the known prevalence of *C. glareolus* in habitats with low-level cover (Southern & Lowe, 1968). Their abundance in plantations was probably due to dense cover of *Rubus* and the standard forestry practice of removing and discarding on the ground the lower, dead branches of conifers.

The relative abundance of *A. sylvaticus* and *A. flavicollis* varied enormously among the four habitats (Table 5.5). In a test of association, the latter was significantly more common in mature, dense woodland and significantly less frequent than expected in secondary woodland, coniferous plantations and grassland. Conversely, *A. sylvaticus* was less frequent than expected in mature woodland and more abundant than expected in secondary woodland, plantations and grassland. Although *A. flavicollis* occurred in grassland adjacent to woodland, it was absent from the more remote grid P; *A. sylvaticus*, on the other hand, penetrated grassland some distance from the nearest woodland habitat (Tables 5.5 and 5.6). This suggests a bias in habitat use; *A. sylvaticus* did not discriminate between habitats whereas *A. flavicollis* was found most frequently in mature habitats with a large amount of *Taxus*. However, the ratio of *A. flavicollis* to *A. sylvaticus* was significantly greater on north-facing slopes than on south-facing slopes ($\chi^2 = 37$, $P < 0.001$; Fig. 5.12). Possibly the prevalence of mature woodland on the north-facing side of the valley was merely coincidental with the north–south bias in captures of *A. flavicollis*.

Table 5.6 *Apodemus flavicollis* as a percentage of all *Apodemus* captures in six distinct habitats on the north-facing slopes of Woodchester Park valley, 1967–1975.

Habitat	%	n
Main grid; mature *Fagus, Taxus*	65.1	350
Mature *Fagus, Taxus*	52.9	119
Fagus, Fraxinus, Ulmus, Corylus	37.3	28
Conifer plantation	12.8	39
Meadow, rough pasture near grid M	23.1	39
Populus plantation with undergrowth of grasses	0	10

Therefore, the analysis was repeated using only data from north-facing locations. Again, numbers of *A. flavicollis* were significantly greater and those of *A. sylvaticus* significantly lower in mature woodland dominated by *Taxus* over rather bare ground. As before, *A. flavicollis* was significantly under-represented in conifers and grassland whereas *A. sylvaticus* was more common than expected in these habitats. Captures on grid M constituted a major part of the total captures in mature woodland (a). There was a significantly lower incidence of *A. flavicollis* among total *Apodemus* on traplines set in mature woodland than on grid M ($\chi^2 = 5.11$, $P < 0.05$; Table 5.6). Although the pattern of captures of *Apodemus* was the same as that for the north-facing slope as a whole (Table 5.6), there was no significant diference in the incidence of *A. flavicollis* in habitat types 1 and 2 on these traplines. In the trapline analyses, the only secondary woodland sampled on the north-facing side of the valley was in the vicinity of grid L (trapline 5 on Fig. 5.12), which is close to more mature open woodland.

In the valley as a whole, *A. flavicollis* was associated with mature woodland, dominated by *Taxus* and *Fagus*, high on the south side of the valley. This woodland, situated on thin calcareous soils, takes a characteristic form; the *Taxus* stands as a dense monoculture under which there is little light and no plant growth. In places this is penetrated by *Ulmus*, *Fagus* and *Quercus*, and is surrounded by other seed-bearing species such as *Fraxinus* and *Corylus* (traplines 1, 3, 4, 8 and 27 on the north-facing slopes, and trapline 23 on the south-facing slopes of the valley). Frequently these woods are situated just above discontinuities in the geological strata where badger setts are often located. Associated with the latter are *Sambucus* and *Rubus*, which in turn add to the abundance and diversity of seeds available to rodents. The largest such area is grid M, with several dense stands of *Taxus* in Leaze Wood. This also had the greatest proportion of captures of *A. flavicollis* (Table 5.6). From 1975 onwards, numbers of *A. flavicollis* declined (Fig. 5.10). Although the causes of this decline are uncertain, there was also an increase in the exposure and mortality of *Taxus* during this period, supporting the contention that *A. flavicollis* was associated with habitat 'a' during the early 1970s.

Spatial distribution and population dynamics of *A. flavicollis* were closely allied in Woodchester Park. Localised areas of high seed production seem critical to overwinter survival. In these areas, which act as refuges, *A. flavicollis* dynamics follow the pattern evident on grid M from 1974 to 1976 (Fig. 5.6), whereas elsewhere dynamics resemble those at Alice Holt Forest (Fig. 5.11) or outlined by Montgomery (1979b). In early summer, as numbers of *A. flavicollis* increase, there is dispersal into woodland and other habitats adjacent to these refuges. This results in later, less spectacular, increases in numbers, which decline again to a very low level by midwinter.

Population dynamics of *A. sylvaticus* and *A. flavicollis* did not corroborate the hypothesis that these closely related species compete. Similarly, there was no apparent relationship between the percentages of *A. sylvaticus* and *A. flavicollis* in total rodent captures at the 27 sites illustrated in Fig. 5.12. Yalden (1971) considered the abundance of *A. flavicollis* to be positively related to the proportion of *Apodemus* in the total catch of rodents. This trend was still apparent with further data but not significant ($r = 0.396$, df 19, $P < 0.1$) where trapline sample size was at least 20. It would appear that *A. flavicollis* inhabits areas of woodland favourable to *Apodemus* in general. However, the absence of any relationship in the distributions of the congeners seems contradictory; if conditions suited both species, then one would anticipate a positive association between species. The lack of a positive correlation may have resulted from two confounding processes: increased suitability leading to more mice of both species and the acquisition of limited resources, food and space, by one species to the disadvantages of the second. Competition for space is examined below.

Spatial distribution of Apodemus *species within woodland*

In the estimation of populations by MRR, it is necessary to ensure that all individuals are equally available for capture, irrespective of their position in the habitat (Southwood, 1978). Catching small mammals on grids of trap-points ensures that all areas of the habitat are sampled in proportion to their prevalence. At any trap-point, traps are set to ensure the maximum number of captures rather than placed at random; in most stratified surveys of animals other than vertebrates, traps are set randomly. In mammal ecology the emphasis is on catching as many individuals in the population as possible close to a known reference point. Capture inhibits the activity of rodents and may affect whether they return to a particular place. Montgomery (1979a) presented some evidence that all captives on grid M tended to return to the trap in which they were captured. The incidence of 'repeat' captures was significantly greater in *A. flavicollis* than in *A. sylvaticus*. Distribution of captures on grids must therefore be used cautiously in extrapolating to the use of space by any particular species or intraspecific class of individuals. Collating data over several sampling periods or, indeed, the whole trapping programme, reduces the impact of the effects of confinement and inter- or intraspecific biases in catches, at the expense of eliminating short-term, potentially interesting, changes in distribution.

There are three central questions concerning the spatial distribution of populations coexisting within a limited space. First, it may be important to establish whether individuals in a population are, as in the majority of species, distributed at random. Montgomery (1980b) demonstrated that captures of *A. sylvaticus* and *A. flavicollis* were clumped during all sampling periods on grid M. Secondly, there may be a positive or negative association in the spatial disposition of the two species. Thirdly, the distribution of captures of a species may be associated with some biological or physical feature of the habitat. Here, the second and third topics are considered in detail.

Southwood (1978) considered that association in spatial distribution between two species may be measured using presence–absence data or data for their abundance in a number of samples. Both methods were applied to data from each sampling period on grid M. Correlation coefficients were calculated between the number of captures of *A. sylvaticus* and *A. flavicollis* at points where either *Apodemus* species was captured. Presence–absence data were based on the incidence of no captures, capture of *A. sylvaticus*, capture of *A. flavicollis* and

Table 5.7 The relationship between captures of *A. sylvaticus* and *A. flavicollis* on grid M, 1974 to 1976. Correlation coefficients were calculated between the number of captures of each species at grid points where any *Apodemus* were captured. Data were transformed as square root $(x + 0.5)$. Hurlbert's coefficient of interspecific association (1969) was calculated using all trap points over each of five nights. Departure from 0, i.e. no association, was tested using the χ^2 test or the Fisher Exact test.

		No. of points	Correlation coefficient	$P <$	Hurlbert's coefficient	$P <$
1974	J	48	− 0.54	0.001	− 0.61	n.s.
	F	75	− 0.34	0.005	− 0.38	n.s.
	M	58	− 0.51	0.001	− 1.00	n.s.
	M	34	− 0.62	0.001	− 0.57	n.s.
	J	59	− 0.54	0.001	− 0.34	n.s.
	A	45	− 0.62	0.001	− 0.43	n.s.
	O	80	− 0.30	0.05	− 0.61	0.001
	D	44	− 0.49	0.001	− 1.00	0.05
1975	F	71	− 0.45	0.001	− 0.44	0.05
	A	63	− 0.44	0.001	− 0.24	n.s.
	J	40	− 0.57	0.001	− 0.53	n.s.
	A	55	− 0.43	0.005	− 0.34	n.s.
	O	60	− 0.36	0.001	− 0.65	n.s.
	D	80	− 0.57	0.001	− 0.70	0.001
1976	F	78	− 0.42	0.001	− 0.62	0.001
	A	69	− 0.54	0.001	− 0.84	0.001
	J	45	− 0.55	0.001	− 0.54	n.s.

capture of both *Apodemus* species at a trap-point with two traps, during one night. Data were collated over a whole sampling period, allowing evaluation of presence–absence data in 480 trap nights (Montgomery, 1980*b*). These data were used to compute Hurlbert's Coefficient of Interspecific Association (CIA) (Hurlbert, 1969), which, like the product moment correlation coefficient (COR), ranges from − 1, complete disassociation, to + 1, complete spatial accord. Both indices were negative throughout the 17 sampling periods, suggesting that, in the woodland of grid M, the distributions of *A. sylvaticus* and *A. flavicollis* were always separate to some extent (Table 5.7). Both CIA and COR were rather variable, suggesting that the spatial relationships of *A. sylvaticus* and *A. flavicollis* changed with respect to some unknown variable.

Glass & Slade (1980), following Terman (1974), proposed that spatial organisation in a community of *Sigmodon hispidis* and *Microtus ochrogaster* depended on interspecific contact, which was determined by the characteristics of the population of the former. The relationship between spatial association of *A. sylvaticus* and *A. flavicollis*, as measured by CIA and COR, and the population parameters of either species was investigated using linear stepwise multiple regression. Regression of the dependent variable, COR or CIA, on a number of independent variables, which were population parameters, was performed to assess the relative merit of seven models or groups of independent variables which potentially might explain the interspecific spatial relationships.

Model 1: Population density. Density of single-species populations.
Model 2: Population structure. Proportion of males, females and juveniles in each population.
Model 3: Reproductive status. Proportion of males, females and all adults in reproductive condition in each population.
Model 4: Dispersion characteristics. Mean, variance and variance : mean ratio of captures of each species.
Model 5: All single-species population characteristics. Variables in models 1 to 4.
Model 6: Interaction between populations. Products of population characteristics of *A. sylvaticus* and *A. flavicollis*, namely density, percentage of males, percentage of juveniles, percentage of reproductive males, percentage of reproductive adults and variance : mean ratio.
Model 7: All possible parameters. All parameters in 5 and 6.

Data for 60 sampling periods on grids M, A, B and C in 1974, 1975 and 1976 were included in the analysis. Data for independent variables were transformed to arcsin or square root $(x + 0.5)$.

Succinct summaries of stepwise multiple regression cannot be made. The Coefficient of Determination is the proportion of the total variation in the dependent variable explained by the regression. It therefore embodies the full analysis, but Wesolowsky (1976) points out that the greater the number of independent variables, the greater the chance of getting a large R^2 where no relationships really exist. Consequently, the number of variables in models was restricted to 1 per 10 samples. Models 5 and 7 were included for completeness and warrant cautious interpretation. Results are presented in Table 5.8.

The influence of population densities (model 1) was different on COR and CIA. A higher proportion of variation in COR was explained in model 1. The population density of *A. sylvaticus* was positively correlated with COR; as population size of *A. sylvaticus* increased, so spatial separation of the *Apodemus* species decreased. However, CIA was less affected by population densities. CIA was negatively related to numbers of *A. sylvaticus*; as the latter increased, so spatial separation also increased. Model 2 variables also explained a certain amount of variation in interspecific spatial relationships. As the proportion of males among *A. flavicollis* increased, CIA decreased and spatial separation became more apparent. No single parameter of population structure was related to COR. Model 3 was also more revealing with respect to CIA; an increase in the percentage of reproductive males

Table 5.8 Proportion of variation explained by linear multiple regression (coefficient of determination, $R^2 \times 100$) in models relating population parameters to spatial association, between *A. sylvaticus* and *A. flavicollis*, as measured by Hurlbert's coefficient of interspecific association and the correlation coefficient. Data were collated for grid M, 1974–1976; grid A, 1975–1976, and grids B and C in 1975, giving 60 samples in all.

Model	Number of independent variables	Variation explained by regression $R^2 \times 100$	
		Hurlbert's (CIA)	Correlation coefficient (COR)
1 Population density	2	7.9	13.7
2 Population structure	6	11.9	8.8
3 Reproductive status	6	10.9	10.5
4 Species dispersion characteristics	6	8.8	23.3
5 All population characteristics	20	37.7	45.1
6 Interaction between species characteristics	6	17.1	13.3
7 All possible parameters	26	53.8	51.7

among *A. flavicollis* resulted in an increase in CIA. Mean captures of *A. sylvaticus* were related negatively to CIA in model 4. As in model 1, an increase in population size, assessed through mean number of captures per point, resulted in an increase in the division of space between *A. sylvaticus* and *A. flavicollis*. COR was more closely related to dispersion characteristics. Some 23.3% of variation in COR could be accounted for by the variables of model 4; mean and variance of captures of *A. sylvaticus* were positively related to COR, suggesting decreased spatial separation as abundance of this species increased, much as in model 1. Means, variances and the calculation of the correlation coefficient are in essence related, so that this result was not unexpected.

The interaction model, 6, accounted for the greatest amount of variation in CIA. The interaction between the percentage of reproductive males in *A. sylvaticus* and *A. flavicollis* was positively related to CIA; as this independent variable increased, so spatial separation became less. Similarly, the product of the percentage of juveniles in *A. sylvaticus* and *A. flavicollis* had a positive effect on CIA. In the relationship between COR and the variables of model 6, the interspecific product of percentage juveniles was negatively related to the measurement of spatial overlap.

As applied here, CIA and COR measure interspecific association over different areas and different periods of time. The former used data where each score was taken overnight, whereas the latter used samples taken over the whole five nights. Spatial separation is a function of time allocated for sampling. If time is short enough, then only animals simultaneously active at any one place would be recorded as positively associated. Over a time scale of several days, animals active in the same place on different nights would appear to be positively related. COR was calculated for the portion of the grid used by either species, usually the major part of the grid (Table 5.8), but CIA included points where neither *Apodemus* species was captured. Therefore the factors governing CIA and COR need not have a common effect. This was examplified by the relationship between numbers of *A. sylvaticus* and spatial separation. As numbers of this species increased, there was an increase in spatial overlap measured by COR, but a decrease in spatial separation as measured by the presence or absence of mice over a single night. This may be interpreted as *A. sylvaticus* using more space, also used by its congener, as its population size rises, but only in the absence of *A. flavicollis*. The increase in spatial overlap between species as the incidence of reproductively active males increased probably resulted from their wider excursions during the breeding seasons (Randolph, 1977). This effect was more evident in *A. flavicollis*.

Multiple regression analyses suggest that population criteria affect the spatial relationships of *A. sylvaticus* and *A. flavicollis* in the woodland of grids M, A, B and C. However, this variation was within the overall constraint that the species were always negatively related in use of space within the habitat. The relationship between the extent of spatial separation and population criteria suggests that competition for space occurred, and resulted in mutual spatial exclusion. This is further indicated by the relative strength of the interspecific interaction model (6) in explaining variation in spatial separation. However, at most, 50% of variation in spatial association was determined by population characteristics (Table 5.8). Of the remaining variation in spatial relationships between *A. sylvaticus* and *A. flavicollis* in their shared habitat, the changing distribution of resources is likely to be the most important predictive variable.

Vegetation surveys, after Elton & Miller (1954), were carried out on grids M, A, B and C in spring 1976. The associations of *A. sylvaticus* and *A. flavicollis* with vegetation structure were similar, thought not quite indentical, on all grids (Montgomery, 1977, 1981). The distribution of captures of *A. sylvaticus* and *A. flavicollis*, as a proportion of total captures on grid M, from 1974 to 1976, are illustrated in Fig. 5.13. Both species were caught at more or less every point of the grid, but clearly the distributions of captures were different in the two *Apodemus* species. Analysis of captures with respect to density of cover in three levels of the vegetation of the main grid indicates that *A. sylvaticus* avoided areas of dense high canopy and was more common in areas with good ground cover (Table 5.9). The latter were

Table 5.9 Mean number of individual *A. sylvaticus* and *A. flavicollis* caught at points of grid M with specified cover types. Data have been collated for 1974 to 1976. Values of d test the significance of the difference in mean numbers of mice at points with less than and more than 60% cover. Data were transformed as square root $(x + 0.5)$. (From Montgomery, 1980b.)

	Cover			
	60% or less	More than 60%	d	$P <$
A. sylvaticus				
high canopy	14.75	7.53	5.43	0.001
low canopy	12.19	14.93	1.08	n.s.
ground cover	11.30	20.71	3.78	0.001
A. flavicollis				
high canopy	9.47	5.54	3.29	0.001
low canopy	7.01	12.25	3.39	0.001
ground cover	8.38	8.00	0.25	n.s.

A. Sylvaticus

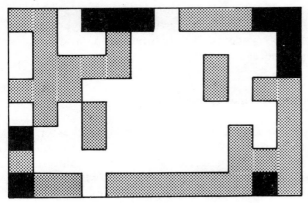

A. Flavicollis

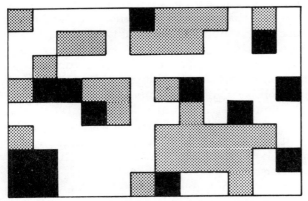

Fig. 5.13 Proportion of total captures of *A. sylvaticus* (*n* = 1747) and *A. flavicollis* (*n* = 1091) at each trap point of grid M, 1974 to 1976.

mostly peripheral and the former mostly central areas of grid M (Fig. 5.13). Captures of *A. flavicollis* were concentrated in areas outside dense high canopy but with good cover at low canopy level. Unlike *A. sylvaticus*, the larger species did not discriminate between areas with dense and not so dense ground cover (Table 5.9). The areas most favoured by *A. flavicollis* were those around the central, dense stands of *Taxus*, often with a tangle of laurel *Prunus laurocerasus* and fallen *Taxus*, which often recommences growth from its main trunk if its roots are still embedded in soil. These low branches are used as silent runways but also form a barrier to avian predators (Montgomery, 1980c).

These associations with different kinds of cover on grid M and elsewhere confirm the spatial division of habitats shared by *A. sylvaticus* and *A. flavicollis*. However, it is uncertain whether the differential exploitation of space within habitats is a product of a competitive or specific process.

Do 'A. sylvaticus' and 'A. flavicollis' compete?

The ecologies of *A. sylvaticus* and *A. flavicollis* at Woodchester Park differ with respect to annual cycles of population size, habitat selection and use of space within shared habitats. These differences may be explained by selection favouring different adaptations to environmental conditions in different species. Alternatively, inter-specific competition, either in the past or at present, may be invoked as an explanatory process (see, for example, Begon & Mortimer, 1981). Interspecific competition necessitates a reduction in fitness of both species but it is possible that amensalism, where one species is inhibited by the presence of a second which remains unaffected, is a more correct description of the relationship of *A. sylvaticus* and *A. flavicollis*. Interspecific competition and amensalism are difficult to demonstrate in natural communities (Hutchinson, 1957; Southern, 1968). Although competition is regarded by many as a central process, occurring widely in all biological communities (Miller, 1967), the paucity of evidence in the field has led some (Andrewartha & Birch, 1954) to question its importance. Since the 1960s, experimental studies, those of Connell (1961) and Grant (1972) being well known, have countered these criticisms.

Reynoldson & Bellamy (1970) prepared a set of conditions which should be verified in attempting to establish competition between species in natural communities and in rejecting other hypotheses which seek differences in the ecology of two or more species. They suggested five criteria:

(1) The comparative distribution and abundance of two potential competitors should be amenable to an explanation based on competition.

(2) Potential competitors should exploit a common resource which actually or potentially is limited, thus forming a basis for competition.

(3) Conspecifics should have the facility for intraspecific competition. This facility may be employed in interspecific relationships.

(4) Both the resource which is being competed for and the popula-

tions should be manipulated separately in the field with predictable results that are compatible with the hypothesis that competition is occurring.

(5) Events following the addition or removal of a competitor should be consistent with the competition hypothesis.

Not all of these must be satisfied in order to be certain that species compete. Reynoldson & Bellamy (1970) emphasise the experimental approach and regard evidence from removal studies as being of prime importance. Here, it is necessary to review the evidence for competition between *A. sylvaticus* and *A. flavicollis*. All but the fourth of the above criteria will be considered.

There was no evidence of competition in the annual dynamics of *A. sylvaticus* and *A. flavicollis* on gird M between 1974 to 1976. However, as numbers of *A. flavicollis* fell from 1975 onwards and those of *A. sylvaticus* increased, though not significantly, the interpretation of long-term changes in abundance is not unequivocally against a competitive relationship between the *Apodemus* species. The change in the abundance of *C. glareolus* from 1972 onwards was a confounding factor which may prove surmountable as more data are added. Relative abundance in different habitats in Woodchester Park also contained little direct evidence of competition. Only one, again rather tenuous, result suggested otherwise. The positive relationship between the incidence of *A. flavicollis* and the proportion of all *Apodemus* in the rodent community (Yalden, 1971) in the absence of any correlation between the proportions of each species, may indicate an interaction where *A. sylvaticus* is prevented from realising its potential population size in the habitats most suitable for *Apodemus*. Spatial separation within habitats was associated with structural features of the plant community rather than being solely a characteristic of the interspecific relationship. Although this conforms to the assumption of interspecific competition, the data may be interpreted in other ways. However, the consistent negative relationship in their distributions was, to some degree, dependent on population characteristics; both parameters of single-species populations and those estimated as the product of population parameters of *A. sylvaticus* and *A. flavicollis* had an influence on the extent of spatial overlap. An increase in population size of *A. sylvaticus* either increased (COR) or decreased (CIA) spatial overlap. The likely interpretation of this result, as *A. sylvaticus* at high densities entering areas of the grid frequented by *A. flavicollis* only when the latter was absent, suggests that *A. sylvaticus* was inhibited in use of space by its congener. There was no evidence for the converse relationship, tilting the balance of evidence towards amensalism rather than interspecific competition.

Table 5.10   Proportion of items found in the stomachs of *A. sylvaticus* and *A. flavicollis* in a spruce forest in southern Moravia, Czechoslovakia. Overlap coefficient, *C*, was calculated after Zaret & Rand, 1971. (From Holisova & Obrtel, 1980.)

	Spring		Summer		Autumn	
	A. sylvaticus	*A. flavicollis*	*A. sylvaticus*	*A. flavicollis*	*A. sylvaticus*	*A. flavicollis*
Fungi	0.4	—	2.4	2.4	2.8	1.5
Mosses	0.3	—	0.7	—	1.1	1.6
Green plants	3.7	3.8	3.4	4.5	5.1	3.4
Bark	—	1.5	—	1.0	0.3	1.2
Roots	—	1.4	—	0.4	—	2.1
Flowers	—	0.9	0.5	0.8	0.4	—
Seeds	27.1	19.2	34.0	29.8	34.1	36.1
Animals	69.6	74.8	60.2	60.6	59.2	56.5
C	0.68		0.77		0.80	

Grant (1972), considering competition between rodent species, suggested that the most likely limiting factors are space and food. These may be closely allied or, indeed, indistinguishable. There can be little doubt that there is considerable overlap in the diets of *A. sylvaticus* and *A. flavicollis* (Miller, 1954; Watts, 1968; Drozdz, 1966; Obrtel, 1974; Obrtel & Holisova, 1974). Holisova & Obrtel (1980) calculated dietary overlap as 80% in a mature spruce forest in Czechoslovakia. Diets of both species are heavily dependent on seeds and small invertebrates, mostly insect larvae (Table 5.10). There are no data on the diet of *Apodemus* species at Woodchester Park but it is probable that their diet consists primarily of seeds of trees with large amounts of animal materials when seed supply is exhausted.

Most definitions of competition require that resources, chiefly food, are actually or potentially limited in their availability (Miller, 1967). The percentage consumption of available food supply is generally low. Hayward & Phillipson (1979), in reviewing the energetics of small mammals in ecosystems, concluded that they consume only 6% or less of the available primary production in any one year. Smal & Fairley (1981), working in a Yew wood in Killarney, calculated average consumption as 13%, though at times it was much greater. These figures suggest a superabundant food supply, but they may be misleading. Supply of seed is irregular, and other animals, mainly granivorous birds, may consume a significant proportion of tree seed production such that food resources for mice are limited. Hoarding of seeds by rodents may lead to contest for seeds even when there is a heavy crop. Watts (1969), reviewing some 18 years of data, concluded that in the deciduous woodland of Wytham Woods, Berkshire, numbers of *A. sylvaticus* were probably limited by food supply one year in two. On balance, the evidence suggests that dietary overlap between *A. sylvaticus* and *A. flavicollis* is high and food may often be limited, thus increasing the likelihood of competition. Competition for space is not at issue since both species share some kinds of woodland. The division of space within that shared habitat may result from competition for space or from exclusion through competition for food.

Birch (1957) distinguished between competition through exploitation of limited resources and direct interference of one animal with another. Interference competition among conspecifics may be viewed as inherent in dominance–subordinancy relationships where some individuals have priority of access to resources. Dominance-subordinancy relationships are apparent, often through the deference of subordinates rather than overt aggression, in laboratory analyses of behaviour of *A. sylvaticus* (Gurnell, 1977). Watts (1969), Flowerdew (1974) and Gurnell (1978*b*) indicate that the consequence of the dominance of adult males over juveniles is the low viability of the latter in early summer. Relationships among adults are possibly important in gaining sufficient of a limited food supply. Stable groups of *A. sylvaticus* in the wild and in laboratory arenas are noted for their low levels of antagonistic behaviour; dominance–subordinancy relationships may be usually expressed through the timing of activity of subordinates to avoid dominants (Bovet, 1972; Garson, 1975). The behaviour of *A. sylvaticus* includes several aspects indicative of intraspecific competition through interference between animals. Avoidance of a conspecific may be easily applicable to interspecific relationships where one species avoids contact with another.

Under laboratory conditions, *A. sylvaticus* and *A. flavicollis* have a consistent relationship. Hoffmeyer (1973) demonstrated that *A. sylvaticus* avoids *A. flavicollis* in small enclosures. Later, Montgomery (1978*b*) found that when *A. sylvaticus* is confronted with *A. flavicollis* in a small arena, it exhibited submissive behaviour in 63 of 70 dyadic encounters. Overt aggression by *A. flavicollis* was rare under these experimental conditions and it is uncertain whether auditory or olfactory cues were important in interspecific encounters. In keeping with the results presented here concerning habitat division and its relationship to specific and interspecific population characteristics, *A. flavicollis* was superior in laboratory analyses. It is unknown as to whether this superiority in interspecific encounters occurs in the wild, but results are consistent and suggest that *A. flavicollis* is not harmed in any way and expends little energy through interspecific contact. It seems reasonable to conclude that *A. sylvaticus* and *A. flavicollis* have the facility for interspecific competition through direct interference.

A removal experiment was conducted in 1975 and 1976, reducing numbers of *A. flavicollis* on grid C and *A. sylvaticus* on grid B from

January 1976 onwards. Populations on grid A were undisturbed and results for 1976 also acted as a control. The results of this experiment afford further, limited, support for the contention that competition is inherent in the relationship between *A. sylvaticus* and *A. flavicollis* (Montgomery, 1981). In the absence of *A. sylvaticus* on B, *A. flavicollis* entered breeding condition earlier in 1976 than on the control grid, A. Early reproduction resulted in an immediate increase in numbers through natality rather than immigration, such that, by early summer 1976, numbers of *A. flavicollis* on grid B reached a much higher level than at any previous time. A very high proportion of this population was juvenile (Table 5.11). Although *A. sylvaticus* also entered breeding condition earlier on the experimental grid, C, numbers did not rise. This disparity in the effect of the removal of the congener on *A. sylvaticus* and *A. flavicollis* conforms with the differences in their population dynamics, where the latter commences recruitment shortly after the start of breeding and the former has low, stable densities in early summer (Adamczewska, 1961; Watts, 1969), rather than reflecting the direction of interspecific relationships. Results from behavioural analyses (Hoffmeyer, 1973; Montgomery, 1978*b*) suggested that the removal of *A. flavicollis* would have a greater effect on *A. sylvaticus* than the converse. The enhanced reproduction and consequent population growth was totally unexpected. Removal of *A. sylvaticus* may simply have had a similar effect to a reduction of the *A. flavicollis* density. Reducing density of rodent populations is likely

Table 5.11 Numbers of adult and juvenile *A. sylvaticus* and *A. flavicollis* appearing on grids A, B and C between February and July 1975 and 1976. Data in 1976 for *A. sylvaticus* on B and *A. flavicollis* on C are numbers removed. (From Montgomery, 1981.)

	1975				1976			
	Ad.	Juv.	Tot.	% juv.	Ad.	Juv.	Tot.	% juv.
A. sylvaticus								
Grid A (control)	39	18	57	31.58	37	5	42	11.90
Grid B (*A. sylvaticus* removed)	28	1	29	3.45	44	4	48	8.33
Grid C (*A. flavicollis* removed)	45	4	49	8.16	34	10	44	22.73
A. flavicollis								
Grid A (control)	26	17	43	39.50	7	11	18	61.11
Grid B (*A. sylvaticus* removed)	14	6	20	30.00	10	36	46	78.26
Grid C (*A. flavicollis* removed)	18	25	43	58.14	14	3	17	17.65

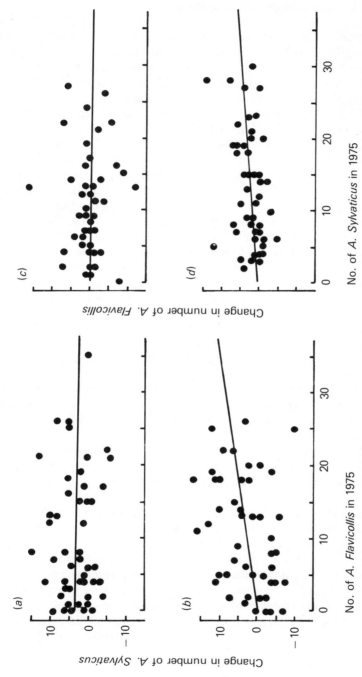

Fig. 5.14 Scatter diagrams where, for each trap point, the change in the number of captures of one species from 1975 to 1976 (June to July) is plotted against the total number of captures of its congener in 1975. (*a*) and (*b*) *A. sylvaticus* on grids A and C, respectively; (*c*) and (*d*) *A. flavicollis* on grids A and B, respectively. (From Montgomery, 1981.)

to result in the effect opposite to that of increasing density, which inhibits breeding in other murid species (Christian, 1971). Also, lower densities created by removal of one or other species may have increased availability of food for the population; enhanced food supply promotes reproduction in *A. sylvaticus* (Flowerdew, 1973).

Removal of a population from its habitat may be followed by an influx of a competing species which normally occupies a distinct habitat. Grant (1969, 1972), for example, found that the removal of *Microtus* from grassland was followed by immigration of *Clethrionomys* or *Peromyscus* from adjacent woodland. No such dramatic results can be achieved when experimenting on species which share one habitat, even if spatial separation is maintained at all times as in *Apodemus* populations at Woodchester Park. During the removal phase of the experiment, it was anticipated that any shift in distribution would be slight and the supposed weaker competitor, *A. sylvaticus*, would exhibit greater release. However, in the absence of their congener, both *A. sylvaticus* and *A. flavicollis* were captured more at trap-points formerly frequented by the absent species (Fig. 5.14). The effects of removal were not strong but neither were they as one-sided as suggested by behavioural analyses, where individuals were forced to share a limited space. Captures of both species were associated with the same characteristic vegetation structure before and after the removal of their congener (Montgomery, 1981). Hence the results of the removal experiment indicate that although interspecific competition may help maintain the spatial segregation of *Apodemus* species in shared habitats, use of space is intrinsically different in the two species.

The relationship of *A. sylvaticus* and *A. flavicollis* in sympatric populations illustrates the complexity of the processes and forces determining species composition of communities. The balance of available evidence suggests that these species do compete for resources in the habitat they share. Their interaction is weak and possibly more typical of relationships among populations in communities with many rodent species. If competition between *A. sylvaticus* and *A. flavicollis* were any stronger, then exclusion at the habitat level might occur. Competition is almost certainly ameliorated by the intrinsic differences in annual cycles of abundance apparent in both sympatry and allopatry. The study of the ecology of the populations of *Apodemus* at Woodchester Park illustrates the necessity for data collected over a sufficient period and over a large enough area to permit a synthesis of dynamics in time and space.

Acknowledgements

It is a pleasure to thank Mr and Mrs A.R. Kelly for their hospitality at Woodchester Park; Fountain Forestry, who also granted access to their property; the many students who plodded the slopes of the valley between 1968 and 1983; the staff and postgraduates of the Department of Zoology, University of Manchester; Dr Mike Begon, who supplied the data for grid L; Mike Taylor and Richard Abbott, for their technical support; and Sally Montgomery and Liz Purdy, for helping in the preparation of this chapter; special thanks are due to Dr Derek Yalden, who started it all and has guided the work with unlimited energy and enthusiasm.

References

Adamczewska, K.A. (1961) Intensity of reproduction of *A. flavicollis* (Melchior, 1834) during the period 1954–49. *Acta theriologica*, **5**, 1–21.

Amtmann, E. (1965) Biometrische untersuchungen zur Introgressiven Hybridisation der Waldmaus (*Apodemus sylvaticus* (L.)) und der Gelbhalsmaus (*A. tauricus* Pallas 1811). *Zeitschrift zoologisches Systematick und Evolutionforschung*, **3**, 103–56.

Andrewartha, H.G. & Birch, L.C. (1954) *The Distribution and Abundance of Animals*. Chicago: University of Chicago Press.

Arnold, H.R. (1978) *Provisional Atlas of the Mammals of the British Isles*. Natural Environment Research Council: Huntingdon.

Ashby, K.R. (1967) Studies on the ecology of field mice and voles (*Apodemus sylvaticus, Clethrionomys glareolus* and *Microtus agrestis*) in Houghall Wood, Durham. *Journal of Zoology, London*, **152**, 389–513.

Aulak, W. (1970) Small mammal communities in Bialowicza National Park. *Acta theriologica*, **15**, 465–515.

Begon, M. (1979) *Investigating Animal Abundance: Capture–Recapture for Biologists*. London: Edward Arnold.

Begon, M. (1983) Abuses of mathematical methods in ecology: applications of Jolly's capture–recapture method. *Oikos*, **40**, 155–8.

Begon, M. & Mortimer, M. (1981) *Population Ecology. A Unified Study of Animals and Plants*. Oxford: Blackwell.

Bergstedt, B. (1965). Distribution, reproduction, growth and dynamics of the rodent species *Clethrionomys glareolus* (Schreber), *Apodemus flavicollis* (Melchior) and *Apodemus sylvaticus* (Linne) in southern Sweden. *Oikos*, **16**, 132–60.

Birch, L.C. (1957). The meanings of competition. *American Naturalist*, **91**, 5–18.

Bishop, J.A. & Hartley, D.J. (1976). The size and age structure of rural populations of *Rattus norvegicus* containing individuals resistant to the anticoagulant poison warfarin. *Journal of Animal Ecology*, **45**, 623–46.

Blower, J.G., Cook, L.M. & Bishop, J.A. (1981). *Estimating the Size of Animal Populations*. London: Allen & Unwin.

Bobek, B. (1973). Net production of small rodents in a deciduous forest. *Acta theriologica*, **18**, 403–34.

Bothschafter, E. (1963). Biometrische Untersuchungen an Gelbhalsmausen (*Apodemus tauricus* Pallas, 1811) und Waldmausen (*Apodemus sylvaticus*

Linne, 1758) aus dem Bayerischen Wald. *Saugetierkundliche Mitteilungen*, **11**, 1–47.

Bovet, J. (1972). On the social behaviour in a stable group of Long-tailed field-mice (*Apodemus sylvaticus*): 2. Its relations with distribution of daily activity. *Behaviour*, **41**, 55–67.

Brink, van den, F.H. (1967). *A Field Guide to the Mammals of Britain and Europe*. London: Collins.

Caughley, G. (1977). *Analysis of Vertebrate Populations*. Chichester: Wiley.

Chitty, D. & Kempson, D.A. (1949). Prebaiting small mammals and a new design of live trap. *Ecology*, **30**, 536–42.

Christian, J.J. (1971) Fighting, maturity and population density in *Microtus pennsylvanicus. Journal of Mammalogy*, **52**, 556–67.

Connell, T.H. (1961) The influence of interspecific competition and other factors on the distribution of the barnacle *Chthamalus stellatus. Ecology*, **42**, 710–23.

Corbet, G.B. (1966) *The Terrestrial Mammals of Western Europe*. London: Foulis.

Corke, D. (1970) The local distribution of the Yellow-necked mouse (*Apodemus flavicollis*). *Mammal Review*, **1**, 62–6.

Corke, D. (1974) *The Comparative Ecology of the Two British Species of Apodemus (Rodentia: Muridae)*. Unpublished Ph.D. thesis, University of London.

Corke, D. (1977*a*) The Yellow-necked mouse *Apodemus flavicollis*, in *The Handbook of British Mammals*, 2nd edn. Corbet, G.B. & Southern, H.N., eds. Oxford: Blackwell, pp. 217–9.

Corke, D. (1977*b*). A combination of extensive and intensive survey techniques for the study of the occurrence of *Apodemus flavicollis* in Essex. *Journal of Zoology, London*, **182**, 171–5.

Corke, D. & Harris, S. (1974). The small mammals of Essex. *The Essex Naturalist*, **33**, 32–59.

Curry-Lindahl, K. (1959). Notes on the ecology and periodicity of some rodents and shrews in Sweden. *Mammalis*, **23**, 389–422.

David, F.N. & Johnson, N.L. (1952). The truncated Poisson. *Biometrics*, **8**, 275–85.

Doi, T. & Iwamoto, T. (1982). Local distribution of two species of *Apodemus* in Kyushu. *Researches on Population Ecology*, **24**, 110–22.

Drozdz, A. (1966). Food habits and food supply of rodents in the beech forest. *Acta theriologica*, **11**, 363–84.

Dunn, E. (1977) Predation by weasels (*Mustela nivalis*) on breeding tits (*Parus* spp.) in relation to the density of tits and rodents. *Journal of Animal Ecology*, **46**, 633–52.

Elton, C. & Miller, R.S. (1954) The ecological survey of animal communities; with a practical system of classifying habitats by structural characters. *Journal of Ecology*, **42**, 460–96.

Elton, C., Ford, E.B., Baker, J.R. & Gardner, A.D. (1931) The health and parasites of wild mouse population. *Proceedings of the Zoological Society of London*, 1931, 657–721.

Evans, D. (1978) The field vole *Microtus agrestis*, in *The Handbook of British Mammals*, 2nd edn. Corbet, G.B. & Southern, H.N., eds. Oxford: Blackwell, pp. 182–97.

Evans, F.C. (1942) Studies of a small mammal population in Bagley Wood, Berkshire. *Journal of Animal Ecology*, **11**, 182–97.

Fairley, J.S. (1982) Short-term effects of ringing and toe-clipping on the recapture of Woodmice (*Apodemus sylvaticus*). *Journal of Zoology, London,* **197**, 295–7.

Flowerdew, J.R. (1972) The effect of supplementary food on a population of Wood mice (*Apodemus sylvaticus*). *Journal of Animal Ecology,* **41**, 553–66.

Flowerdew, J.R. (1973) The effect of natural and artificial changes in food supply on breeding in woodland mice and voles. *Journal of Reproduction and Fertility* (Supplement), **19**, 259–69.

Flowerdew, J.R. (1974) Field and laboratory experiments on the social behaviour and population dynamics of the Woodmouse (*Apodemus sylvaticus*). *Journal of Animal Ecology,* **43**, 499–510.

Flowerdew, J.R. (1976) Techniques in mammalogy. Chapter 4. Ecological methods. *Mammal Review,* **6**, 123–59.

Flowerdew, J.R. (1977). The wood mouse *Apodemus sylvaticus,* in *The Handbook of British Mammals,* 2nd edn. Corbet, G.B. & Southern, H.N., eds. Oxford: Blackwell, pp. 206–170.

Flowerdew, J.R. (1978). Residents and transients in Woodmouse populations. In *Population Control by Social Behaviour* Ebling, F.J. & Stoddart, D.M., eds. London: Institute of Biology, pp. 49–66.

Flowerdew, J.R. & Gardner, G. (1978). Small rodent populations and food supply in a Derbyshire ashwood. *Journal of Animal Ecology,* **47**, 725–40.

Fullagar, P.J. & Jewell, P.A. (1965). Marking small rodents and the difficulties of using leg rings. *Journal of Zoology, London,* **147**, 224–8.

Garson, P.J. (1975). Social interaction of Woodmice (*Apodemus sylvaticus*) studied by direct observation in the wild. *Journal of Zoology, London,* **177**, 496–500.

Gebczynska, Z. (1966). Estimation of rodent numbers in a plot of Querceto–Carpinetum forest. *Acta theriologica,* **11**, 315–28.

Glass, G.E. & Slade, N.A. (1980). Population structure as a predictor of spatial association between *Sigmodon hispidus* and *Microtus ochrogaster. Journal of Mammalogy,* **61**, 473–85.

Grant, P.R. (1969). Experimental studies on competitive interaction in a two-species system. I. *Microtus* and *Clethrionomys* species in enclosures. *Canadian Journal of Zoology,* **47**, 1059–82.

Grant, P.R. (1972). Interspecific competition among rodents. *Annual Review of Ecology and Systematics,* **3**, 79–106.

Grodzinski, W., Pucek, Z. & Ryzkowski, L. (1966) Estimation of rodent numbers by means of prebaiting and intensive removal. *Acta theriologica,* **11**, 297–314.

Gurnell, J. (1975) Notes on the activity of wild wood mice, *Apodemus sylvaticus,* in artificial enclosures. *Journal of Zoology, London,* **175**, 219–29.

Gurnell, J. (1976) Studies on the effect of bait and sampling intensity on trapping and estimating wood mice, *Apodemus sylvaticus. Journal of Zoology, London,* **178**, 91–105.

Gurnell, J. (1977) Neutral cage behavioural interaction in wild wood mice, *Apodemus sylvaticus* (Linne, 1758). *Saugetierkundliche Mitteilungen,* **25**, 57–66.

Gurnell, J. (1978a) Observations on trap response in confined populations of wood mice, *Apodemus sylvaticus. Journal of Zoology, London,* **185**, 287–97.

Gurnell, J. (1978b) Seasonal changes in numbers and male behavioural interaction in a population of wood mice, *Apodemus sylvaticus, Journal of Animal Ecology,* **47**, 741–55.

Gurnell, J. (1981) Woodland rodents and tree seed supplies. In *The Worldwide Furbearer Conference Proceedings*, Chapman, J.A. & Pursley, D., eds. Falls, Chard, Virginia, USA: R.R. Donnelly & Sons, pp. 1191-1214.

Gurnell, J. (1982) Trap response in woodland rodents. *Acta theriologica*, **27**, 123-37.

Haitlinger, R. (1969) Morphological variability in the Wroclaw populations of *Apodemus sylvaticus*. *Acta theriologica*, **14**, 285-302.

Hamar, M., Simonescu, V. & Theiss, F. (1966) Biometrische und zoogeographische Untersuchungen der Gattung *Apodemus* (Kaup, 1829) in der Sozialistischen Republik Rumanien. *Acta theriologica*, **11**, 1-40.

Hansson, L. (1968) Population densities of small mammals in open field habitats in south Sweden in 1964-1967. *Oikos*, **19**, 53-60.

Hansson, L. (1971). Small rodent food, feeding and population dynamics. *Oikos*, **22**, 183-98.

Hayne, D.W. (1949) Two methods of estimating population from trapping records. *Journal of Mammalogy*, **30**, 399-411.

Hayward, G.F. & Phillipson, J. (1979) Community structure and functional role of small mammals in ecosystems. In *Ecology of Small Mammals*, Stoddart, D.M., ed. London: Chapman & Hall, pp. 135-211.

Hedges, S.R. (1966) *Studies on the Behaviour, Taxonomy and Ecology of Apodemus sylvaticus (L.) and A. flavicollis (Melchior)*. Unpublished Ph.D. thesis, University of Southampton.

Hedges, S.R. (1969) Epigenetic polymorphism in populations of *Apodemus sylvaticus* and *A. flavicollis* (Rodentia, Muridae). *Journal of Zoology, London*, **159**, 425-42.

Heinrich, G. (1951) Die deutschen Waldmause. *Zoologische Jahrbucher (Systematik)*, **80**, 99-122.

Heptner, W.G. (1959) Communication in Peshev, T. & Georgiev, G. (1961).

Hoffmeyer, I. (1973) Interaction and habitat selection in the mice *Apodemus flavicollis* and *A. sylvaticus*. *Oikos*, **24**, 108-16.

Hoffmeyer, I. & Hansson, L. (1974) Variability in number and distribution of *Apodemus flavicollis* and *A. sylvaticus* in S. Sweden. *Zeitschrift für Saugetierkunde*, **39**, 15-23.

Holisova, V. & Obrtel, R. (1980) Food resource partitioning among four myomorph rodent populations coexisting in a spruce forest. *Folia Zoologica*, **29**, 193-207.

Hurlbert, S.H. (1969) A coefficient of interspecific association. *Ecology*, **50**, 1-10.

Hutchinson, G.E. (1957) Concluding remarks. *Cold Spring Harbor Symposium in Quantitative Biology*, **22**, 415-27.

Jensen, T.S. (1975) Trappability of various functional groups of the forest rodents *Clethrionomys glareolus* and *Apodemus flavicollis*, and its application to density estimations. *Oikos*, **26**, 196-204.

Jolly, G.M. (1982) Mark–recapture models with parameters constant in time. *Biometrics*, **38**, 301-21.

Judes, U. Von (1979) Untersuchungen zur Okologie der Waldmaus (*Apodemus sylvaticus* Linne, 1758) und der Gelbhalsmaus (*Apodemus flavicollis* Melchior, 1834) im Raum Kiel (Schleswig-Holstein). *Zeitschrift für Saugetierkunde*, **44**, 81-95.

Kikkawa, J. (1964) Movement, activity and distribution of the small rodents *Clethrionomys glareolus* and *Apodemus sylvaticus* in woodland. *Journal of Animal Ecology*, **33**, 259-99.

King, C.M. (1980) The weasel *Mustela nivalis* and its prey in an English woodland. *Journal of Animal Ecology*, **49**, 127–59.

Kratochivil, J. (1970) Die Hodengrosses als Kriterium der europaischen Arten der Gattung *Apodemus. Zoologica listy*, **20**, 293–306.

Lack, D. (1944) Ecological aspects of species-formation in Passerine birds. *Ibis*, **86**, 260–86.

Lincoln, F.C. (1930) Calculating waterfowl abundance on the basis of banding returns. U.S. Dept. of Agriculture Circular No. 118, pp. 1–4.

Matthews, L.H. (1952) *British Mammals*. London: Collins.

Mermod, C. (1969) Ecologie et dynamique des populations de trois rongeurs sylvicoles. *Mammalia*, **33**, 1–57.

Miller, R.S. (1954) Food habits of the Woodmouse, *Apodemus sylvaticus* (Linne 1758) and the Bank vole, *Clethrionomys glareolus* (Schreber, 1780) in Wytham Woods, Berkshire. *Saugetierkundliche Mitteilungen*, **2**, 109–14.

Miller, R.S. (1967) Pattern and process in competition. *Advances in Ecological Research*, **4**, 1–74.

Montgomery, W.I. (1976) On the relationship between Yellow-necked mouse (*Apodemus flavicollis*) and Woodmouse (*A. sylvaticus*) in a Cotswold valley. *Journal of Zoology, London*, **179**, 229–33.

Montgomery, W.I. (1977) *Studies on the Ecology of Two Sympatric Species of* Apodemus (*Rodentia: Muridae*). Unpublished Ph.D. thesis, University of Manchester.

Montgomery, W.I. (1978a) Studies on the distributions of *Apodemus sylvaticus* (L.) and *A. flavicollis* (Melchior) in Britain. *Mammal Review*, **8**, 177–84.

Montgomery, W.I. (1978b) Intra- and interspecific interactions of *Apodemus sylvaticus* (L.) and *A. flavicollis* (Melchior) under laboratory conditions. *Animal Behaviour*, **26**, 1247–54.

Montgomery, W.I. (1979a) An examination of interspecific, sexual and individual biases affecting rodent captures in Longworth traps. *Acta theriologica*, **24**, 35–45.

Montgomery, W.I. (1979b) Seasonal variation in numbers of *Apodemus sylvaticus, A. flavicollis* and *Clethrionomys glareolus. Journal of Zoology, London*, **188**, 283–6.

Montgomery, W.I. (1980a) Population structure and dynamics of sympatric *Apodemus* species (Rodentia: Muridae). *Journal of Zoology, London*, **192**, 351–77.

Montgomery, W.I. (1980b) Spatial organisation in sympatric populations of *Apodemus sylvaticus* and *A. flavicollis* (Rodentia: Muridae). *Journal of Zoology, London*, **192**, 379–401.

Montgomery, W.I. (1980c) The use of arboreal runways by the woodland rodents, *Apodemus sylvaticus* (L.), *A. flavicollis* (Melchior) and *Clethrionomys glareolus* (Schreber). *Mammal Review*, **10**, 189–95.

Montgomery, W.I. (1981) A removal experiment with sympatric populations of *Apodemus sylvaticus* (L.) and *A. flavicollis* (Melchior) (Rodentia: Muridae). *Oecologia*, **51**, 123–32.

Morris, R.D. & Grant, P.R. (1971) Experimental studies of competitive interaction in a two-species system. IV *Microtus* and *Clethrionomys* spp. in a single enclosure. *Journal of Animal Ecology*, **41**, 275–90.

Muller, von J.P. (1972) Die Verteilung der Kleinsauger auf die Lebensraume an einen Nordhang im Churer Rheintal. *Zeitschrift für Saugetierkunde*, **37**, 257–86.

Niethammer, J. (1969) Zur Frage der Introgression bei den Waldmausen

Apodemus sylvaticus und *A. flavicollis* (Mammalia, Rodentia). *Zeitschrift zoologische Systematik und Evolutionforschung*, **7**, 77–127.

Obrtel, R. (1974) Comparison of animal food eaten by *Apodemus flavicollis* and *Clethrionomys glareolus* in lowland forest. *Zoologica listy*, **23**, 35–46.

Obrtel, R. & Holisova, V. (1974) Character of food eaten by *Apodemus flavicollis* and *Clethrionomys glareolus* in a lowland forest. *Lynx*, **16**, 37–45.

Parker, R.E. (1979) *Introductory Statistics for Biology*. London: Edward Arnold.

Peshev, T. & Georgiev, G. (1961) Studies on the taxonomy of some populations of *Apodemus sylvaticus* (L. 1758) in Bulgaria. *Acta theriologica*, **5**, 185–202.

Petrusewicz, K. & Andrzejewski, R. (1962) Natural history of a free-living population of house mice (*Mus musculus* L.) with particular reference to grouping within the population. *Ekologia Polska Series A*, **10**, 85–122.

Randolph, S.E. (1977) Changing spatial relationships in a population of *Apodemus sylvaticus* with the onset of breeding. *Journal of Animal Ecology*, **46**, 653–76.

Reynoldson, T.B. & Bellamy, L.S. (1970) The establishment of interspecific competition in field populations, with an example of competition in action between *Polycelis nigra* (Mull.) and *P. tennuis* (Ijima) (Turbellaria, Tricladida). *Proceedings of the Advanced Study Institute on Dynamics and Numbers in Populations*, Oosterbeek, 1970, 282–97.

Saint-Girons, M.C. (1973) *Les Mammiferes de France et du Benelux*. Paris: Doin.

Schumacher, F.X. & Eschmeyer, R.W. (1943) The estimation of fish populations in lakes and ponds. *Journal of the Tennessee Academy of Science*, **18**, 228–49.

Smal, C.M. & Fairley, J.S. (1980) The fruits available to small rodents in two woodland ecosystems. *Holarctic Ecology*, **3**, 10–18.

Smal, C.M. & Fairley, J.S. (1981) Energy consumption of small rodent populations in two Irish woodland ecosystems. *Acta theriologica*, **26**, 449–58.

Smal, C.M. & Fairley, J.S. (1982) The dynamics and regulation of small rodent populations in woodland ecosystems of Killarney, Ireland. *Journal of Zoology, London*, **196**, 1–30.

Smyth, M. (1966) Winter breeding in woodland mice, *Apodemus sylvaticus*, and voles, *Clethrionomys glareolus* and *Microtus agrestis*, near Oxford. *Journal of Animal Ecology*, **35**, 471–85.

Sokal, R.R. & Rohlf, F.J. (1981) *Biometry. The Principles and Practice of Statistics in Biological Research*, 2nd edn. San Francisco: W.H. Freeman.

Southern, H.N. (1968) A review. *Journal of Animal Ecology*, **37**, 723–4.

Southern, H.N. (1973) a yardstick for measuring populations of small rodents. *Mammal Review*, **3**, 1–10.

Southern, H.N. & Lowe, V.P.W. (1968) The pattern of distribution of prey and predation in Tawny owl territories. *Journal of Animal Ecology*, **37**, 175–98.

Southern, H.N. & Lowe, V.P.W. (1982) Predation by Tawny owls (*Strix aluco*) on Bank voles (*Clethrionomys glareolus*) and Woodmice (*Apodemus sylvaticus*). *Journal of Zoology, London*, **198**, 83–102.

Southwood, T.R.E. (1978) *Ecological Methods with Particular Reference to Insect Populations*. London: Chapman & Hall.

Stoddart, M.D. (1982) Does trap odour influence estimation of population size of the short-tailed vole, *Microtus agrestis*? *Journal of Animal Ecology*, **51**, 375–86.

Tanton, M.T. (1965) Problems of live trapping and population estimation for the Woodmouse, *Apodemus sylvaticus*. *Journal of Animal Ecology*, **34**, 1–22.

Terman, M.R. (1974) Behavioural interactions between *Microtus* and *Sigmodon*. A model for competitive exclusion. *Journal of Mammalogy*, **35**, 705-19.

Vereschchagin, N.K. (1959) *Mammals of the Caucasus. History of the Formation of the Fauna*. Leningrad: Izdakelstvo Akademii Nauk. Translation from Israel Program for Scientific Translations.

Watts, C.H.S. (1968) The foods eaten by Wood mouse (*Apodemus sylvaticus*) and the Bank vole (*Clethrionomys glareolus*) in Wytham Woods, Berkshire. *Journal of Animal Ecology*, **37**, 25-41.

Watts, C.H.S. (1969) The regulation of Wood mouse (*Apodemus sylvaticus*) numbers in Wytham Woods, Berkshire. *Journal of Animal Ecology*, **38**, 285-304.

Wesolowsky, G.O. (1976) *Multiple Regression and Analysis of Variance: Introduction for Computer Users in Management and Economics*. New York: Wiley.

Winer, B.J. (1971) *Statistical Principles in Experimental Design*. New York: McGraw-Hill.

Witte, G. (1964) Introgression bei *Apodemus flavicollis* und *A. sylvaticus*. Biometrische Untersuchungen an *Apodemus* Populationen des Monte Gargano (Suditalien). *Bonner zoologische Beitrage*, **15**, 159-77.

Yalden, D.W. (1971) A population of the Yellownecked mouse *Apodemus flavicollis*. *Journal of Zoology, London*, **164**, 244-50.

Yalden, D.W. (1974) Population density in the common shrew *Sorex araneus*. *Journal of Zoology, London*, **173**, 262-4.

Zaret, T.M. & Rand, A.S. (1971) Competition in tropical stream fishes: support for the competitive exclusion principle. *Ecology*, **52**, 336-42.

Zedja, J. (1966) Habitat selection in *Apodemus agrarius* (Pallas, 1778) (Mammalia: Muridae) on the border of the area of its distribution. *Zoologica listy*, **16**, 15-30.

Appendix 1 Scientific and common names of plant species mentioned in text

Acer pseudoplatanus	Sycamore
Allium ursinum	Ramsons
Buxus sempervirens	Box
Corylus avellana	Hazel
Crataegus monogyna	Hawthorn
Epilobium angustifolium	Rosebay Willowherb
Fagus sylvatica	Beech
Fraxinus excelsior	Ash
Larix decidua	European Larch
Mercurialis perennis	Dog's Mercury
Picea sitchensis	Sitka Spruce
Prunus laurocerasus	Cherry Laurel
P. lusitanica	Portugal Laurel
Quercus cerris	Turkey Oak
Q. robur	English Oak
Sambucus nigra	Elder
Taxus baccata	Yew
Ulmus glabra	Wych Elm

6   R.R. Baker

Moths: Population estimates, light-traps and migration

Introduction

For over a century, the most widely used and productive way to catch night-flying moths has been by the use of light-traps. Moths fly towards the light and then enter, and are constrained by, the trap. On a good night in summer, even in Britain, a single light-trap may sometimes capture over 1000 individuals.

Most light-traps are designed not to harm the captured moths and, with certain precautions, the insects remain relatively fit and healthy until subsequent release. At first sight, therefore, light-traps offer an ideal method by which to capture moths when trying to estimate the size of the population in a particular area.

Every June and July between 1976 and 1983, students from Manchester University have used light-traps to estimate the population of the various moth species in the vicinity of Woodchester Park Field Centre in Gloucestershire. Moths were caught, marked and released and their population sizes estimated using standard methods (Blower *et al.*, 1981). Some of the results obtained are shown in Tables 6.1 and 6.2. In 1983, for example, the population of the Dot moth, *Melanchra persicariae*, was estimated at about 400. We conclude that somewhere in Woodchester Park in July 1983 there existed 400 Dot moths that collectively formed the population sampled by the light-traps. What is not clear is the area over which these individuals were dispersed and whether, in this unknown area, there were other Dot Moths not included in the estimate.

The aim of this paper is to discuss the nature of the population of moths estimated by mark, release, recapture techniques when the moths are captured in a light-trap. The search leads first to a consideration of moth migration and orientation. Eventually, a picture emerges of the population that is being estimated.

Methods

Over the period 1976–1983 we have tried a number of variations on a basic mark, release, recapture scheme in attempts to control for different complications. Some indication of the details that have varied is given here, but none is critical to the main point of discussion.

Two types of light-trap have been used (Fig. 6.1): a 'portable' trap with an ultraviolet (UV) fluorescent tube powered by a 12 V car battery; and a larger trap with a mains-powered 125 W mercury-vapour bulb. Although constant within any one year, the type and number of light-traps used from year to year has varied (between one and four). Some years, portable traps were placed on paths along the edge of woodland 1 km or so from the Field Centre. Usually, however, the larger type was used and placed on lawns and among trees within 50 m

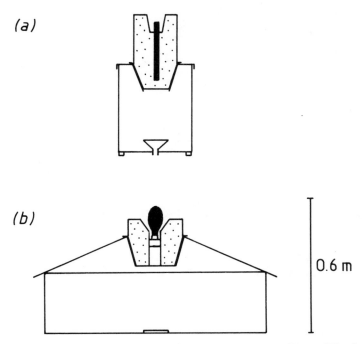

Fig. 6.1 Light-traps used in mark, release, recapture studies at Woodchester Park. (*a*) Portable trap with fluorescent UV tube powered by 12 V car battery; (*b*) mains-operated trap with 125 W mercury-vapour bulb. Lights are shown in black; baffles (to intercept moths flying near to light) are stippled. Both traps are part-filled with egg boxes each night to provide a large surface area on which the moths can settle. Rain water is funnelled from both traps out of a gauze-covered outlet at the base.

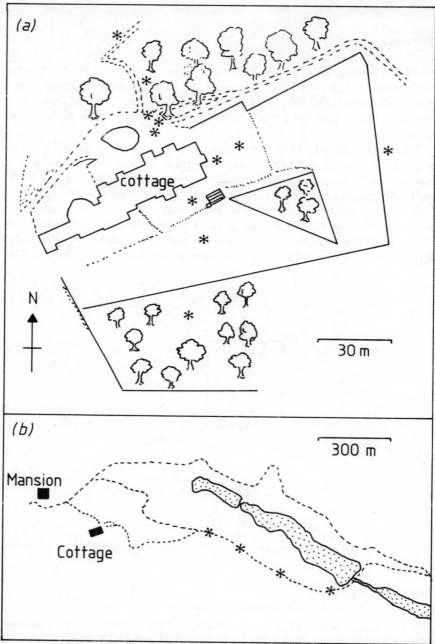

Fig. 6.2 Schematic maps to show approximate positions of light-traps around the Field Centre Cottage during mark, release, recapture studies. (Trap positions shown by asterisks.) (*a*) Positions at which mains-operated traps were sited around the Cottage between 1979 and 1983. Two to six sites were used in any given mark, recapture series. (*b*) Sites occupied by portable traps, 1976–1978. Four traps were used each year. Stippling shows lakes; dashed lines, paths.

of the Field Centre (Fig. 6.2). The distance between adjacent sites ranged from about 10 to 100 m.

Traps were set up during the day and lights were switched on at dusk. As soon as possible after dawn the following morning, but always between 0400 and 0700 GMT, each trap was plugged with polythene and, if necessary, moved to a shaded position until emptied between 0830 and 1200 GMT. All moths were identified and counted, but only the commoner species were marked.

Moths to be marked were usually placed individually in glass tubes and a dot of coloured paint was applied to a wing from the head of a bent, entomological pin embedded in a wooden handle. Different-coloured paint was used each day. Some years, a moth to be marked was held in the hand and an individual number was written on a wing using a felt-tip pen.

After marking, moths were placed in keep-nets and provided with cotton wool soaked in sugar-water. Nets were then placed in a cool, shaded and undisturbed site for the rest of the day. Marked moths were gently shaken into long vegetation from the keep-nets at about 2000 GMT, before dusk but after the main period of risk from bird predation. Site of release varied but most often was within about 10 m of the nearest light-trap. Lights were switched on between 1 and 2 h after release of the moths. The following morning, while being identified and counted, captured moths were checked for the presence of marks from previous nights.

All population estimates have been made between mid-June and late July, each series usually lasting for 6 days. In most years, one series at the end of June was followed by a second series in mid-July, there being about 10 days between the end of the first series and start of the second.

Population size was calculated by the methods of both Jolly and Fisher & Ford (Blower *et al.*, 1981). More often than not, however, recaptures were so few and erratic that only the Fisher & Ford method, using as it does a survival rate averaged over the whole period of study, allowed estimates to be made for the majority of nights that the traps were operational.

Results

Tables 6.1 and 6.2 summarise all population estimates and survival rates for individual species over the period 1976–1983. Table 6.3 gives the median capture per night and the median population estimate in each year for the two commonest species.

Such data could be used to discuss night-to-night (Table 6.1) and

Table 6.1   Some population estimates (Fisher & Ford's method) for the most common species of moths at Woodchester, 1976–1983.

	Capture day, June					Capture day, July				
	2	3	4	5	6	2	3	4	5	6
1976										
Heart-and-Dart	—	—	71	4946	4905	—	—	—	—	—
White Ermine	156	139	444	189	173	—	—	—	—	—
Poplar Hawk	6	4	18	11	7	—	—	—	—	—
1978										
Heart-and-Dart	—	—	—	—	—	634	1389	1340	—	1338
LYU	—	—	—	—	—	840	709	607	362	558
Buff Ermine	73	89	152	131	—	—	—	—	—	—
Mottled Beauty	231	114	109	696	2020	—	—	—	—	—
1980										
Heart-and-Dart	44	738	132	256	35	176	313	733	188	78
LYU	—	—	—	—	—	—	—	—	215	187
1981										
Heart-and-Dart	35	22	123	113	55	250	197	167	514	225
LYU	—	—	—	—	—	134	217	90	50	42
Dot	—	—	—	—	—	37	269	86	180	45
1982										
LYU	—	—	—	—	—	66900	68155	4569	11909	64100
Flame	821	1943	1243	628	1620	—	—	—	—	—
1983										
Heart-and-Dart	—	—	—	—	—	1357	2759	785	1167	1987
Dot	—	—	—	—	—	417	379	251	335	584

Species: Large Yellow Underwing (LYU) (*Noctua pronuba*); Heart-and-Dart (*Agrotis exclamationis*); Dot (*Melanchara persicariae*); Flame (*Axylia putris*); Mottled Beauty (*Cleora repandata*); Poplar Hawk (*Laothoe populi*); Buff Ermine (*Spilosoma lutea*); White Ermine (*Spilosoma lubricipeda*).

Table 6.2   Survival rates (Fisher & Ford's method) for some of the most common species of moths at Woodchester, 1976–1983.

Species	1976	1977	1978	1979	1980	1981	1982	1983
Heart-and-Dart, June	0.20	—	—	—	0.06	—	—	—
Heart-and Dart, July	—	—	0.52	—	0.37	0.87	—	0.47
LYU, June	—	—	—	—	—	—	—	—
LYU, July	—	—	0.20	—	0.50	0.33	0.46	—
Dot, July	—	—	—	—	—	0.83	—	0.62
Flame, June	—	—	—	—	—	—	0.72	—
Poplar Hawk, June	0.20	—	—	—	—	—	—	—
Mottled Beauty, June	—	—	0.50	—	—	—	—	—
White Ermine, June	0.56	—	—	—	—	—	—	—
Buff Ermine, June	—	—	0.43	—	—	—	—	—

Species: as Table 6.1.

Table 6.3 Comparison of median number caught and median population estimate for two species of moths.

Species	1976	1977	1978	1979	1980	1981	1982	1983
Caught								
LYU, June	8	0	6	3	39	1	57	1
LYU, July	—	—	148	29	58	53	348	13
Heart-and-Dart, June	245	3	27	9	101	7	62	14
Heart-and-Dart, July	—	—	98	24	36	13	107	78
Population estimate								
LYU, June	—	—	—	—	—	—	—	—
LYU, July	—	—	607	—	201	90	64100	—
Heart-and-Dart, June	4905	—	—	—	132	55	—	—
Heart-and-Dart, July	—	—	1338	—	188	225	—	1357

Species: as Table 6.1.

year-to-year (Table 6.3) population fluctuations. However, if the population estimates are to be more useful or meaningful than simple capture data, we need to know just what is the population that consists of, for example, 55 individuals of Heart-and-Dart Moth *Agrotis exclamationis* in June 1981. It is this question with which the remainder of this paper is concerned.

Discussion

Distance of response to light-traps

Although, at most sites, trees obscured direct view of our light-traps at distances greater than about 20 m, on some nights the sphere of illumination produced by the traps was visible to the human eye from distances of a kilometre or even more. Clearly, if moths were attracted to this illumination from such distances, we could begin to discuss our population estimates in terms of the moth population of the valley.

Bowden & Morris (1975) calculated background levels of illumination for different phases of the Moon and estimated the distance at which light from a 125 W mercury-vapour lamp was equal to background illumination. On this basis they suggested that, on moonless nights, moths may well respond to light-traps at distances of up to 0.5 km. Support for this suggestion could be taken from electroretinographic studies (Agee, 1972). The threshold of response to a 15 W 'black' (UV) lamp is sufficiently sensitive for detection of the light from such a distance. Direct behavioural studies, however, lead to different conclusions.

Experiments on the distance of response to a 15 W 'black' bulb have been performed using: (a) concentric circles of pans filled with oil and water to trap insects that landed on their surface (Hartstack *et al.*, 1968); and (b) orientation cages (Stewart *et al.*, 1969). Their results seem to indicate orientation primarily from much shorter distances than 500 m, perhaps no further than 1–6 m.

Sotthibandhu (1978) used tethered but free-flying Large Yellow Underwing moths, *Noctua pronuba*. Precautions standard for experiments on goal orientation (Baker, 1984*a*) were taken, controlling particularly for the possibility of compass orientation. For every test at a particular distance in one direction from the light, Sotthibandhu carried out another test at the same distance in the opposite direction. Testing began at a distance of 30 m from a 125 W mercury-vapour lamp, with a view to moving further away to determine the distance at which orientation towards the light ceased. Instead, Sotthibandhu found no evidence for light orientation until the moth was only 3 m from the light.

Baker & Sadovy (1978) used free-flying moths to test Sotthibandhu's claims. 'Masking', 'withdrawal' and 'ratio' experiments were designed in which the sphere of influence of one light-trap was used to mask, interfere with, or compete with the sphere of influence of other light-traps. Large Yellow Underwing and Heart-and-Dart moths were marked and released at known distances from a number of traps. Identification of the degree of separation of traps at which interference or masking seemed to disappear, and determination of the ratio of moths recaptured in traps at different distances from the release site, allowed the radius of the sphere of influence to be calculated. Sotthibandhu's claim was supported, the moths apparently responding to a 125 W mercury-vapour lamp from a distance of about 3 m.

A population estimate of 55 Heart-and-Darts in 1981 would have seemed unrealistically low had the population being estimated been that within a 500 m radius of the light-traps taking the sample. On the other hand, as an estimate of the population within a 3 m radius of the traps, such a figure seems unrealistically high. The estimate of 400 Dot moths for 1983 seems even more unrealistic, especially when it is observed that in that year the two lights were placed on the short grass of a lawn.

Obviously, the population of moths we are estimating does not 'live' within the sphere of influence of the lights but is one that is at risk of entering that sphere from outside. The next question we have to answer, therefore, is how far individuals are likely to travel and thus over what area there are moths at risk of entering the sphere of influence of our light-trap(s).

Lifetime tracks and migration

A moth is laid as an egg in a place determined for it by its mother. Some time later it dies in a place determined by its own migrations. As it travels through time and space on its way from birth to death, it traces an invisible path, its lifetime track (Baker, 1978, 1982). As moths are relatively small and mostly nocturnal, it is hardly surprising that we know virtually nothing about their tracks, and it is often helpful to seek comparisons with the better understood tracks of butterflies. For one moth, however, there is firm evidence that individuals may die more than 100 km from where they were born.

Each year, the Oriental Armyworm moth (*Pseudaletia separata*) first appears on the wing in spring in southern China, spreads north to Korea, then retreats with the Sun to more southerly latitudes in autumn. Rather than moving as a block, the population seems to ebb and flow across the land with the seasons, the curve of population density with latitude having a mode; a wave that washes north in spring and summer, then south in autumn. Movement of this wave is due, at least in part, to the movement of individuals over long distances. In a classic mark, release, recapture study, Li *et al.* (1964) showed that some individuals travel 1000 km or more from their release site in a few days.

The ebb and flow of the Oriental Armyworm population through long-distance migration to the north in spring and summer and to the south in autumn seem analogous to the better understood and better documented shifts in population of the Monarch butterfly, *Danaus plexippus*, in North America (maps in Baker, 1978, 1984b). Mark, release, recapture studies (e.g. Urquhart, 1960; Urquhart & Urquhart, 1978) show that individuals travel distances of up to 3000 km across country.

In Europe, a seasonal ebb and flow of population apparently similar to that of the Oriental Armyworm moth in Asia and Monarch butterfly in North America is shown by the Silver-Y moth (*Plusia gamma*). The species shows preferred compass orientation to the NNW in spring and summer and to the S in autumn (Williams, 1958; Baker, 1978). Eventually, long-distance travel by individuals over hundreds or even thousands of kilometres seems almost certain to be demonstrated, not only for the Silver-Y but also for the Humming Bird Hawk moth (*Macroglossum stellatarum*) and those other Hawk moths with comparable population shifts documented by Williams (1958).

In the tropics, outbreaks of the African Armyworm moth (*Spodoptera exempta*) often spread northwards from Tanzania through Kenya to Ethiopia with the rainy season, and it has been hypothesised that individuals migrate over distances of several hundred kilometres (Brown & Swaine, 1966). In a combined optical and radar study, Riley *et al.* (1983) collected circumstantial data that individuals may travel 20 km or more in a single night.

Cross-country travel by butterflies is not confined to those species, such as the Monarch, that show gross latitudinal shifts of population with the seasons. Individuals of species, such as the Small White (*Pieris rapae*) and Small Tortoiseshell (*Aglais urticae*), that show no such obvious population shift are nevertheless seen to travel across country in a more or less straight line between suitable habitats where they pause for a few minutes, hours or days to feed, roost, reproduce, etc. (Baker, 1968a, 1969). The main difference between species is the length of time individuals spend in each suitable habitat before once more leaving to travel across country (Baker, 1969). Observed rates of cross-country travel suggest *Pieris* spp. may travel tens or hundreds of kilometres across country in their lifetime (Baker, 1978, 1984b), a possibility confirmed by mark, release, recapture experiments on these and other European species (Roer, 1968, 1969, 1970).

The reasons for such mobility of individual butterflies and moths have been discussed at length elsewhere (Baker, 1978, 1984b). Some of the consequences to the population of this mobility of individuals have also been evaluated. For example, one result is that the mosaic dispersion of a species through space is forever changing through time. This dynamic mosaic is strikingly illustrated for some British moths by Taylor & Taylor (1977) using nationwide light-trap data. A second result of individual mobility is, paradoxically, within-habitat stability of numbers. Taylor & Woiwod (1980) demonstrate that 263 moth species, caught over 6 years by light-traps at 53 sites in Great Britain and adjacent mainland Europe, show a spatial and temporal stability at the different sites that is a power function of mean population density over an area and through time. I have suggested (Baker, 1984b) that both of these population effects are the unselected consequence of mobile individuals each making the best decision (Baker, 1978) over when to stay in a habitat and when to leave. Yet a third result of individual mobility may be the smoothing of regional differences in morph frequency of polymorphic species.

Many moths are polymorphic for wing coloration, the best studied examples perhaps being the various manifestations of industrial melanism. Classically, such moths are predominantly melanic in industrial areas and predominantly typical in less industrial areas. Bishop & Cook (1975) point out, however, that at least for the Scalloped Hazel (*Gonodontis bidentata*), Peppered (*Biston betularia*) and Large Yellow Underwing (*Noctua pronuba*) moths there appears to be correspondence between the distance individuals travel and the area

Table 6.4 Night of first recapture for individuals of two cohorts of moths caught and marked on first night of trap-operation.

Capture night	Recapture nights					
	1	2	3	4	5	6
Heart-and-Dart	263	30	3	0	0	0
LYU	150	10	1	0	1	0

Species: as Table 6.1.

of patches of relatively constant morph frequency. Thus, *N. pronuba* has a more or less constant morph frequency throughout Britain (Cook & Sarsam, 1981). Individuals are long-lived (an average in the laboratory of 55 days for males, 75 for females; Singh & Kevan, 1965) and we may guess that the span of their lifetime track is at least 100 km and probably much more.

Table 6.4 shows the frequency distribution of recapture intervals for individuals of *N. pronuba* and Heart-and-Dart as obtained from light-trap data from Woodchester. Although the occasional individual may be recaptured several days after release, most individuals are never seen again. These and all the other data in this section suggest that many of the populations of moths we are trying to estimate at Woodchester Park consist of mobile individuals that may spend a relatively short time in the vicinity of our light-traps. When we consider the implications of the light-trap response itself, this suggestion is strengthened.

Migratory orientation and light-traps

Some moths enter light-traps; some migrate across country. If the two were connected, we should have to consider the possibility that our estimated population consists of migrants. One way the two could be connected is if light-traps catch migrant moths by confusing their orientation mechanism. This section discusses what is known about moth orientation, first in relation to migration, then in relation to light-traps. Although there is more direct evidence on orientation than on the nature of the lifetime track, there is even less agreement among entomologists.

Radar studies have shown that strong-flying moths maintain orientation during cross-country migration, not only on moonlit and starlit nights but also under heavily overcast conditions (Schaefer, 1976). Experiments on at least one species, the Large Yellow

Underwing, demonstrate a range of reference systems that would allow compass orientation under such a variety of conditions.

The compound eyes of moths are known to have a spectral and intensity sensitivity that should allow them to perceive almost as many stars as can Man (Cleve, 1964) and, on starlit nights, Large Yellow Underwings orient by a dorsal, visual source that moves across the sky at the rate of about $16°/h$ (Sotthibandhu & Baker, 1979). Stars or star patterns on the celestial equator are implicated. On moonlit nights, the same species orients with respect to the Moon (Sotthibandhu & Baker, 1979); on overcast nights by the geomagnetic field (Baker & Mather, 1982).

Moon, star and geomagnetic orientation systems are integrated such that as a Large Yellow Underwing switches from one reference system to another, it is able to orient in roughly the same compass direction (Baker & Mather, 1982). On clear nights the moth, like birds (Wiltschko & Wiltschko, 1978), may select its migration direction by the geomagnetic field but maintain that direction by the stars or Moon (Baker & Mather, 1982).

Large Yellow Underwings do not compensate for the movement of Moon or stars across the sky during the night (Sotthibandhu & Baker, 1979). In the same way, those migrants among temperate butterflies that simply travel from one suitable habitat to another, with no specific destination, orient by the Sun but do not compensate for its movement across the sky during the day (Baker, 1968a,b, 1978, 1984b). In contrast, butterflies migrating to specific destinations or zones (such as the Monarch butterfly in temperate regions and Brown-Veined White (*Belenois aurota*) in seasonally arid regions), if they also orient by the Sun, must compensate for its movement during the day (Baker 1978, 1984b). Any moths, such as the Silver-Y, Oriental Armyworm, and African Armyworm, that show comparable migratory behaviour in the same regions, are predicted (Baker, 1978) to show similar compensation for the movement of the Moon during the night.

Some authors have argued (e.g. Johnson, 1969; Taylor *et al.*, 1973) that even if moths and other insects do have a range of compass orientation mechanisms, these are irrelevant to migration, cross-country travel being the result of downwind displacement. In apparent contradiction to this view, it has long been known from visual observations (Common, 1954; Williams, 1958) that migrating moths maintain their direction of travel over a wide variety of wind speeds and directions. Johnson (1971) argues, however, that visual observations of low-flying individuals are irrelevant to an understanding of population shifts, which he considers are due to long-distance travel by higher-flying and wind-displaced individuals.

Radar studies suggest that small, weak-flying moths, such as the

Spruce Budworm (*Choristoneura fumiferana*), do indeed travel across country by downwind displacement (Schaefer, 1976), though it is still not clear if they only elect to fly when the wind is blowing in a particular direction (Baker, 1978; Sotthibandhu & Baker, 1979). For large, strong-flying moths, however, radar studies have shown that migratory direction is maintained over a wide range of wind speeds and directions (Schaefer, 1976).

Despite the weight of combined visual and radar evidence that the larger moths, as well as butterflies and other strong-flying insects, migrate across country in preferred compass directions, it was clear from a recent discussion meeting at the Royal Entomological Society of London (Baker, 1981) that the whole question of orientation and displacement in insect migration remains contentious. Specifically for moths, two attempts have been made to demonstrate downwind displacement from field observations of migration. Remarkably, though both attempts see no support in their data for the hypothesis of compass orientation, neither actually test their data against this hypothesis.

Taylor *et al*. (1973) analysed visual observations of the Silver-Y (*Plusia gamma*) in Britain. They claimed that whereas the moth may not travel downwind by day, it does so at night when the greatest cross-country displacement would be achieved. They concluded, therefore, that any compass orientation by the moths was irrelevant to their migration strategy. When the data were reanalysed (Baker, 1978), it was found that by day and night over land, and by day even over the sea, moths travelled with a preference for the expected compass direction (NNW in spring and summer; S in autumn: Williams, 1958; Baker, 1969), irrespective of wind direction. The apparent support for downwind displacement obtained by Taylor *et al*. was the spurious result of frequent coincidence between downwind direction and preferred compass direction.

Riley *et al*. (1983) analysed radar observations of the African Armyworm moth (*Spodoptera exempta*) made in Kenya, first at the end of February, then at the beginning of April. This time of year is roughly the period of northward passage of the main rainfall zone of the area, the inter-tropical convergence zone (ITCZ). Indeed, wind direction changed significantly between the February and April observations (Watson's $U_{9,9}^2 = 0.285$; $P = 0.005$; Batschelet, 1981), mean wind direction veering from NE to E/ESE. This suggests that in February the main body of rain was to the south of the observation site whereas in April it was, if in any direction, to the north. According to the models in Baker (1978), therefore, we should expect the moths in February to have a preference to travel with a vector to the south and in April to travel with a vector to the north. This is what was observed (Fig. 6.3),

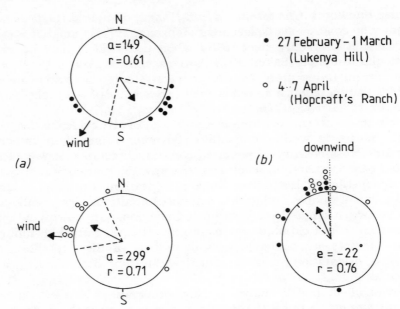

Fig. 6.3 Analysis of flight direction of African Armyworm moth (*Spodoptera exempta*) in Kenya in relation to compass and wind directions. (*a*) Mean compass direction of cross-country travel in February and April. Each dot is the mean direction of travel of moths as determined by radar. Arrows inside circles show the mean vector ($a°$, r, where $a°$ is the mean direction and r is the length of the mean vector; Batschelet, 1981) of the dots. Dashed lines show 95% confidence limits of the mean vector. Arrows outside circles show mean wind direction over all observations. (*b*) Mean direction of travel relative to downwind. Dots as in (*a*) but relative to wind direction at time of observation. Data for April are laterally inverted to accommodate predictions of compass-orientation hypothesis. Conventions as in (*a*) except mean direction is the mean difference (or error, $e°$) between moth track direction and downwind direction. (Data from Riley *et al.*, 1983, Table 5.)

moth track direction changing significantly ($U_{9,10}^2 = 0.291$; $P < 0.005$) between the two months. In fact, the mean track direction of the moths changed by 150° (from SE to WNW) compared with a change in mean wind direction of only 63°. Moths should have preferred to travel anticlockwise of downwind in February and clockwise of downwind in April. When we control for the possibility of these compass preferences, the 18 observations tabulated by Riley *et al.* (1983) are no longer consistent with downwind displacement ($e = 22° \pm 21°$, where downwind direction is given by $e = 0°$; $P < 0.05$; Batschelet, 1981).

Without presenting data, Riley *et al.* specifically reject the possibility of Moon orientation because the Armyworm moths 'did not orientate towards the moon's bearing nor did they appear to orientate at any consistent angle to the moon'. The authors seem unaware that neither of these characteristics would be expected during Moon orientation by the Armyworm (Baker, 1978; Sotthibandhu & Baker, 1979), and that therefore radar data for such a species are unsuitable to provide a critical test of the Moon-orientation theory.

Although there is by no means general agreement, the bulk of the critical evidence to date supports the view that moths make use of compass orientation during cross-country travel. Compass information may be used to select migration direction, to identify the compass direction of the wind, and/or to compensate totally or in part for the influence of cross- or headwinds. The question of interest in this chapter, however, is whether there is any connection between compass orientation during migration and orientation to a light-trap.

Experiments on the Large Yellow Underwing show that the angle at which an individual moth orients to the Moon's azimuth (i.e. the point on the horizon perpendicularly beneath the Moon's disc) is the same as the angle at which it orients to the artificial light source on a light-trap (Sotthibandhu & Baker, 1979). The implication is that the moth mistakes the artificial light source for the Moon, a suggestion originally made by von Buddenbrock (1937). If this suggestion is correct, the problem emerges of why moths should respond to an artificial light source at a distance of only 3 m whereas they respond to the Moon at a distance effectively of infinity.

Using tethered moths, Sotthibandhu (1978) found that the distance at which several species responded to a 125 W mercury-vapour lamp raised 9 m above ground level was much greater than for the same lamp only 0.6 m above ground level as on a light-trap, the distance being of the order of 10–17 m. The angle of elevation of the light source is, therefore, important, as might be expected if the response to the light is a Moon-orientation response.

When near to the ground, as on a light-trap, a light is below the height of most flying moths, and individuals are often seen to fly overhead, a few metres above ground level, without apparently responding to the light. Others are seen suddenly to dive down to ground level. This behaviour is often a response to bats flying overhead (Roeder, 1975) but also occurs in the apparent absence of bats and may be a response to the light. If it is, it could be interpreted (Baker & Sadovy, 1978) as an attempt to restore a Moon substitute, the artificial light, to an acceptable elevation so that dorsal rather than ventral ommatidia are illuminated (Sotthibandhu & Baker, 1979). Once a moth is near or on the ground, of course, the elevation of a light 0.6 m above the ground can approach that of the real Moon, depending on the distance of the moth from the light. Perhaps the explanation for moths responding to a light 0.6 m above the ground on a light-trap from a distance of only 3 m is that at greater distances the apparent elevation is not a close enough approximation to that of even a newly risen Moon (Baker & Sadovy, 1978).

Angle of elevation cannot be the only factor involved in Moon recognition, otherwise, when the artificial light is raised 9 m above ground level, the distance of response would be greater than the 10–17 m observed by Sotthibandhu (1978). Spectral composition (Mikkola, 1972), light intensity (Bowden & Morris, 1975) and the physical size of the light (Baker & Sadovy, 1978) are all likely to be important. The lightbulbs used by Sotthibandhu (1978) have a horizontal diameter of 7.5 cm and a vertical diameter of 12 cm. As the Moon changes phase, its apparent horizontal diameter changes greatly but the vertical diameter is much more constant. This vertical dimension subtends to a point on the Earths surface an angle of $0.518°$ (diameter = 3456 km; distance = 382 170 km). The vertical dimension of Sotthibandhu's lightbulb subtends the same angle to a point at a distance of 13.27 m (Baker & Sadovy, 1978). This is much nearer the 10–17 m that a moth near the ground responds to a light source 9 m above the ground (Sotthibandhu, 1978) than it is to the 35–519 m, depending on Moon phase, latitude, etc., at which the light source has the same level of illumination as the Moon (Bowden & Morris, 1975).

Unlikely though it may at first seem, therefore, the available evidence suggests that von Buddenbrock (1937) was correct and light-traps catch moths that mistake the artificial light for the Moon. It follows that moths respond to the light-trap when unable to recognise that the artificial light is not the Moon. As long as the light is bright enough and has an appropriate spectral composition, the critical factors in the moth making a 'mistake' are first the elevation and secondly the vertical dimension of the light source. An individual will only make such a mistake and enter the light-trap, however, if in a physiological state to make use of Moon orientation.

Some insects use a celestial body, such as the Sun or Moon, for orientation towards a familiar goal over relatively short distances of a kilometre or so. Perhaps the best-known example is the use of the Sun by Honey Bees (*Apis mellifera*) in travelling between their hive and other resource sites (von Frisch, 1967). Although not insects, various beach-living crustaceans are known to use the Moon for similar goal orientation as they travel up and down the shore between tideline and roosting zones (e.g. Papi & Pardi, 1963).

Clearly, therefore, some of the moths caught in a light-trap could be individuals that normally use the Moon as an aid to goal orientation within their familiar area (Baker, 1978, 1982). Some may even have taken advantage of the presence of the artificial light in their home range and adopted it as a landmark in its own right. Such scanty evidence as is available, however, suggests that such 'local' individuals are swamped by the number of migrants that enter a light-trap.

First, there appears to be a better correlation between light-trap catch and volume of migration as determined by radar (Schaefer, 1976) than between light-trap catch and suction-trap catch (Taylor & Carter, 1961) in the same area. Secondly, light-traps next to nectar-bearing plants are ignored by the feeding moths (R.R. Baker, unpublished data). Thirdly, in most species, males are probably more migratory than females (Baker, 1978) and predominate in light-trap catches. Exceptions seem often to be species, such as the Large Yellow Underwing, in which females have a long pre-oviposition period (Singh & Kevan, 1965) and which, therefore, are probably more migratory.

If light-traps catch primarily cross-country migrants, it would explain why they do not capture all species of moths in the vicinity (Taylor & Carter, 1961). Indeed, comparison of moths captured in adjacent light-traps and suction-traps may be a way to identify the more migratory species. Similarly, comparison of the times of night that moths enter suction- and light-traps may indicate the partitioning of local and more migratory flight periods during the night (Baker, 1979).

Most moth migration, as observed by radar, occurs at heights of tens or hundreds of metres above ground level (Schaefer, 1976; Riley *et al.*, 1983). At such heights, moths are unlikely to respond to light-traps on the ground. If it is the migrant population that is being caught, therefore, it is likely to be during a low-flying phase at the initiation or termination of migration (Baker & Sadovy, 1978).

Light-traps can catch only those individuals that orient at an angle to the light of less than 90°. It follows, therefore, that they should also catch only those individuals that orient at less than 90° relative to the Moon's azimuth (Baker & Sadovy, 1978). Such individuals will be those that travel across country roughly to the south ± 90°. Sotthibandhu (1978) and Sotthibandhu & Baker (1979) showed that Large Yellow Underwings captured in a light-trap do indeed show a preference to orient to the south, a finding that was confirmed by Baker & Mather (1982). Moreover, Baker & Mather found that the preference to fly south was manifest with respect to the geomagnetic field as well as to the celestial cues studied by Sotthibandhu & Baker (1979).

Studies of butterflies have shown that whereas each individual shows a preference to orient at a particular angle to the Sun's azimuth, individuals differ in their preferred angle (Baker, 1969, 1978, 1984b). The population shows a so-called 'direction ratio', a frequency distribution of preferred angles. Different species have different direction ratios, and many species also have different direction ratios at different times of year. Theoretical models have been developed that account for observed variation in butterflies and allow prediction of direction ratios in other insects, such as moths. For example, those species with a flying season that spans both spring/summer and autumn and have lifetime tracks more than about 100 km in length (i.e. straight-line distance from birth site to furthest-from-birth site) show a predominance of northerly (to be precise, in Britain, of north-northwesterly) orientations in spring and summer and of southerly orientations in autumn. Those species with shorter flying seasons or lifetime tracks have all orientation preferences represented equally.

If the same is true for moths, it follows that, for every southward-flying individual estimated to be present in our population in spring and summer, there should be one or more northward-flying individual(s) that is (are) not included. This is because such individuals, with a preference to fly away from the Moon, should respond to the light-trap by flying away from it. Such individuals can indeed be seen among those that enter the sphere of illumination from the light-trap.

Our only attempt to test this hypothesis was carried out in 1982 using the Large Yellow Underwing. Some moths were captured in a light-trap the night before the test; others were captured by hand among leaf litter on the forest floor. The prediction from theoretical models of the direction ratio of butterflies (Baker, 1969) was that hand-caught moths should show a preponderance of individuals that prefer to orient to the NNW (337.5°), whereas moths caught in a light-trap should show the usual preponderance to the S (180°).

The moths were tested using the orientation cage and analytical technique described by Baker & Mather (1982). Cross-shaped perspex cages were rotated through 180° every 10 min and the number of individuals was counted in each of the four arms of the cage. Mean direction of movement for each 10 min period was calculated by circular statistics (Batschelet, 1981). These means were then tested against the predicted directions of NNW for hand-caught moths and S for individuals caught in a light-trap. On the first night, with fresh and active moths, the hypothesis was significantly supported (Fig. 6.4). On the second night, after 36–48 h in captivity, the moths were less vigorous and the pattern disappeared.

This important experiment needs to be repeated next time a species of moth is common enough for a satisfactory sample of hand-caught moths to be obtained. For the moment, the available evidence seems to suggest that light-traps sample only a part of the migratory population: those with a preference to fly roughly south.

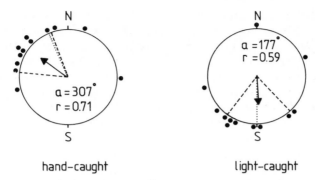

hand-caught   light-caught

Fig. 6.4   Test of hypothesis that hand-caught Large Yellow Underwings should prefer to orient NNW whereas those caught in a light-trap should prefer to orient S. Each dot is the mean direction of movement of moths in an orientation cage during a 10 min period. Arrows show the mean vectors (see Fig. 6.3) for the dots. Dotted lines show predicted orientation directions. Dashed lines show 95% confidence limits of mean vector. (Drawn from data obtained by I. Anderson & N. Paul.)

Population estimated

When mark, release, recapture experiments on moths began at Woodchester, the aim was the same as for the other animals described in this book: to estimate the number of moths in the vicinity of the trap. It now seems that, although some of the moths captured may be resident in the area, the majority are likely to be visitors; cross-country travellers pausing briefly on their journey as they exploit local resources. Moreover, they may only be moths en route to the south.

If necessary, a crude correction factor could be applied to the estimated population size to make allowance for that unsampled section en route to the north. Models of the direcion ratio (Baker, 1969, 1978) suggest that in spring and summer the total population is usually two or three times greater than just the southwards-flying sector. In autumn, the factor is about 1.5. However, unless we can identify the area occupied by our estimated population of migrants, such correction seems pointless.

Mark, release, recapture methods require marked and unmarked individuals to have an equal probability of capture within the population to be estimated (Blower *et al.*, 1981). In the case of moths, where first we estimate a population, then try to decide what has been estimated, the principle can be reversed: the population is that for which marked and unmarked individuals have an equal probability of capture.

In our experiments, marked moths were released before dark at distances from the trap(s) always greater than 3 m (the effective radius of attraction) but rarely greater than 10 m. There is an obvious danger, therefore, that when they become active, a portion of the marked moths will immediately enter the radius of influence of the trap. However, this danger may not be as serious as it might seem.

It is well known that different species of moths enter light traps at specific and different times of night (Taylor & Carter, 1961; Hitchen *et al.*, 1969). Comparisons of light-trap and suction-trap catches, however, show that failure to catch a species in light traps at a particular time of night does not necessarily indicate that the moth is inactive (Taylor & Carter, 1961). Taylor & Carter interpreted their results in terms of the interaction of light-trap emission and background levels of illumination. An alternative (Baker, 1979) is that suction-traps catch moths involved in feeding and other localised movements whereas light-traps catch those initiating or terminating cross-country migration. On either explanation, it follows that, before they once more become responsive to light, moths released 10 m from the trap may well disperse and mix with unmarked individuals over a relatively wide area.

The size of this area of mixing around the trap(s) is unknown. It is given by the area occupied at the beginning of the night by those unmarked moths with which, on average, marked moths share an equal probability of capture during the course of the night. In the future, some indication of the dimensions of this area may be obtained by releasing different cohorts of marked moths in different dispersions (i.e. some at a point; some scattered), at different distances and in different directions from the trap. As yet, however, we cannot even guess at these dimensions.

If the estimated population is primarily a population of migrants, we have to consider the meaning of the formal estimates of 'survival' that are calculable (Table 6.2) from mark, release, recapture data (Blower *et al.*, 1981). Presumably a moth leaves the population if it never again uses orientation to a light source and is thus never again at risk to capture. Some of the likely causes of egress are obvious, such as death. Others are less obvious, such as 'drifting' away from the area by means (e.g. pilotage or even wind displacement) other than light orientation. Yet others are downright paradoxical. For example, a moth that becomes resident in the area effectively egresses from the estimated population (unless, of course, it uses light for goal orientation within its familiar area). A 'survivor', therefore, as measured by survival rate, is an individual that does none of these things, but may eventually leave the area by light orientation.

The nature of the population estimated by mark, release, recapture when moths are caught in a light-trap still seems far from clear. If analogy helps, the situation seems similar to attempting an estimate of the number of motorists using the service area of a motorway by sampling cars as they enter the area from, and exit on to, the southbound carriageway.

Mark, release, recapture or just capture?

Table 6.3 compared population estimates and number of individuals captured for two species of moths, and earlier the question was mooted of whether the estimates from mark, release, recapture data were in any way more useful than simple capture data. We are now in a position to address this question.

If mark, release, recapture techniques, when applied to moths caught in light traps, do not estimate the population *in* the area, but those entering and leaving the area, and if the size of 'the area' is itself uncertain, the technique may not seem very useful. After all, presumably the raw capture data also provide an index of the number entering and leaving 'the area'. Moreover, simple capture data are obtained with far less effort and can be obtained every year. In contrast, population estimates can only be made if a species is common enough to obtain recaptures. Even then, unless large numbers of marked moths are recaptured, the confidence intervals to the population estimates are enormous. When population estimates can be made, however, they have a number of advantages, most of which derive from the notorious night-to-night variation in light-trap catch.

The number of moths caught in a trap on a given night can be related to weather conditions (e.g. Williams, 1940); the precise location of the trap, to within a few metres (Baker, 1979); and to distance of response (Sotthibandhu, 1978). Some variation should be due to night-to-night changes in the number of moths in the vicinity and the proportion primed to migrate, precisely the parameters we are trying to estimate. The remainder, however, is due to variation in the efficiency of the light-trap and needs to be controlled. In principle, such control is a feature of mark, release, recapture methods and thus makes their use preferable to the use of simple capture data. Two examples illustrate the point.

Observation shows that not all moths that pass within 3 m of a light-trap eventually enter the trap. Although apparently orienting towards the light, their momentum or strong winds may carry them beyond the 3 m radius and away. Others dive, or are blown, into the grass and stay there for the remainder of the night, many to be eaten by birds the following morning. Night-to-night variation in wind strength will thus influence the number captured. However, as long as marked and unmarked individuals behave the same and are exposed equally to the same risks, the population estimate is unaffected.

Some student projects have involved placing marked moths inside a light-trap at the beginning of a night and then measuring rates of escape and disappearance until the normal time of opening the trap the following morning. Moths do escape during the night but greatest losses occur after dawn, particularly if the sun happens to shine on the trap. In addition, unless precautions are taken, predatory birds such as House Sparrows (*Passer domesticus*) actually enter the trap to remove moths. Variation in the strength of the morning sunlight and in the abundance of predatory birds thus influences the number counted in the trap when it is opened. Once again, however, as long as the probability of escaping or being eaten is the same for marked and unmarked individuals, population estimates will be unaffected, except in so far as predation reduces the population.

Attempts to estimate night-to-night and year-to-year fluctuations in the number of moths pausing in an area during cross-country migration have a choice of techniques. On the one hand, there is the labour-intensive system of mark, release, recapture with inbuilt controls for variation in trapping efficiency. On the other is the less-intensive system of number captured, with its guarantee of producing a data point in years when a species is too scarce for mark, release, recapture to be applied.

Raw capture data are unreliable because of variation in trap efficiency; population estimates measure their own unreliability in terms of huge confidence limits. Neither method may seem very appealing, but weighing heavily in their favour is the fact that a better method does not yet exist.

Acknowledgements

Much of the work described here was carried out, or at least pioneered, by students, often working unsocial hours under arduous conditions with minimal obvious reward. In 1981 and 1982, they were supervised by Jon Delf. I am grateful to them all.

References

Agee, H.R. (1972) Sensory response of the compound eyes of adult *Heliothis zea* and *H. virescens* to ultraviolet stimuli. *Annals of the Entomological Society of America*, **65**, 701–5.
Baker, R.R. (1968*a*) A possible method of evolution of the migratory habit in

butterflies. *Philosophical Transactions of the Royal Society*, (B), **253**, 309–41.

Baker, R.R. (1968b) Sun orientation during migration in some British butterflies. *Proceedings of the Royal Entomological Society of London* (A), **43**, 89–95.

Baker, R.R. (1969) The evolution of the migratory habit in butterflies. *Journal of Animal Ecology*, **38**, 703–46.

Baker, R.R. (1978) *The Evolutionary Ecology of Animal Migration*. London: Hodder & Stoughton.

Baker, R.R. (1979) Celestial and light-trap orientation of moths. *Antenna*, **3**, 44–5.

Baker, R.R. (1981) Orientation and displacement in insect migration: insect migration discussion meeting. *Antenna*, **5**, 26–7, 70–2.

Baker, R.R. (1982) *Migration: Paths through Time and Space*. London: Hodder & Stoughton.

Baker, R.R. (1984a) *Bird Navigation: Solution of a Mystery?* London: Hodder & Stoughton.

Baker, R.R. (1984b) The dilemma: when and how to go or stay, in *The Biology of Butterflies*, Vane-Wright, R.I. & Ackery, P., eds. London: Academic Press, pp. 279–96.

Baker, R.R. & Mather, J.G. (1982) Magnetic compass sense in the Large Yellow Underwing moth, *Noctua pronuba* L. *Animal Behaviour*, **30**, 543–8.

Baker, R.R. & Sadovy, Y.J. (1978) The distance and nature of the light-trap response of moths. *Nature, London*, **276**, 818–21.

Batschelet, E. (1981) *Circular Statistics in Biology*. London: Academic Press.

Bishop, J.A. & Cook, L.M. (1975) Moths, melanism and clean air. *Scientific American*, **232**, 90–9.

Blower, J.G., Cook, L.M. & Bishop, J.A. (1981) *Estimating the Size of Animal Populations*. London: Allen & Unwin.

Bowden, J. & Morris, M.S. (1975). The influence of moonlight on catches of insects in light traps in Africa. Part III. The effective radius of a mercury-vapour light-trap and the analysis of catches using effective radius. *Bulletin of Entomological Research*, **65**, 303–48.

Brown, E.S. & Swaine, G. (1966) New evidence on the migration of moths of the African Armyworm *Spodoptera exempta* (Wlk.) (Lepidoptera, Noctuidae). *Bulletin of Entomological Research*, **56**, 671–84.

Buddenbrock, W. von (1937) *Gundriss der vergleichenden Physiologie*. Berlin: Oldenbourg.

Cleve, K. (1964) Der Anflug der Schmetterlinge an Künstliche Lichtquellen. *Mitteilungen der Deutschen entomologischen Gesellschaft*, **23**, 66–76.

Common, I.F.B. (1954) A study of the ecology of the adult bogong moth, *Agrotis infusa* (Boisd.) (Lepidoptera: Noctuidae), with special reference to its behaviour during migration and aestivation. *Australian Journal of Zoology*, **2**, 223–63.

Cook, L.M. & Sarsam, V. (1981) Polymorphism in the moth *Noctua pronuba* (L.). *Heredity, London*, **46**, 443–7.

Frisch, K. von (1967) *The Dance Language and Orientation of Bees*. London: Oxford University Press.

Hartstack, A.W., Hollingsworth, J.P. & Lindquist, D.A. (1968) A technique for measuring trapping efficiency of electric insect traps. *Journal of Economic Entomology*, **61**, 546–52.

Hitchen, J.M., Hitchen, E.T., Jackson, C.M. & Meers, G.H.A. (1969) The flight times of some nocturnal moths. *Entomoligist* **102**, 80–5.

Johnson, C.G. (1969) *Migration and Dispersal of Insects by Flight*. London: Methuen.

Johnson, C.G. (1971) Comments at a meeting. *Proceedings of the Royal Entomological Society of London*, **36**, 33–6.

Li, Kuang-Po, Wong, Hong-Hsiang & Woo, Wan-Sei (1964) [Route of the seasonal migration of the Oriental Armyworm Moth in the eastern part of China as indicated by a three-year result of releasing and recapturing marked moths.] (In Chinese with English summary.) *Acta Phytophylacica sinica*, **3**, 101–10. (From: *Review of Applied Entomology* A, **53**, 391.)

Mikkola, K. (1972). Behavioural and electrophysiological responses of night-flying insects, especially Lepidoptera, to near-ultraviolet and visible light. *Annales Zoologici fennici*, **9**, 225–54.

Papi, F. & Pardi, L. (1963). On the lunar orientation of sandhoppers (Amphipoda: Talitridae). *Biological Bulletin*, **124**, 97–105.

Riley, J.R., Reynolds, D.R. & Farmery, M.J. (1983) Observations of the flight behaviour of the armyworm moth, *Spodoptera exempta*, at an emergence site using radar and infrared optical techniques. *Ecological Entomology*, **8**, 395–418.

Roeder, K.D. (1975) Moths and ultrasound, in *Animal Behavior: Readings from Scientific American*, Eisner, T. & Wilson, E.O., eds. San Francisco: W.H. Freeman, pp. 46–54.

Roer, H. (1968) Weitere Untersuchungen über die Auswirkungen der Witterung auf Richtung und Distanz der Flüge des kleinen Fuchses (*Aglais urticae* L.) (Lep.: Nymphalidae) im Rheinland. *Dechemiana*, **120**, 313–34.

Roer, H. (1969) Zur Biologie des Tagpfauenauges, *Inachis io* L. (Lep.: Nymphalidae), unter besonderer Berüchsichtigung der Wanderungen im mitteleuropaischen Raum. *Zoologischer Anzeiger*, **183**, 177–94.

Roer, H. (1970) Untersuchungen zum Migrationsverhalten des Trauermantels (*Nymphalis antiopa* L.) (Lep.: Nymphalidae) *Zeitschrift für angewandte Zoologie*, **4**, 388–96.

Schaefer, G.W. (1976) Radar observations of insect flight, in *Insect Flight*, Rainey, R.C. eds. London: Blackwell, pp. 157–97.

Singh, M.P. & Kevan, D.K.McE. (1965) Notes on three common British species of agrotid moth. *Entomological Record and Journal of Variation*, **68**, 233–5.

Sotthibandhu, S. (1978) *Behaviour of Moths in Relation to Light Traps*. Ph.D. thesis, University of Manchester.

Sotthibandhu, S. & Baker, R.R. (1979) Celestial orientation by the Large Yellow Underwing moth, *Noctua pronuba* L. *Animal Behaviour*, **27**, 786–800.

Stewart, P.A., Lam, J.J. & Blythe, J.L. (1969) Influence of distance on attraction of tobacco hornworm and corn earworm moths to radiations of a blacklight lamp. *Journal of Economic Entomology*, **62**, 58–69.

Taylor, L.R. & Carter, C.I. (1961) The analysis of numbers and distribution in an aerial population of Macrolepidoptera. *Transactions of the Royal Entomological Society of London*, **113**, 369–86.

Taylor, L.R. & Taylor, R.A.J. (1977) Aggregation, migration and population mechanics. *Nature, London*, **265**, 415–21.

Taylor, L.R. & Woiwod, I.P. (1980) Temporal stability as a density-dependent species characteristic. *Journal of Animal Ecology*, **49**, 209–24.

Taylor, L.R., French, R.A. & Macauley, E.D.M. (1973) Low altitude migration and diurnal flight periodicity; the importance of *Plusia gamma* L. (Lep.: Plusiidae). *Journal of Animal Ecology*, **42**, 751–60.

Urquhart, F.A. (1960) *The Monarch Butterfly*. Toronto: University Press.

Urquhart, F.A. & Urquhart, N.R. (1978) Autumnal migration routes of the eastern population of the monarch butterfly (*Danaus p. plexippus* L.; Danaidae; Lepidoptera) in North America to the overwintering site in the Neovolcanic Plateau of Mexico. *Canadian Journal of Zoology*, **56**, 1759–64.

Williams, C.B. (1940) An analysis of four years' captures of insects in a light trap. Part II. The effects of weather conditions on insect activity; and the estimation and forecasting of changes in the insect population. *Transactions of the Royal Entomological Society of London*, **90**, 227–306.

Williams, C.B. (1958) *Insect Migration*. London: Collins.

Wiltschko, R. & Wiltschko, W. (1978) Relative importance of stars and the magnetic field for the accuracy of orientation in night-migrating birds. *Oikos*, **30**, 195–206.

Index